MW00659034

EYE OF THE HURRICANE

an autobiography

Other books from World Scientific by the author

SERIES IN MODERN APPLIED MATHEMATICS

Vol. 1 – **Mathematical Methods in Medicine** *Bellman*

Vol. 2 – **Quasilinearization and the Identification Problem** *Bellman & Roth*

RICHARD BELLMAN

EYE OF THE HURRICANE

an autobiography

World Scientific

Published by

World Scientific Publishing Co. Pte. Ltd.
5 Toh Tuck Link, Singapore 596224
USA office: 27 Warren Street, Suite 401-402, Hackensack, NJ 07601
UK office: 57 Shelton Street, Covent Garden, London WC2H 9HE

British Library Cataloguing-in-Publication Data
A catalogue record for this book is available from the British Library.

EYE OF THE HURRICANE

ISBN-13 978-9971-966-00-3
ISBN-10 9971-966-00-X
ISBN-13 978-9971-966-01-0 (pbk)
ISBN-10 9971-966-01-8 (pbk)

To Kirstie and Eric

PREFACE

Why write an autobiography?

In the first place, I have been in interesting places at interesting times, New York City, Princeton, Los Alamos, RAND, Center for the Study of Democratic Institutions, to name a few. I think that others will be interested to get a glimpse of these places through my eyes.

In the second place, I have always found personal essays, biographies, and autobiographies very valuable. Reading about the inertia, stupidity and prejudice faced by others has made me more philosophical. It is very important to know that others have had the same troubles. I hope that this account will also be useful.

Finally, there is the opportunity to speak freely. In writing a mathematical paper, one tries to be rigidly impersonal. In writing an autobiography, one has the chance to explain and express opinions. Besides, it is very interesting to see if one can discern a pattern and to know how large a role chance played in one's life.

ACKNOWLEDGMENTS

Many friends have read the manuscript and made helpful comments.

I would particularly like to thank Elaine Haight Anderson with whom I discussed many of the social events of the '50s and '60s; Herb Bailey with whom I exchanged many reminiscences about Princeton and who gave the publisher's viewpoint of the Kahn book; Brownlee Haydon who furnished much information about the early days at RAND and about above surface nuclear testing; Ted Harris who was a fellow graduate student at Princeton and a fellow mathematician at RAND; Jo Ann Lockett who supplied much information about the scientific life at RAND; Tom Runyon who gave a valuable perspective as a non-mathematician and non-RANDite; Charlene Smith who edited the whole manuscript and added much information about the early days at USC; and finally Ernst Straus, who gave much information about the Institute for Advanced Study and supplied much information about Einstein which would not be accessible otherwise.

All of these people also made valuable comments concerning the manuscript.

My wife, Nina, edited and improved the manuscript considerably.

Rebecca Karush patiently typed version after version of the manuscript.

Santa Monica, 1978

CONTENTS

CHAPTER 1

GROWING UP IN NEW YORK CITY

I was born in 1920, a wartime baby. My father, John James Bellman was twenty and my mother, Pearl Saffian Bellman, was eighteen. They took one frightened look at me and promptly gave me to my mother's mother, my grandmother, to raise for the first few years. The responsibility of raising an infant was too much for a twenty-year old and an eighteen-year old. I was not a husky baby and she had to work very hard. She took me to many clinics.

My father's father ran a small grocery store on Bergen Street near Prospect Park in Brooklyn. My father was born there. According to my father, his father's father had made uniforms for the Czar and was quite wealthy. My father's father was a socialist and had the habit of sticking propaganda in the pockets of the uniforms. A recruit showed this propaganda to his officer who showed it to the secret police, the Okrana, who sent men around to investigate. My father's father got afraid and that was how he came to America.

He did not run the grocery store well. He was made to be a rich man's son, and could never adjust to working for a living.

He came from the Kiev area. The name Bellman is Swedish. We know historically that the Swedes went down as far as Kiev. Whenever I go to Stockholm I have some fun. The name "Bellman" in Sweden is like Shakespeare in the United States. Carl Michael Bellman was a very famous Swedish poet and there are many places and dishes named after him. As a matter of fact, people in Sweden usually think I am joking when I use the name "Bellman".

However, Carl Michael Bellman's family emigrated to Sweden from Germany in the 17th century. The name, therefore, may be German in origin.

My father belonged to the second set of children. His father married twice, having seven children by the first wife and six children by the second. My father's father died before I was born and my father's mother died when I was one year old. As a result, I never knew either of my paternal grandparents. Neither my father nor his sisters ever mentioned their mother. I neither know her first name, nor her maiden name, nor where she came from.

My father told me that there was a very disgraceful scene at the death-bed of his father. The children by the first marriage scrambled for his possessions while he was still alive. I never met any of my father's half-brothers or sisters. I am sure that many of the people named Bellman came from this marriage.

When I speak of my grandfather and grandmother below, I shall mean my mother's father and mother.

My mother's mother, born Mildred Apple, was brought up in Philadelphia in a wealthy family. She was born in Germany and came to this country at about the age of four. Her father had been a Graf in Germany. He was driven out of Germany by the anti-Semitic measures of Bismarck. One of her proudest possessions was an invitation her mother had received for a ball for the Kaiserling's reception. My grandfather, Samuel Saffian, had been born in Poland. He said his family had lived in Poland for about 100 years. Before that, they lived in Armenia. I think he was of Catholic origin. However, he practiced no religion. At the age of twelve, he was forced to leave the house by a wicked stepmother. He made his way to England, and at the age of fourteen he embarked for America. He landed in New York with one kopek in his pocket. He went to a saloon and filled himself on the free lunch. When he offered to pay with the kopek, the bartender just laughed.

He also had an address in New York. When he got to that address, the man of the house answered the door and said, "We don't have enough to feed ourselves," and shut the door. Fortunately, his wife took pity on the young boy and took him in.

In some way he made his way to Philadelphia where his older brother was a plumber. How his older brother got to Philadelphia and became a plumber, I don't know.

One day, my grandmother looked through the window of her finishing school and saw my grandfather, who had become a handsome young dandy. It was love at first sight and they eloped. My great-grandmother was furious at this and promptly disinherited her. She promised never to set foot in my grandmother's house and kept this promise faithfully. I suspect that my great-grandmother was outraged at the fact that my grandfather was a plumber.

When my grandfather was about seventy-five, I asked him about my grandmother's mother. All he would say was, "That fat sow!" He was a good hater.

He was also very stubborn, a family characteristic. The phone company wanted to charge him for a call to California, quite expensive in those days. He pointed out that he had not made the call and didn't even know anybody in California. The phone company threatened that unless he paid they would remove the telephone. He told them to go ahead and do it. However, they were reluctant to do so because he had one of the original telephones, a Butterfield number. They said he could make outgoing calls but receive none. He wouldn't let anybody use the phone. When my grandmother wanted to talk to my mother and aunt, she had to go to the candy store around the corner. Finally, the phone company gave in and restored the service.

My grandfather moved from Philadelphia to New York, to 439 E 76th Street, the heart of Yorkville. This was a German-Hungarian neighborhood.

It was a very rough neighborhood. Every night, the doors were securely locked with many locks and a screen was put over the plate-glass window. Before the screen, the window had been broken by bricks several times.

There was a saloon on every corner. Although this was during prohibition, they were protected by the police. When my grandmother sent me to the grocery store around the corner to get a quart of milk, I had to be careful not to step over the drunks on the sidewalk.

At that time New York was run by Tammany Hall. Every time my grandfather tried to get a license, the examiner wanted to be bribed. Finally my grandfather clipped out of the paper a story about an examiner who was sent to jail for taking bribes and put that in the opened drawer. He got his license.

During prohibition my grandfather took advantage of his plumbing knowledge to build a still so that he and my grandmother could have their schnapps.

On his first attempt, he blew out the side of the house.

My father met my mother at the beach and promptly fell in love with her. I imagine it was a family custom. All he knew was her first name, Pearl, and that she worked in a large department store in Manhattan. With typical persistence, he stationed himself at the exit of each department store at five o'clock and asked, "Do you know a girl named Pearl?" In this way he tracked my mother down, and after many vicissitudes they were married.

Pearl was a very popular name in those days, after Pearl White of the movies. There were three Pearls in my family, which caused a bit of confusion.

As I said above, my father had several brothers and sisters. The oldest sister, Pearl, or Peg as she liked to be called, became a lawyer and married a lawyer, Alfred Klein. I will say more about him.

Alfred started out as a reporter in New York and then became a lawyer and moved to Washington. Eventually, he became the top legal officer for civil service. Peg, although she had the privilege of presenting cases before the Supreme Court, never practiced. She devoted her time to social work, particularly to runaway girls.

My father had four sisters. One, I never knew, Dorothy, because she died when I was quite young. Another, Beth (Elizabeth), married a candy store owner in Newark and had one son, Murray, a very distant cousin. The third, Augusta (Gus), became a buyer for a big New York department store and used to go to Europe every summer. I well remember how impressed I was that she even used taxis.

I always enjoyed my visits to Beth in Newark. They meant free candy, reading all the magazines, and a gift of a toy. Also, we took the tubes, which was an exciting experience. It was a thrill to go to a different city.

My father's younger brother, Bunny, was the black sheep of the family. My father and he never got on well. He was a bookie to the White House, Harry Hopkin's personal bookie. Every once in a while he would disappear. I found out later that he would go to Canada to let the statute of limitations take over. It seems that he was a little forgetful. He had the habit of selling tickets for a benefit and forgetting to put on the benefit.

He married the boss's daughter and somewhere I have two Catholic first cousins by that marriage.

There was a great deal of intermarriage in my family. My grandmother's younger sister, Anna, had married into the Harrison family. Her husband's name was Benjamin Harrison, Uncle Ben. He was a wealthy corporation lawyer, and also a socialist. I well remember the arguments in my grandfather's house. My father at that time was a devout Republican and used to argue quite vehemently with my Uncle Ben. Uncle Ben was hard of hearing and wore a hearing-aid. Whenever the argument went against him he would turn off the hearing-aid.

These arguments took place in the parlor of my grandmother's house. It was a typical Victorian parlor. As was the custom in those days, the living quarters were behind the shop. Directly behind the plumbing store was the parlor and behind that was the kitchen. The bedrooms were upstairs.

Uncle Ben and Aunt Anna used to drive up from Philadelphia in his Packard. These arguments took place at Thanksgiving and Christmas, at which times we had family gatherings.

One of my grandmother's relatives in Philadelphia had been partners with Guggenheim at one time, but although I heard the story many times, I never got the relationship straight. All I know is that we were almost very wealthy.

I suspect that my grandfather was of Catholic origin, and that was one of the reasons my grandmother's mother was against the marriage.

My father's younger brother, Bunny, mentioned above had married a Catholic girl. My mother's younger brother had married a non-Jewish girl in his first marriage. I suspect also that my father was also only one-half Jewish. Possibly, that is why he never mentioned his mother.

My mother had two siblings, an older sister, Sylvia, and a younger brother, Arthur. I was very close to both of them.

My Aunt Sylvia had several beaus, including Mark Connolly, who wrote "Green Pastures". However, nothing came out of these, with the result that my mother married before my aunt did. That was not proper in those days.

My aunt got married when I was about four years old. I was page boy at the wedding, wearing a little Lord Fauntleroy costume which I hated. My job was to carry the ring on a velvet cushion.

Sylvia's husband was Jacob Rosen, "Uncle Jack". He had originally studied engineering and then went to night school to become an accountant. In those days people with the name "Jacob Rosen" didn't get jobs as engineers.

My Aunt Sylvia had a very prosaic life. Her one chance of adventure was during World War I when she worked at Brentano's, the famous bookstore. For some reason, she was a great favorite of the Japanese who worked at the consulate. The secret service approached her to go out with them and pump them for secrets. They promised that she would be well protected.

When my grandfather heard of this, he exploded, "I will not have my daughter a Mata Hari."

My grandfather had a gleaming white toilet bowl in the window. Both my aunt and my mother pleaded with him to take it out, since it embarrassed them when their beaus came calling. My grandfather pointed out that he was a plumber after all, and besides, he was very proud of this fixture which was just coming into vogue. It stayed in the window.

Arthur was an esthete. At a time when other people brought candy or cake, he always brought flowers and wine. He was also quite artistic. He did many things, and that was the trouble. He never stayed with one thing very long, and that did not endear him to my grandfather.

He was also an excellent camper and hunter. He tried to give me several rifles and hunting knives, which my mother made me give back. Each time she added some words for her younger brother.

He was also a very good athlete. He played soccer with the leading amateur team of New York City. Finally, he put all this together, selling sporting goods for Davega, a well-known sporting goods store in New York.

Arthur's second wife was Sandra, a German refugee. She was a very pretty and very nice woman and we became good friends. She and her three friends had been skiing in Switzerland when they received a telegram telling them not to return. Her three friends disregarded the warning, returned to Germany, and were killed in gas chambers. Her whole family was exterminated by the Nazis.

Arthur and Sandra lived in the same rooming house. That is how they met. Arthur got the flu and Sandra nursed him. In return he taught her colloquial English. Being mischievous, another family characteristic, he could not resist teaching her four-letter words. He got a great deal of amusement when she used them in conversation. However, the joke backfired when he took her to parties.

The same practical joke was played on Browning. There is a famous line when he talks about the nun's twat. He was told this meant cloak. It does not.

Naturally, I was raised as an atheist. This was quite easy since the only one in the family that had any religion was my grandmother, and she was of German stock. Although she believed in God, and went to the synagogue on the high holy days, there was no nonsense about ritual. I well remember when I went off to the army, she said, "God will protect you." I smiled politely. She added, "I know you don't believe in God, but he will protect you anyway."

I know many sophisticated and highly intelligent people who are practicing Catholics, Protestants, Jews, Mormons, Hindus, Buddhists, etc., feel strongly that religion, or lack of it, is a highly personal matter.

My own attitude is like Lagrange's. One day, he was asked by Napoleon whether he believed in God.

"Sire," he said, "I have no need of that hypothesis."

My father was a very handsome man and my mother was very jealous of him, probably justifiably. Whenever she nagged him about that he would get very angry and break up some furniture. He enjoyed breaking up furniture because he enjoyed putting it together again. He was quite mechanical. Whenever they had a fight, I was sent to the candy store to get some cigarettes.

I well remember one such occasion when they were having a fight. I had tears running down my cheeks and I thought, "How I wish I believed in God now."

I was a very skinny child. Both my parents were very attractive people. When they walked down the street with me, they were often stopped by strangers who said, "Aren't you ashamed to mistreat a child that way?" Every meal was an ordeal. My father tried to remedy the situation by having me eat two pieces of bread with every meal. My cousin Lou, who was my pediatrician, made up a foul-tasting mixture for me to take three times a day. It was my first experience with health food.

My grandmother did her part by inventing Indian tea, a mixture of milk and tea. Many years later, I was talking about this and used the expression, "Indian tea". Seeing the look of puzzlement on the face of the person I was talking to, I suddenly realized my grandmother had invented this term.

The two curses of my childhood were bed-wetting and fear of the dark. The bed-wetting went away at a relatively late age, about thirteen. Every technique was tried with no success. The best thing to do was not to drink after dinner. I used to have dreams of drinking water, but this technique of abstinence was pretty effective. Even when I was thirteen, I worried about spending the night in a friend's house.

Why I was afraid of the dark, I don't know. But I well remember the elaborate ritual which I had for turning out the lights and jumping into bed whenever my parents went out. From time to time I have lost this fear of the dark. From time to time it recurs.

My mother was a terrible cook. She had a magic touch, everything she tried she ruined. Fortunately, my father was an excellent cook and he would often make the meals on Saturday and Sunday. I well remember some of the things he made, as well as the things my mother made.

When I married Nina, I said, "For heaven's sake don't cook the way my mother did."

Also, my grandmother was a wonderful cook, even though she used an antiquated stove. Probably, that is why my mother and her older sister were bad ones. We used to get together on Thanksgiving and Christmas. My grandmother would deliberately make too much so that my mother and my aunt had lots of leftovers to take home. My chore in a few days was to return the container.

I adored my grandmother. She never said a harsh word to me. She was about five feet tall with blond hair and blue eyes. She had a will of iron, yet was quite feminine. As a matter of fact, all the women in my family, on both sides, were strong and feminine. I got quite used to it, and expect it.

My grandmother often embarrassed me. When I was eighteen, I was my present height and weight, about six feet tall and 174 pounds. Whenever we travelled together she would try and stand to let me sit. If I had to carry a bundle she would try to carry it.

Why she was so diminutive, she didn't know. Both her brothers were over six feet and her father was a red-bearded giant.

When I was much younger, we lived near the Grand Concourse and played a game which still makes me shudder. The object of the game was to run across the street and see how narrowly a car could miss you. The driver would slam on his brakes and curse us. Occasionally, one would stop his car and chase us. Since we knew the terrain well, we never got caught.

In junior high, we would jump off the platform when the train was coming and jump on the platform just in time. It is a good thing that mothers don't know what their little darlings are doing.

When I was older, we moved to another part of the Bronx, 1805 Longfellow Ave. We played many games. I remember that we used to play marbles, "Hit and Span", a very unsanitary game because it was played in the gutter, and deliveries were still made by horse and wagon. Then we would play several games involving checkers. One involved hitting checkers off a crack in the sidewalk. For that purpose we had "shooters". These shooters were highly polished and had some lead in the center to give them weight.

We also played a game called "Skelley". This involved going from boxes numbered one to thirteen and then the reverse. It was a game of great skill.

We also played "One-a-Cat", an antecedent of baseball. Finally, we played various ball games.

Many of the games were quite old, as I found out reading various books on children's games. Many of them can be recognized in the famous painting by Breughel.

Girls had their own games, principally skipping rope, jacks, and hop-scotch. In skipping rope, two girls turn the rope and a third or fourth stayed in the middle avoiding the rope. It required great nimbleness when two ropes were used, turned in opposite directions. While turning the ropes, the girls chanted songs which I'm sure went back to Elizabethan times or before.

I tried skipping rope several times but never mastered it and gave it up. I had more luck with jacks and became quite proficient at it, but never as good as the girls. Hop-scotch was too simple, and I seldom played it.

In the schoolyard every morning, we played "Ring-O-Leaves". Occasionally, we played soccer with a rubber ball. This was played enthusiastically and involved a lot of kicks in the shin. As a result, my shins are quite serrated.

I had many toys as a child. Partly this was due to the fact that Aunt Beth and her husband ran a toy store in Newark. Partly it was due to the fact that my father enjoyed the mechanical toys, like erector sets and trains. The game, however, that intrigued me was a question and answer game in which one put one lead of a battery on the question and other lead on the answer. If the answer was correct, there was a buzz. It was a primitive computer.

Many of the applications in medicine and social sciences are no more sophisticated. They could have, and should have, been done 25 years ago. Why they were not is an interesting chapter in human psychology. Progress is always painfully slow.

I am left-handed. When I entered public school, left-handed children were forced to learn to write with their right hands. I still remember the torment. I started stuttering and was allowed to return to the use of my left hand. In those days, teachers were very much interested in penmanship. There was something called the Palmer method in which you were not allowed to rest your elbow on the table while writing. It was hard enough for right-handed people but you can imagine the contortions of a left-handed person. When I was in my teens, I developed a more natural style of writing. I sometimes amuse my classes by showing them that the older method allows me to write straight up the board. As a result, I have three signatures, two with my left hand and one with my right. For many years I kept the older signature for banks and official documents.

One day, while strolling down Broadway I passed a store where they advertised computer analysis of your writing. Since it wasn't very expensive, I was quite curious and gave them samples of both the older and newer styles of writing. It was amazing how accurate the analysis was.

Being left-handed is a great advantage in athletics. One is accustomed to right-handed opponents, but they are not accustomed to left-handed ones. In a game like tennis, the opponent hits the ball to what is the backhand of a right-handed player, but it is the forehand of a left-handed player. For any player, it is the forehand that is usually much stronger.

I also believe that there is a strong correlation between left-handedness and creativity. Being left-handed in a right-handed world, one is constantly forced to examine every situation carefully. Nothing can be taken for granted. One gets used to looking at the world with fresh eyes.

Actually, very little is understood about creativity. There have been very creative people who have been very poor students, like Newton. It was a myth that Einstein was a poor student, actually he was a very bright child. There have been creative people who have been child prodigies, like Mozart and Wiener. Examples can easily be given to buttress any theory. It is like the Bible where careful quotations can support any moral position.

I was painfully shy when young. Every semester, I had to face the terror of reciting in class. I stayed home on those days, and usually did my reciting on the last day of the term.

I also was afflicted with telephone deafness, a condition which persisted well into my teens. I had several embarrassing incidents as a result.

In high school and college, I forced myself to give talks to get over this shyness.

I had many of the ingredients of an unhappy child, but I wasn't. I think the reasons were three-fold. To begin with I got a lot of love and attention. I was an only child and on my mother's side, an only nephew and grandchild as well. On my father's side, I had only three cousins, and two of them I saw at infrequent intervals. Secondly, I lived in a world of ideas, and was surrounded by people who were eager to listen to these ideas, and had many ideas themselves. Finally, I was a good athlete, which made life in the streets very pleasant.

When I was about ten, we moved from the Bronx to Brighton Beach in Brooklyn. Because of the large commissions my father made, our family fortunes improved considerably. We lived in a very luxurious apartment house in Brighton Beach. It had such features as a doorman, elevators, incinerators, and even a tap for taking a saltwater bath.

The year before, we had spent the summer in Brighton Beach in a bungalow on Neptune Avenue and Sixth. The sewers were not very good. Whenever it rained, it flooded. My father was quite a dandy. He wore spats and a flower in his buttonhole. However, when it flooded, he had to take off his shoes and stockings, roll up his pants, and come into the house that way. It's a picture I will never forget.

Brighton Beach was a middle-class community while Coney Island community. That meant that it was not completely built up and there were many fields to play in. Secondly, we were next to the boardwalk, which extended about two miles from Manhattan Beach to Seagate. Thirdly, there was the beach and the ocean. Fourthly, we were very close to Coney Island.

Brighton Beach was a middle class community while Coney Island was definitely a poor community. The two were separated by Ocean Parkway. However, it was an easy walk from Brighton Beach to Coney Island. Every night in the summer we would walk there and have some food and watch the side-shows.

The main street of Brighton Beach was Brighton Beach Avenue, along which the elevated ran. It made a terrific racket. It was a constant source of aggravation to me that my parents could sleep through this but woke up when I made the slightest sound when I came in late. I had a running battle with my father about staying out. He wanted me to be home by nine o'clock.

We were only a few hundred yards from the beach, but I never enjoyed it. I had a wool allergy. The combination of a woollen bathing suit and wet sand made every trip to the beach an ordeal. The beach was very crowded in the summer, and the people were not very attractive, as can be imagined. The ocean was always very cold and always contaminated. This combination was never made public because of business.

My father, however, loved the beach. He was a great swimmer and thought nothing of swimming to Rockaway in an afternoon, a distance of seven miles back and forth. He also enjoyed playing a form of medicine ball with the lifeguards. He had a running battle with the police. In those days, we were firmly in the grip of puritanism. It was against the law for a man to take off his top at the beach. This irked my father no end, and he would see how much he could cut out of the top. Finally, he got the idea of cutting out everything but the seams. This led to many arguments with the police. After several years, common sense prevailed and this regulation was quietly ignored.

The only time I enjoyed the ocean was when it rained. Then the waves got very high because of the wind, and the rain made the water seem warmer. I learned how to body surf, which was dangerous during a storm. Every year several people got struck by lightning. But, I never worried about that.

In the evening, we would congregate on the boardwalk. Unfortunately, mosquitoes also would congregate. For some reason, they would not bite my father, but they loved me. To this day I have a great abhorrence of mosquitoes.

There was a great deal of political activity in Brighton Beach. The population was divided into three parts: the Zionists, the communists, and those who wanted none of either. In addition, there were many types of Zionists and communists. In the fall, when my annual bone bruise made handball impossible, I would amuse myself on the weekends by listening to the arguments on the boardwalk.

I stayed apart from political activity. I figured that my first job was to get myself established scientifically. When my opinion was worth something, I would take stands.

Life was full of rituals. On February 14, St. Valentine's Day, one made a valentine and sent it to one's best girl, anonymously. Not until much later, did I buy them. On Easter Sunday, there was the parade of Easter bonnets and old cars down Fifth Avenue. In 1940, Betty Jo and I even strolled in the Easter parade for an hour or so. When summer came, the screens were put on to keep out the bugs, the awnings were put out to keep out the sun, and the rugs came up. This involved a liberal use of mothballs and the rugs were rolled up.

At the end of the summer, the screens came down and the rugs were put down. Also, there was a week in Coney Island called the Mardi Gras week. During the day, there were parades of high school bands and fire-engine companies from all over the state. During the nights, it was the custom to throw a lot of confetti. Theoretically, one was supposed to buy this. It was cheaper to pick it up from the ground. One looked for pretty girls and stuffed confetti in their mouths. A good time was had by all.

During the summer, every Tuesday, there were fireworks. In September, there was the first day of school, always a time of excitement and confusion. Sometime in September, there were the Jewish holidays. The most important of these is Yom Kippur, the Day of Atonement. Since Brighton Beach was a Jewish community, everything stopped on that day. We stood on the boardwalk, dressed in our Sunday best, completely bored. One family resolutely played handball. This shocked many people.

At the end of October, there was Halloween. It was the custom to chalk people's backs on Halloween. This probably was a remnant of some medieval practice. I never found out why this was done.

In November, there was Thanksgiving. This meant a feast at my grandmother's house.

In December, there was another feast on Christmas Day and the Christmas holidays.

During the plush period, every Sunday, we would walk down Sheepshead Bay to have a seafood dinner at one of the restaurants. We usually had dinner at Lundy's, a shore dinner, which included chicken and lobster. We paid the stupendous price of $2.50 for this.

New York is a wonderful city to be poor in. It has many free attractions. In order of importance to me, they were the Forty-Second Street Public Library, the Metropolitan Museum of Art, the Museum of Natural History, and the Bronx park zoo. I knew the first three by heart. I spent many happy hours in the Forty-Second Street Library and in the museums.

In the Metropolitan Museum, my favorite place was the Hall of Armor. In the Museum of Natural History, my favorite place was the Hall of Dinosaurs.

Every Sunday, my father and I would explore another part of the city. He took me around to all the churches and all the museums. He was very interested in history and communicated this interest to me.

I well remember walking along Forty-Second Street in 1927. My father showed me a headline. Lindberg had just flown across the ocean solo. My father said that this was a historic headline. Overnight "Lindy" became a world hero.

Unfortunately, Lindberg fell under the influences of Alexis Carrel in connection with the construction of an artificial heart. Carrel was a French fascist, and both Lindbergs became fascists. His wife, Anne Morrow Lindberg even wrote a book, "The Wave of the Future". She was a big disappointment to her father who was an ambassador.

Before World War II, Lindberg got involved with Nazi groups and soon was a front man for all kinds of isolationists and anti-Semitic statements.

When the Japanese attacked, he wanted to fly in the air force. However, Roosevelt and others well remembered his attitudes and would not let him.

When he died a few years ago, he was not given a hero's funeral. Too many people remembered his statements.

We were not supposed to be poor, but were ruined by the Depression. My father had tried many things and found that being a dress salesman best suited his abilities. He opened up many areas in the South that were closed to New York manufacturers.

One of his favorite stories was about the time he was travelling through Texas. He had made a vow not to get into trouble. During the long train ride, a big Texan came through the train bellowing, "Who is Jewish?" My father said nothing. Again the Texan came through the train repeating his question. Again my father said nothing. When the Texan came through the third time, that was too much for my father. Squaring his shoulders, he stood up and said, "I am Jewish. What about it?" The Texan looked at him and said, "Why didn't you say that before. We need a third for pinochle."

As I said, we were not supposed to be poor. As a matter of fact, just before the great Depression, my father had decided to go into business for himself. Then the Depression struck. My father was offered many jobs. By the time he decided to take these, they were not available. Then he was offered others for less money. By the time he decided to take these, they were not available too. We went all the way down.

My father took the Depression personally instead of seeing that it was a world cataclysm. He got bleeding ulcers and then heart trouble which eventually killed him. I always describe him as a victim of the Depression.

Fortunately, my grandfather had made a great deal of money during the First World War. Thus he was able to support himself, my family, my aunt's family and my uncle, Arthur.

Finally, my father took a job with the WPA. This was not a peaceful existence because agencies were always running out of money. Fortunately, my father had a friend in the front office who had him transferred in the nick of time. It was a little like Eliza jumping from ice flow to ice flow just ahead of the blood hounds.

My father had decided to wait out the Depression by taking a trip to Bermuda. Like many people, he thought it was only a matter of a few weeks. It was not a good decision. Although the trip was placid, it used up all our savings.

At about the age of twelve, I became interested in psychology. In those days we had an adolescent problem. I was naturally curious what symptoms I was supposed to develop. I think my lifelong interest in psychology dates from then. One of the fringe benefits was that one read a great deal about sex.

New York City is composed of five boroughs, Manhattan, Brooklyn, the Bronx, Queens and Richmond. I know Manhattan fairly well. It has many interesting streets and sections. Two of the streets, Broadway and Fifth between 42nd St. and 59th St., I knew by heart. Many a time I walked up both streets.

New York University, the Courant Institute to be specific, is in the heart of Greenwich village. Fifth Avenue begins there and I often used to walk up to the hotel where Nina and I were staying, Essex House, a very pleasant walk. Greenwich Village is an interesting area which I knew after I had left New York. When I lived in New York, I could not afford to go to its restaurants and nightclubs.

New York City has many good restaurants because it has many ethnic groups. I only got to know these restaurants after I had left the city.

Brooklyn, I know a little, mainly the areas which are covered by the subway. Nevertheless, there are huge areas of Brooklyn which I have never been to.

The Bronx I only know slightly. Any trip to the Bronx would involve an extensive use of maps and I would usually get lost.

Queens, although I have visited several times, I don't know at all.

Richmond, I never even visited.

My taste in the arts was formed by the museums and the books at home. In art, I have always been interested in the art of the Renaissance and the Flemish school.

We had a fairly good library. We had the Harvard classics, the complete works of Gauthier, Smollett, Mark Twain, Shakespeare, and others. In addition, we had a large number of single volumes. All of this was supplemented by the neighborhood library.

Mark Twain was my favorite. I particularly enjoyed "Tom Sawyer", "The Connecticut Yankee in King Arthur's Court", "Innocents Abroad",. and "Essays New and Old". The essay on James Fenimore Cooper should be read by every aspiring writer, and parts of it would be quite useful for a course in operations research.

Mark Twain had a great influence on me, my ideas, my sense of humor, and my writing style.

Three individual volumes were favorites of mine: Robinson Crusoe, Gulliver's Travel and Ivanhoe. Few people know that there is a second part to Robinson Crusoe in which he travels across Russia.

I particularly liked the third voyage of Gulliver to the flying island of Laputa. Swift got many of his ideas by reading the transactions of the Royal Society. He had a great time poking fun at science. The trouble is that many of the ideas there are good ones. The line between a good idea and poor idea is not clear cut. I always remember what Aldous

Huxley said, "The universe is strange. It is stranger than you think. It may be stranger than you can think."

Great care must be exercised in applying "common sense" to the study of the physical universe. Take gravity for example. Thanks to the efforts of Newton, Einstein and many others, we now possess useful mathematical descriptions. But we understand no more about the nature of this mysterious force than Archimedes did. Many other examples can be furnished by relativity theory and quantum mechanics.

I also read and re-read Ivanhoe. Later on, when I read Quentin Durward, I thought this was a much better work.

We had a number of biographies. My favorites were two by Hackett, one on Francis the First, whom I liked and the other about Henry the Eighth, whom I didn't. We also had a fine biography of Washington by Woodward. Washington is one of my heroes. He could hold his own intellectually with people like Jefferson, Hamilton or Adams. In addition, he was a man of high moral principles. I doubt very much that he would have stood by when Jenner and McCarthy called Marshall a traitor, and I doubt very much whether these words would have been uttered if Jenner and McCarthy knew that they had Washington to deal with instead of Eisenhower.

It always irked me when Eisenhower was compared to Washington.

I read voraciously. When I was young, I read "Baseball Joe", "Tom Swift", "The Rover Boys", and so on. My father added to these with the books he had read as a boy, which were far superior. I particularly enjoyed the works by Henty.

Nick Carters were still available. I read at least one every time we visited Aunt Beth.

I also read Horatio Alger. His name has become synonymous with hard work. But, if one reads the stories, one finds that he is always achieving fame and fortune by rescuing heiresses from runaway horses, drowning, burning buildings, thugs, and the like.

I also read various adventure magazines like, "The Shadow" and "Doc Savage".

As I got older, I read the adventure novels by H. Rider Haggard, Jeffrey Farnol and Rafael Sabatini.

Haggard had a good knowledge of Africa, particularly of the Zulus. He had a high admiration for them and indeed they are an admirable people. From Jeffrey Farnol I learned a little English history. From Sabatini, I learned a lot more and a great deal of Italian history. Sabatini was a professional historian before he turned to writing.

When I was twelve, I felt I had read enough fiction and concentrated thereafter on non-fiction, paleontology, archaeology, philology, history, biography, and books about science, like those by Paul de Kruif and "Crucibles" by Jaffee.

I also discovered Montaigne. I read and re-read his essays. He became a model of a civilized man. This was particularly remarkable when one considers when he lived.

Three heroes of mine, Twain, Montaigne and Washington stood up under adult scrutiny.

In music, we had a good collection of light classical music such as, "Song of India". It was not until I went to college that I developed my liking for Bach, Mozart, Beethoven and the like.

I made my social money in several ways. When I went to high school and college, I did tutoring. I also worked at various jobs.

When I was eighteen, I was a counselor at a camp. When I was nineteen, I ran a ping-pong parlor right off the boardwalk. When I was twenty, I was a scoutmaster at a settlement house on the lower east side. I made most of my money playing handball with older men and gambling. To make money playing handball, I would play with my right hand. The older men had money and were not very good players.

I would gamble at pinochle. My Aunt Sylvia would often see me from a window playing cards and was often disturbed by this. I would try to console her, that I didn't enjoy gambling at all. I only did it to make money.

Even today when I give many talks, I get a bit of stage fright before each one. I always tell myself glumly, "You didn't have to accept this invitation, you could have been home comfortably in a chair." What consoles me is the knowledge that once I get started I will do well, and that many actors and actresses have the same problem.

Lou Berlinrood was an enormous help when I was growing up. My father was quite authoritarian. Lou, however, was a doctor and my father had to listen to him. Lou constantly advised tolerance and patience.

Lou was always welcome in our house. Both my parents were very fond of him and conversely. The relationship between Lou and my father was never made clear. I had the impression that he was some sort of cousin. His mother and an older sister had died in a tenement fire and my father's mother had been very kind to Lou. His father had been a pushcart peddler before opening a clothing store which he ran with the help of Lou's older brother, Sol, a very nice man. Lou often said that he had been a member of a gang that used to steal from the Five and Ten. All the other members of the gang ended up either in the East River or in the electric chair at Sing Sing. Lou ended up being a doctor.

Lou often scandalized my mother. He went to dances where he danced with black girls.

Lou loved to feed me. I had developed the habit of dropping in at his office on Saturday afternoon. In the morning, I would go either to the museums or the Forty-Second Street Library. I would read something while waiting for him to take care of his last patient. Then we would have lunch together and very often spend the rest of the afternoon talking about various things.

He never forgot the time when he took me out to lunch, and after I finished, he asked me if I wanted anything else. "Yes," I replied, "another lunch." I started all over again and finished another lunch easily. I had quite an appetite in those days. What is ironical, is that now that I can afford to eat anything, I have to diet.

At that time, Lou was doing research on piknolepsy. The adjective "piknos" means false. The symptoms of piknolepsy are exactly like the symptoms of epilepsy. One can only tell the difference by means of brain waves. These experiments made a deep impression on me. They showed me what can be done in medicine using the techniques of physics and engineering. Much later, I realized how much could be done using the techniques of mathematics and computers.

I wrote up Lou's results for him, and as a result I knew quite a lot about piknolepsy when I was sixteen. In general, Lou taught me a great deal about medicine in a painless manner. He was full of entertaining stories. I learned from him about allergies and placebos. In addition, one of his hobbies was tracking down cases of syphilis. He was firmly convinced you can only catch syphilis by direct sexual contact.

When an eight-year old boy was admitted to Bellevue with syphilis, he thought at last he had a case which contradicted the general theory. However, he was very cautious. One day when talking to the boy, J. P. Morgan's yacht sailed down the East River. Lou had contacts with many famous people by treating their children. He promised the boy a ride on the yacht if the boy would tell him how he caught syphilis.

This was the story. The boy, although eight years old, was big for his age. Consequently, he was a member of a gang of boys who were ten to twelve. The family had a great deal of money, but had to live in Hell's Kitchen because that was the only apartment they could find. In Hell's Kitchen, there were many gypsies. These gypsies had a belief that sexual intercourse with a virgin would cure venereal disease. And that is how the boy caught syphilis.

When I was about sixteen, Lou decided that I ought to have my teeth fixed up. He knew a family of dentists and arranged this easily. Going to the dentist was quite an ordeal in those days. Although novacaine was just coming in, many dentists were reluctant to use it. In the first place, it meant learning new techniques. Often, giving the shot was more painful than the drilling. Sharp and small needles had not been developed yet. Furthermore, the novacaine took about forty-five minutes to "take". Consequently, many dentists said, "I have to know when it hurts."

Many people insisted upon a complete anesthetic to go to the dentist. Johnny Broderick, the tough New York detective who thought nothing of beating up racketeers on sight and going into a room after a cornered killer, would climb out through the window of the waiting room unless accompanied by a friend.

Fortunately, I had two anesthetics.

I had just discovered books on vector analysis and was entranced by the subject. My experience with geometry had prepared me for this.

Also, I wanted to learn something about tensor analysis, which was necessary for relativity theory. I was quite disappointed that tensor analysis was just notation. Furthermore, the mathematics of relativity theory is not difficult or interesting at all. Philosophically, it is quite interesting, but mathematically it is rather dull.

Secondly, the dentist had a very pretty nurse. The dentist stood on the right and the nurse on the left. Occasionally, she assisted him in some activity. When she did so, she would lean over to hand him some instrument or other. Whether by accident or design, when she did so, she would lean her crotch against my left hand. I was petrified by this, and was so busy making sure that I didn't move a muscle, that I paid little attention to the drilling.

The dentist was a Henry Georgeite, a single taxer. Poised over me with the drill, he made me promise to go to several meetings. I thought it wise to agree. As I suspected, the meetings were very dull. I did my usual trick, which I have done at innumerable parties, dinners and meetings. I let the sound flow around my head and thought about mathematics.

I didn't know about painless dentistry until I met Charlie Goldstein. I suggested to him that the second method of anesthetic wasn't bad. He agreed, but his wife was his nurse.

When I first came to Charlie, he asked me to leave through the side door. I used to turn so green that he was afraid I'd scare his other patients.

My mother was a Victorian. I received no sex education but many dire warnings about wicked older women who preyed on young boys. The nature of this preying was not specified. For years I looked in every doorway and every window hoping to find a wicked older woman. I had no luck. Much later I found wicked older women but by that time I was generally older than them.

My father wanted me to go to West Point; we compromised on the Boy Scouts. I was not enthusiastic about the Boy Scouts, but my father was very militaristic. He loved to wear his army uniform, and often would accompany me on hikes. I well remember all the equipment I used to take on those hikes.

I was supposed to be an Eagle Scout. Eddie Kanner, Jerry Janoff and I went through the ranks together: Tenderfoot, Second Class, First Class, Star, and Life. Unfortunately, since I couldn't go to camp long enough I never got Camping and Bird Study, which were required for

Eagle. Boy Scout camp was eight dollars a week. My parents managed to scrape up enough so that I could go for two weeks. I am sure I could have gone for a longer time if I had wished. However, I was not enthusiastic about it and although I had more than the twenty-one merit badges required, I didn't have the right ones.

Every year we made a project. One year, I decided to make a knotboard. I used a picture in a dictionary and had a great deal of fun figuring out the knots from this picture. There are many interesting mathematical questions connected with knots. Gauss devised an interesting integral which determined whether two curves are knotted or not. Artin wrote a paper on braids, an interesting combination of group theory and topology.

One of the members of my patrol was Mickey Rich, whose older brother was Buddy Rich who became the famous drummer. Buddy always carried a pair of drumsticks with him and would practise on everything he passed, the lids of garbage cans and the railings of the boardwalk.

All in all, I think the Boy Scouts was a waste of time, but I did make several friends, and gained valuable experience as editor of the newspaper.

In addition, I did enough hiking to last me a lifetime. Although I like nature and have been through the National Parks several times, at nighttime I like to sleep in a comfortable motel or hotel.

Two of my friends were daredevils, and did many risky things. However, I could do one trick they couldn't. I could vault over a mailbox. The sight of that concrete spike would always dampen their ardor.

Our scoutmaster and assistant scoutmaster, Al and Leon Harvey, were paternal twins. Also, the junior assistant scoutmasters, Gene and Leon Marcus were paternal twins. Closely associated with the troop was Jerry Schoen. At the time he had a girlfriend, Geraldine, who had a younger friend, Sylvia. That is how I met Sylvia.

Al and Leon were struggling cartoonists. Finally, everything clicked and they founded Harvey Comics which became very successful.

Many boys wanted to join the troop but were not allowed to by their parents who thought the Boy Scouts were too militaristic. One of them was Murray Hammwerker. He was a very nice boy and would have been an asset to the troop. But the real disappointment was the fact that his father was Nathan Hammwerker who owned the famous Nathan's in Coney Island. Every time we looked at Murray, we thought of all the free hot dogs and French fries that he represented.

It was an all-Jewish troop except for Clement Schuck. Clement was the son of a janitor of one of the apartment houses on Brighton Sixth Street. The father was a very nice man, but the mother was an ardent Nazi. She infected Clement, who wasn't very bright, with this disease.

I got to know Clement very well since we took hiking merit badge together. Every day for months, we walked to Prospect Park and back, a distance of about five miles. Clement would entertain me by telling me the illegal tactics that various football coaches had taught him. Clement was about six feet tall and very solidly built. He would play football for a Catholic high school for a year until expelled for low grades. It was necessary to watch Clement at all times since his idea of a good practical joke was to throw a block into you.

Clement decided to form a secret army. He drove Marty Klein out to the wilds of Long Island at three o'clock in the morning and revealed his plan. Marty was to be his second-in-command. Considering the time and the place, Marty thought it wise to accept.

Clement joined the Nazi army by way of South America and probably perished in Russia.

There was also a Girl Scout troop in the neighborhood. One of the members of the troop was Zelda Weintraub, who lived in a fancy house in Manhattan Beach. She had the best of everything and well she might. I learned years later that her father, Martin Weintraub, was the principal lawyer for Murder, Inc.

World War I had been a giant lark for my father. He wore a uniform, rode a motorcycle between New York and Philadelphia as a courier, and did not go overseas. The same held for many of the American Legionnaires and members of the JWV. This had been a very glamorous period for them. They had no realization of the grim realities of war.

My father participated a great deal in these veterans' organizations. He was so anxious to be an officer that he even was the chaplain of the American Legion post. Knowing my father's views on religion, I found this very funny. Not so funny were the street fights between the Bund and the JWV. The Bund would drive a sound truck into a predominantly Jewish neighborhood and start spewing forth Nazi propaganda. The JWV combated this with a flying squad. As soon as they heard the sound truck, they sent out this squad. A street fight would ensue. By the time the police arrived, there was usually blood on the streets.

A fact of my teens was illness, not mine but my mother's and father's. My father got ill when I was about fifteen, and my mother when I was about sixteen. For a long while, one was in one hospital and one was in another. Consequently, I used to visit one on Monday, Wednesday, and Friday, and the other on Tuesday, Thursday, and Saturday. On Sunday I would visit them both. Since I was an only child, this made me quite used to being alone.

CHAPTER 2

HIGH SCHOOL AND COLLEGE

I was very fortunate in knowing exactly what I wanted to be. I wanted to be a theoretical physicist. As a matter of fact, I didn't even know that professional mathematicians existed. I had read the popular books on science by Jeans, Eddington, Einstein, and others. In addition I read the book, "Crucibles" by Jaffee and the various books by de Kruif. After the age of about thirteen, however, I concentrated on mathematics and science, with an occasional book on archaeology or philology.

When I was younger I had thought of being a research biologist. As a matter of fact, my family wanted me to be a doctor. Lou was always bringing around slides, microscopes and scalpels. My mother took one look at the scalpels and insisted that he take them back. Furthermore, he was always taking me to Bellevue. But, it was obvious I was not interested in being a doctor.

Several summers, I worked in first aid stations and at the beach but I couldn't stand the sight of stitching. We had many cases of that type because people stepped on broken glass in the ocean. The main advantage of working in a first aid station was eating the ice-cream which policemen confiscated. This ice-cream was confiscated from young kids who wanted to make some money selling ice-cream on the beach illegally. Naturally, the concessionaires complained.

When I was about eleven, my father, an inveterate browser in second-hand book stores, brought home Schultze's "Elementary and Advanced Algebra". I went through it as a book of puzzles. To this day I remember certain parts and it may well be that it had an influence on certain mathematical theories. In any case, knowing algebra made me a star pupil in junior high. Nevertheless, at that time I thought mathematics was only useful for theoretical physics.

When I came to the section on the solution of two simultaneous linear equations, I discovered the use of determinants by myself. I used to practice getting the solution mentally using the rule for evaluation of determinants. Of course I was anticipated by Cramer by several hundred years. What is ironical is that Cramer's solution which is so useful theoretically is of no use computationally.

As I said in Chapter I, as a result of the Depression we went all the way down. We had to move from Brighton Beach and for a while we lived in Bensonhurst. While living in Brighton Beach I went to an elementary school in Coney Island. Brighton Beach being a new area did not yet have a school of its own. From this elementary school I went to junior high, thereby skipping another year. I had already skipped one year. It was nice to skip two years, which were mostly a waste of time but it made it hard on my athletic career. I had to compete against boys who were much older.

Coney Island was a rough area. On the way to school, children from Brighton Beach were regularly held up for their spending money.

In elementary school, I decided to try out for the track team. However, at the first meeting, the coach caught me whispering something and banished me. That was the end of my athletic career in elementary school.

Junior high combined three years, the 7th, 8th and 9th years into two. One went from junior high directly into third term of high school. In junior high, I took a year of algebra and a year of French. I discovered in junior high that I had a flair for design. Also, in junior high, we had to take woodworking. I made the only three-legged table that would not stand up.

My best friend in junior high was Chester Kallman. We drifted apart when we went to high school, but when we went to junior high, we spent many hours together. Subsequently, he became the companion of W.H. Auden and they did much work together. In particular, they translated many Italian operas.

In junior high, I made my first geometric discovery. I observed that vertical angles were equal. Of course, I had no notion of a proof. However, I still remember the thrill of discovery.

My father during the plush period had gotten some furniture and other things from Sloanes. When the Depression hit he should have given them back rather than trying to keep up the payments. As a result we were constantly hounded by collection agents. For this reason, we had to move constantly. My memory of this period is continually crating and uncrating books. Finally, when I went to high school, Abraham Lincoln High School, we moved back to Brighton Beach. Abraham Lincoln High School is situated on Ocean Parkway about six blocks from the beach. In nice weather, it was a pleasant walk. When the weather was not good, which is usual in the winter time in New York, it was an ordeal. When the weather was really bad, most of the students stayed home and classes were very cozy.

One of the advantages of living back east is the change of seasons. Winter means snow and snow means snowball fights. I had very accurate aim with the snowball which got me into trouble frequently. I observed, however, that in a snowball fight, no matter how accurate I was it was easy for the other person to dodge my snowball. Consequently, I used the following strategem. I would lob a snowball with my right hand, and while the other person was watching that, I would throw one with my left hand. Thus, I learned the principle of decoys, which I wrote about at RAND in connection with far more deadly missiles.

When I graduated from junior high school I got no medals or awards. I always had a very mature attitude towards medals and awards and I didn't think much of them. I had very definite ideas of what I wanted to learn and how I wanted to learn it. I had no intention of letting the establishment interfere.

I soon learned that the average teacher of elementary, high school and college was the enemy of the bright students. These people with their rigidity and lack of understanding had no desire for a penetrating question which would expose their ignorance. Fortunately, there were many good teachers around. This was especially true during the Depression. Many gifted people taught in high school to make sure of a regular job. Many brilliant people took jobs as policemen, firemen and sanitation workers to get a pay check.

Some years ago, Time magazine had a story that the squash champion at Harvard was the son of a New York City policeman. The story amused me greatly. I knew the family well in Brighton Beach and knew how brilliant they all were. The father was an example of what I was saying above.

I constantly adhered to Abel's dictum, "Read the masters, not the pupils." However, my mother was very disappointed. Seeing how unhappy she was, I promised her that when I graduated from high school I would win a few to make her happy. When I graduated I won the mathematics, English, history, and Latin medals. I would have won the medals in physics and economics too, but the teachers in these subjects wouldn't let me take the competitive exams, since they wanted the medals for their pets.

I regarded the course in physics as a collection of parlor tricks, and the course in economics as just plain foolish. I imagine my attitudes showed.

For the graduation ceremony, I got a new suit and new shoes which were quite slippery. When I went up on the stage to receive these medals, I fell flat on my face.

There was a great advantage in being an atheist. One had the Jewish holidays and the Christmas holidays as well.

Lincoln's birthday, February 12, and Washington's birthday, February 22, were holidays. Lincoln was a fine man but in my opinion greatly overrated. I feel that the only reason so much is made of him is because he was shot.

Abraham Lincoln High School had a good curriculum. It had two types of programs, one for those going on to college and one for those going to work. The commercial course offered typing and shorthand. I often thought how useful these would have been and how I would have preferred to take them rather than read Macbeth and Hamlet. The reading of Shakespeare is quite traditional and has little relevance to the problems of contemporary life. In high school, I took one more year of algebra, intermediate algebra, one year of geometry, and a semester of solid geometry. Geometry is a very sophisticated subject and should not be given in high school. The necessity of the axiomatic approach was never explained and I feel sure that it was not understood by the instructor. In addition, I always felt that the first few theorems of Euclid were quite fishy. The idea of picking up and moving a dimensionless object seemed absurd.

In addition, I took two more years of French. I enjoyed French and knew that it was necessary to know the language both for mathematical purposes and for general culture.

In high school, I was on the mathematics team. We had a dedicated coach, Julius Frielich, who spent hours with us almost every afternoon. During these sessions, we learned various parts of algebra and various puzzles as well.

English books were very helpful. They had good texts and good problems. Norman, Norman Greenspan and I would constantly challenge each other with these problems. We were particularly interested in constructions. I have no great ability at geometry, but the subject had always fascinated me. Edna St. Vincent Millay wrote, "Only Euclid has looked upon beauty bare" and I agree with her.

She was certainly right about geometry having beautiful results, but other parts of mathematics had beautiful theorems too. It is impossible to describe the beauty of mathematics, just as it is impossible to describe the appeal of music. Just as different people prefer different types of music, different mathematicians prefer different parts of mathematics. De gustivus non disputandum.

Norman was my closest friend in high school and college. I often had dinner at his house. His mother was an excellent cook, and I enjoyed her cooking enormously. She even ordered an extra bottle of milk for me.

When I made dinner for myself, I would mix a can of hash and a can of green peas. This was tasty, quick and cheap, an ideal combination. When I felt particularly hungry, I would get two generous roast beef sandwiches for fifteen cents, non-kosher. Kosher ones were two for a quarter. Or, I would get three apple strudel for a nickel. Food in New York was plentiful and cheap.

Norman's father worked in the post office, probably making about $3,000 a year, which was a lot of money in those days. As a result, Norman could indulge in his hobbies. In high school, he was interested in magic. He even had a special jacket with rubber-lined pockets and all kinds of elastic so that things could snap from one arm to another. In college, he became interested in photography. This was very convenient for me. Whenever I wanted to meet a girl, I would have Norman take a picture of her. The rest followed a predictable pattern.

After several years, Norman's family moved from Brighton Beach to Neck Road, two stops away from Brighton Beach and a very easy walk. We often used to congregate at his house and at two o'clock in the morning we would save a nickel's carfare by walking on to the station. At Neck Road the subway ran on the surface.

One of my friends made the mistake of doing this trick at two o'clock in the afternoon on a Sunday. He was promptly arrested by a plainclothes subway policeman and marched through the whole train and then booked at the King's Highway police station. His belt and shoelaces were taken away as a precaution against suicide, which made his mother hysterical. He got off with a warning by pleading that he was a scoutmaster, which he was. This was fortunate since he became an officer during the war.

Norman was on the mathematics team too, as was Paul Brock, and Peter Chiarulli.

There was an excellent book on modern geometry by Nathan Altschiller-Court. In college, I took a course in modern geometry using the book by Roger Johnson. I will say more about him below.

When I was a junior, the top man in the city in mathematics was Harry Schwartz of Boys High. He went to Columbia and gradually changed from mathematics to mathematical statistics to economics. This was on the advice of a well-meaning faculty member who said that Jews didn't get jobs as mathematicians. Today he is the science and economics editor of the New York Times.

We had an inter-scholastic algebra league, consisting of various high schools, such as New Utrecht, Boys High, and Stuyvesant, as well as others. While I was senior, my chief rival was I.A.L. Diamond of Boys High. Although I was top man in the city during my senior year, when it came to the final competition, I loafed. I only got two out of five while Diamond got five out of five. As a result, Diamond and I tied and we both shared a medal.

Diamond went to Columbia, where he changed from mathematics to writing. He wrote the class play four years in a row. I often jokingly said that the I.A.L. stood for inter-scholastic algebra league. Imagine my surprise when I read a gossip column several years ago and found out that I was right. The story is the following.

When Diamond was at Columbia he worked on the college magazine, "The Spectator". One day, the editor said, "Diamond, there are too many Jews on the magazine. You have to do something about your first name, which happened to be Israel. Diamond agreed and henceforth used the initials I.A.L. Many years later, when he and Billy Wilder won an Oscar, I wrote to him and suggested that he scratch my name on the Oscar since we shared a medal. I don't know whether he followed this suggestion.

The second big interest in high school was Latin. I have always been interested in philology and was delighted at the opportunity to take Latin. It is a very practical language because with French and Latin it is easy to read mathematical Italian, Spanish, Portuguese, and Rumanian. Abraham Lincoln High also offered Spanish, German and Italian. My father stimulated my interest in etymology. His explanations were often wrong but always interesting.

The second year of Latin was devoted to Caesar's commentaries. The third year was devoted to Cicero. The fourth year was devoted to Virgil. I enjoyed Caesar and Cicero. I read many of Cicero's speeches and essays. I read a little Virgil but found it very artificial and soon tired of the decipherment.

My Latin teacher, Lucy Maria Prescott, wanted me to become a classicist or a philologist. Although I retained my interest in classics and philology, I felt that the field was much too narrow. I have always thought that theoretical physics and mathematics give one a much broader scope.

She was a wonderful person and very inspiring. I remember many of the things she said and did. She often quoted the remark, "Culture is what remains after all knowledge has gone." She also wanted to show that Latin was quite relevant. At the beginning of every class, students were encouraged to write on the board various words. When class began she would write down the Latin originals. One day, mischievously, I wrote "vagina" on the board. Without hesitation, she wrote "equals sheath". I learned a great deal from that episode. This was a fine example of grace under pressure.

My third interest in high school was in writing. There was a special course, a journalism course, for people interested in writing. However, I felt that this would be too much work in addition to the mathematics team and Latin. Consequently, I stayed in the regular English courses. It gave me great satisfaction, however, to win various competitions which the people in journalism did not.

One of the difficulties I had in high school was that my mother wanted to keep me a little boy. Consequently, up until the sixth term of high school I wore knickers. In addition, my father thought I looked very good in a beret. This was not exactly the headgear for New York City, and I got into many fights because of it.

Another difficulty, which I also had in college was that I didn't look like the high school teacher's image of a scholar. I looked more like an athlete, and a not very bright athlete. To this day, at parties, I often respond to the question as to what I do by saying that I am a tennis coach. I get tired of the automatic response to the statement that I am a mathematician.

In my senior year, I decided to look into some other teams. First, I looked at the chess team. However, I knew enough to know I was not a good player and didn't know anything about the theory of chess. Hence, I gave that up quickly.

Next, I looked into the tennis team. Although I could have had a place on the team, I realized I was not a strong player, and decided to let a friend, Eddie Kanner, who was two years behind me have the experience.

The trouble with tennis is that one had to buy a racket, restring it from time to time and buy balls. I learned to play tennis by borrowing rackets occasionally and using rackets which people had thrown away. In addition, there was a middle-aged woman who had two good rackets and always brought a new can of balls. However, she hated to run and always stood in one spot. This was very good for my accuracy, because no matter where she hit the ball I had to return it to her.

I was, however, a good one-wall handball player.

When I played another candidate for the team I beat him 21-0. I had studied the game very carefully. What I would do is to stand at the extreme right hand of the service line and angle my serve in such a way that the ball went into the middle of the next court to the opponent's left hand. If he returned it, it was generally a weak return and I could do many things with it. If he shifted over, I would serve right down the line and he didn't have a chance to return it. However, the coach didn't like my style of play, and chose the other candidate for the team. After all these years the injustice still rankles.

I analyzed other athletic games I played the same way. I found that there was tremendous stylization. The people who played the games were more interested in form than content. They seemed to have forgotten that the primary object of the game was to win.

For example, in basketball, they liked to dribble close to the basket for a lay-up. When they shot, they held the ball with two hands. That was bad for two reasons. In the first place, it gave ample notice that a player was going to shoot. In the second place, it was easy to block.

When I played, I refused to expend all that energy on dribbling. When I got the ball, I shot. Furthermore, I developed the ability to shoot with one hand, either hand. This unconventional play did not make me popular, particularly since it won. However, I had decided early that I was not out to win popularity contests. Now this style of play is standard.

When I played, I had to watch out for elbows, knees, and tripping legs. This merely added to the zest of playing.

In baseball, being left-handed was a great advantage. In the first place, one is a step closer to first base. In the second place, it is easier to bat against a right-handed pitcher. When the pitcher is left-handed, it becomes a disadvantage. Consequently, I became a switch hitter, long before Mickey Mantle.

My first allegiance was to the Yankees. The Yankee Stadium was only a few stops before the one we used. At the time, we lived on Longfellow Avenue and used the 174th Street station. From the train, one could see the outfield of the Yankee Stadium.

When the Dodgers got Jackie Robinson, I switched my allegiance. The story of how Jackie Robinson broke down the racial barrier is very dramatic and very inspiring. When the Dodgers came to Los Angeles, Eric and I went regularly to the ball games. We tried the seats in various parts of the stadium, and found that we got the best view of the field from the bleachers, the cheapest seats. When we splurged and got more expensive seats, we would move down in the late innings. Often, we would end up behind the dugout of the visiting team. Eric amused himself by shouting insults at the visiting manager. Disappointingly, no foul ball ever came close to us.

In tennis, in serving to the forehand court, either one could serve down the line to the backhand, or, when the player shifted over, serve in the other direction. In the backhand court, a twist serve would pull the player all the way off the court. Then, a forehand shot would usually score the point.

Although, this game usually won, I didn't like it. When I came to California, I developed the "big" game, a booming serve followed by a smashing overhead or net shot. I did this until I pulled a back muscle. For several months I drove on one side waiting for it to heal. Finally, when I had convinced myself that I was dying of back cancer, I went to see Emil Seletz. He examined me, and assured me that I had merely pulled a back muscle and he had me feel the spasm. He reminded me that I was not eighteen anymore. After that, I did not play the big game regularly.

In track, I usually ran the 100, 220 or 440. I wasn't enthusiastic about the 100-yard dash because one had little time for strategy. In 220 and 440, however, I developed a simple technique for winning. I would run behind the leader until about 25 yards from the finish, and then forge ahead.

I was never interested in swimming. The ocean was always too cold. The principal reason, however, was that swimming was my father's best sport. He would think nothing of swimming from Brighton Beach to Rockaway and back, a distance of about seven miles. He was an excellent athlete, and loved to play medicine ball with the lifeguards.

I also never liked golf. I was given two sets of golf-clubs, one by Arthur and one by a friend. However, I could never develop an interest in the game, and always thought of it as an old man's game.

We also played football on the beach. One could not run very fast, but one couldn't get hurt when tackled. I played quarterback. One day, when running through the line, I was punched in the nose and got a bloody nose. While lying on the back, waiting for the bleeding to stop, I decided that football was not a game for me. From that point on I played touch-tackle. Here, my abilities at passing and running made sure that I won most of the time.

My grade average for the first four terms was about 80. I got good grades in mathematics, Latin, French, and English. What pulled my average down was the social sciences. I had the habit, which I still have, of stating the main points and letting the details go. This is not the way to proceed in the social sciences.

Actually, I knew a great deal of European history, due to stamp-collecting. My father and I had a joint collection, and it is amazing how much history and geography one learns painlessly from stamp-collecting. However, I had a very disagreeable teacher in European history and we disliked each other immensely. In addition, he was a very poor teacher with little understanding of the subject.

My Aunt Peg was very worried about my average. She offered me a trip to Washington, a month's stay, if I would raise my average to 90. This was a very powerful inducement. I knew exactly what to do. All that was necessary in the social sciences was to belabor the obvious. It is very much like the story of how one tells a joke to the English. First, one says that one will tell a joke, then one tells the joke, then one says that he has told a joke. Actually, this is a libel. The English, as a rule, have a very good sense of humor, far better than the Americans.

Without difficulty, I raised my average to 90. Actually, I have always been interested in history, and related subjects. Unfortunately, in high school up until the last semester I had a succession of very dull teachers in these areas. Consequently, I had no desire to please them at all.

Washington is a great city to visit. It has many features of interest. I had a map showing these and walked over the entire city looking at these. I soon knew the Library of Congress and the Smithsonian very well. My Aunt Peg and Uncle Alfred, having lived in Washington for many years, had many good contacts there. They arranged for me to go in the stacks at the Library of Congress. There I saw many rare manuscripts. In particular, I was able to see many examples of incunabula. Also, I was able to go behind the scenes at the White House. There were official tours, but naturally, they did not enter certain rooms. I was able to go into these rooms and even sit in the President's chair where he made major decisions. This was a big thrill.

I even walked up to the top of the Washington monument. I felt this should be done once.

You may be sure that I kept my average above 90 so that I could go back next year.

In January 1937, I graduated from high school and began college. I started my college career at CCNY, City College of New York. It has two campuses, one at 137th in Manhattan, for general students, and one at 23rd Street for those interested in business administration.

CCNY looked like a university. It is built in Gothic style and had at that time a very strong faculty and very good students. It had very high admission standards, and the student body competed furiously with each other. We had, in many ways, the cream of the New York City high school system. I doubt whether this condition holds today. These people have much more money and with the lowering of various prejudice barriers send their children to the ivy league colleges.

I was accustomed to travelling on the subway to school since I had to do that in junior high. Going to CCNY involved about a one-hour trip each way. It wasn't bad either way, Brighton Beach and 42nd Street were ends of the line and I always got a seat. I would tuck myself away and although it was noisy, one learned to disregard the noise. In the morning, I would do my homework on the train. In the evening I would read something.

The trip from Brooklyn to Manhattan involved going over a bridge. This was welcome because it meant fresh air. Below, there was a large rock on which someone had painted, "Jesus Saves". Every morning I made a joke to myself, "Jesus saves but the Bank of America gives 4%."

When the weather was bad, I could stay underground taking the IRT. When the weather was nice, I would walk up 42nd Street to the Eighth Avenue line. This was a new subway at the time, and the trains were very clean and relatively noiseless. However, the reason why I would take the Eighth Avenue subway was that I could look at the attractions in the burlesque houses on 42nd Street. In the morning I would walk up one side and in the evening I would walk up the other side. In this way, I saw all the posters. The foremost burlesque house was Minsky's. At that time, Gypsy Rose Lee was appearing there. Unfortunately, the price of admission was sixty cents. Much as I wanted to go, I could not see spending that vast amount of money. Naturally, I regret this now.

The most desirable scholarship was the Pulitzer scholarship. This was four years free tuition to Columbia and $1,000 a year. I found out about this scholarship in the following way. Some friends of mine had a blank map of Europe and were trying to place various cities on it. I asked them what they were doing and why.

The Pulitzer scholarship involved taking exams in all high school subjects. Since this involved a very long time, the examinations were given in two parts. Naturally, the best people in the city competed, about 600. I didn't expect to win, but I thought it would be fun to compete. The 600, as a result of the examinations were narrowed down to thirty. From this thirty, twelve were awarded scholarships. Then there was a personal interview on the basis of the examinations and the interviews and twelve scholarships were given out. I made it to the field of thirty and then had an interview. I put on my best suit, my only suit, a white shirt and a tie, and went up to Columbia for the interview. In the course of the interview, the interviewer asked me what my interests were. I told him I wanted to be a theoretical physicist and had read about quantum mechanics and relativity theory.

The interviewer asked what I knew about these subjects. I knew enough to know that they were highly mathematical and could not be described in words. So I answered, truthfully, that I knew nothing. I knew immediately that was the wrong response and that I would not receive the scholarship.

I have always been cursed with this terrible objectivity. I should have just recited back what the books said.

Alfred had grown up with Ritt, a professor of mathematics at Columbia. That contact would have been very helpful to me at that time. Why Alfred never told me about that I don't know.

Registration at CCNY for an entering freshman was a nightmare. First it was necessary to decide what subjects one would take. I think for the first semester, I had differential calculus, physics, English composition, French, speech, physical education (gym), and military science.

I was always interested in military science, and when I read the description of the course it seemed quite fascinating. To my horror, I found that it was RCTC, and the first session was devoted to map reading. The Boy Scouts again! I quickly went to see the colonel in charge of the RCTC and dropped the course. CCNY had a very large RCTC unit, probably the largest in the country, because of the free uniform and two weeks vacation in the summer. It even had a communist cell.

The procedure of registration involved choosing a feasible program, looking at the board to make sure that all the selected classes were open, and standing on line to have the program O.K.'d. Standing on line took about one-half hour. Just as one reached the point where the program was to be O.K.'d, a class was closed. Then it was necessary to get out of line all over again. It was a real frustration dream.

I ended up with classes at nine o'clock in the morning and four o'clock in the afternoon.

I didn't mind this, since I had nothing else to do anyway. I would usually spend my time browsing in the library, going to the great hall at noon and listening to the organ, and going to the student house and playing records. There were three records there. One was a selection from Carmen, including the famous Toreador song. I have always like Carmen and played this record over and over.

The course in differential and integral calculus was a good one. We used an excellent book, Granville, Mith and Longley. The course in physics was given in the usual fashion. A demonstration was given by a senior professor and then we had sections to discuss various results. Fortunately, I had a very bright young man as instructor in my section. In my discussion with him, I learned a good deal of mathematics. In particular, I learned about Huyghens' principle. The instructor in English composition had been a reporter for the New York Times. On the first day of class, he had us all write essays. When he read mine, he felt it would be a waste of time for me to attend class. Instead, he gave me a reading list. This included "Tristram Shandy", "Erewhon", and "Ulysses" by James Joyce. All I had to do was read all the books and write a book report on each of them.

James Joyce was an excellent writer and Ulysses was well worth reading. He wrote a subsequent book, "Finnegan's Wake", which I tried to read but gave up after a few pages. He tried and failed. The stream of consciousness method is not a very good way to communicate. He deserves a tremendous amount of credit for trying.

Since I had done very well in French in high school, I was not forced to take first year French in college. I went immediately into second year French. The first semester was French literature of the 19th Century, people like Victor Hugo, Alexander Dumas, etc. The instructor Roget, had been born in France. He was a man of about fifty. He would have each of us translate a paragraph and then translate a paragraph himself. After his first translation, I raised my hand and told him that the translation was not correct. Naturally, he was very indignant. I pointed out that the translation was totally technically correct but not colloquial. At first, he was very angry with me but after a while we became very good friends.

As expected, I did not get good grades in speech. Consequently, when I transferred to Brooklyn College I was not given credit for these and had to take four terms of speech at Brooklyn College. I often jokingly said that I was majoring in speech. I was quite fortunate to pass these courses. My final speech each semester was, "Why I Dislike Speech Teachers".

Entering freshmen at CCNY had to take a sort of college aptitude test. Great emphasis was put upon this test. I think the national average was 180, and the average for CCNY was 220. Since I was accustomed to working under time pressure, and much of the test was on mathematics and language, I got about 360. This attracted the attention of various people.

I had an interview with somebody in the placement office, and as a result of my high score was allowed to mark the examinations during the break between semesters. I worked eight hours a day, and made twenty dollars a week that way for two weeks. A princely sum in those days. Considering the size of the entering class, and the way the examination was very carefully graded, I soon knew the examination by heart. I think there were 600 questions all together, a large enough number so that no one was able to finish the examination.

My chief memory of the period was one of hunger. My grandfather had given me one dollar a week for carfare and lunch. One dollar a week covered the carfare, leaving nothing for lunch.

Lunch was rather cheap. For eight cents, you could get a big bowl of soup and three pieces of bread. For five cents more, you could get a big serving of succotash. Most days I did not have lunch. As a matter of fact, I very clearly remember that my chief fantasy on the subway train going home was that we would be marooned and have to turn cannibal. I would look at my fellow passengers and wonder who I would eat first.

Often, I got so hungry, I would have lunch and have no fare for the way home. Sometimes, a friendly guard would hear my tale of woe and let me through the gate. Sometimes, I borrowed money from my last period instructor, Roget.

At CCNY, I decided to resume my athletic career, going out for the track team. The gym had an indoor track and the coach told me to run around the track 100 times a day. I did this once or twice and got bored and gave up the activity.

I used to amuse myself boxing with big fellows. They were very poor boxers and I made them human punching bags. One day, a fellow about 5 feet 5 inches wanted to box with me. At first, I refused, saying I would hurt him. He said not to worry that I wouldn't hurt him. We started boxing. After a few seconds, he hit me in the kidneys. I deflated like a balloon. I thought that was an accident and I started sparring again. A few seconds later he did the same thing. I decided then and there that boxing was not for me, and have never boxed again.

When I transferred to Brooklyn College, I was technically an entering freshman there. Consequently, they wanted me to take the college aptitude examination. I pointed out that I had already taken it. However, bureaucracy is bureaucracy. I decided to teach them a lesson. I imagine that I got 598 out of 600. I made no effort to get a perfect score. As a matter of fact, I didn't waste time reading the questions. You can imagine what this did to all the curves they drew.

In 1938, I transferred to Brooklyn College. There were several reasons for this. In the first place, Brooklyn College had a new campus at Flatbush Ave. and Avenue Eighth. In the second place, the new campus was only about twenty minutes from Brighton Beach by subway. But the most important reason was that Brooklyn had girls. Although, legally there was no reason why there were no girls at CCNY, I think there were about three in the whole school. This was obviously a very undesirable state of affairs. The faculty at CCNY was much stronger, as was the student body. However, I figured that I could supply the intellectual stimulation myself.

At Brooklyn College, I continued my efforts to be a theoretical physicist. What I thought I would do is major in mathematics, because that took little work, and spend most of my time learning theoretical physics. To begin with, I had to take mechanics, and electricity and magnetism. To my dismay, I found both courses intolerably dull. At the end of the semester, I was eleven experiments behind in one course and twelve in the other. There were thirteen experiments all together. Each experiment took hours to do and even longer to write up. The instructors insisted that I make up the experiments. I didn't care about failing a course, but I had a state scholarship of $100 a year which would be terminated if I did fail a course. Consequently, I got the write-up of the experiments in mechanics from one friend, Norman, and the write-up of the experiments in electricity and magnetism from another. I will never forget that the instructor in mechanics looked over the write-ups and asked me how the results compared with theory. Of course, I didn't have the slightest idea. However, I said without batting an eye, "Within the limits of experimental error." Fortunately, that satisfied him and he asked no further questions.

It was clear that I was not to be a theoretical physicist. Consequently, with a sigh, I decided to stay a major in mathematics and that is how I became a mathematician.

In Brooklyn College, I took eight good courses which isn't bad.

One was a course in projective geometry. It was given by Roger Johnson, and I am sorry that I still don't have his notes. I think a good tribute to him would be to publish a book on that elegant topic.

One of the most elegant theorems in projective geometry is that concerning the eleven-point conic. Properly specialized, this becomes the famous nine-point circle.

There is a story connected with this. A well-known French mathematician, Bloch, killed his parents and castrated himself. This was considered bizarre behavior even for a mathematician and he was put in an insane asylum where he continued his mathematical research. A Paris journalist heard about this and went to see Bloch. To entertain the journalist, Bloch told him about the two imaginary points at infinity which lie on every circle.

The journalist went out shaking his head. Obviously a fine mind had cracked.

Roger Johnson also wrote an excellent book on modern geometry. Unfortunately, when that course was given, he was not the instructor. The instructor was an ass who knew very little geometry. Consequently, I did not bother to go to class. I went instead to our table in the cafeteria, leaving instructions that if he got stuck he could call me. From time to time, some student would come down to get me. Then I would go to the classroom, find out what the difficulty was, show him how to get around it, and return to the cafeteria.

Then, I took four terms of Greek.

In order to have this course I had to arrange to get five other people. Four of these were easy to obtain. They were people of Greek descent. Modern Greek is very close to classical Greek. Consequently, these four wanted an easy A. I found one other character who wanted to study classical Greek.

Our teacher for three of the four semesters was Helen Gordon Pope, with whom I became quite friendly. But, she was not happy when I gave a talk describing how Aristotle had held back medieval science. Probably the anti-experimental bias of Aristotle was due to the fact that experiments required work and only slaves did work.

As a matter of fact, the Utopia of Plato is based on slavery as was Athens itself.

The first year we read Xenophon, the Anabasis and the Symposium. The Anabasis was quite interesting and the Symposium, except the expurgated parts, quite dull. The second year we read Homer. Greek grammar is very complicated and the vocabulary has little resemblance to English although it is an Indo-European language. However, the word order is very much like English. Consequently, it is not necessary, in general, to know the grammar in order to understand what is written.

The Greeks were not at all the people the Victorians would have us believe they were. Take the white marble statues, paint them, put precious jewels in the eyes and wigs on their heads, and you begin to have some idea of what the Greeks were like. Add the low status of women and the standard practice of homosexuality and you begin to realize what a near Eastern people the Greeks were.

In view of this cultural heritage, it is all the more remarkable, the many contributions the Athenians made to civilization. On the other hand, Sparta was the model for Nazi Germany. Mathematics did not begin with the Greeks. The Egyptians and the Mesopotamians did an enormous amount of work. A good account of this may be found in the book, O. Neugebauer, *The Exact Sciences in Antiquity* (Princeton University Press, Princeton, New Jersey, 1952).

I also read widely in etymology and philology. I even bought Perry's Sanskrit grammar in order to see what paradigms of Sanskrit were like. I studied enough to convince myself that I can learn Sanskrit if I would put in enough time.

In the high school library, I had come across a book talking about the Bacon-Shakespeare controversy. It was obvious to me that Baconians were cranks. It was also clear to me that the man called Shakespeare did not write all the plays ascribed to him. My theory is that he wrote the potboilers, like "Titus" and "Andronicus", while the major plays and the sonnets, like, "Hamlet" and "Macbeth", were written by more educated and more sophisticated people. In those days, it was neither fashionable nor politically wise to be the author of a play.

I also read with interest the controversy whether all of Homer was written by one person. I don't think this will ever be settled, and I have no opinion one way or the other.

It was in Greek that I discovered that I had a good memory. I had observed that I never took notes but put that down to a personal idiosyncrasy. Not taking notes gave me ample time to listen to the instructor. Occasionally, they said something worth listening to. Usually I just day dreamed or occupied myself doing some mathematical problems.

Having a good memory is obviously an advantage. It also is a disadvantage. In those days, I did mathematics instinctively. I had little need for theory because as a new fact came along I merely tucked it away for further reference. It was only when I began teaching myself, and particularly when I came to writing books, that I found it essential to understand theory.

I also took a good course in English literature. The first semester was devoted to older works like that of Chaucer. Chaucer was in addition a good mathematician. He wrote a work on the astrolabe. The second semester was devoted to 18th century English literature.

Finally, I took a course in Elizabethan drama given by the chairman of the English Department. He had a very good theory. In order to understand Elizabethan drama, it was necessary to understand Italian history. Consequently, I read Machiavelli. In order to understand Italian drama, it was necessary to understand Roman drama. To understand Roman drama it was necessary to understand Greek drama. To understand Greek drama it was necessary to understand Mesopotamian and Egyptian mythology. In this way, I did extensive reading and got a good overview.

The worst course I took in college, which should have been the best course, was philosophy. This gave me quite a down on the subject which I didn't get over until I had to grapple with philosophical questions in connection with the use of the computer and the study of social systems.

Another boring course, which should have been very exciting, was government. On the final exam there was a question which counted for quite a lot asking for the differences between the democratic and republican procedures for nominating a presidential candidate. All I knew was that one convention was held before the other. In true social science fashion, I expounded on this theme for page after page. I got a C on the exam and C in the course. Shades of the theory of games!

We also had a mathematics club to which I went occasionally. The only talk I remember is one by Courant. He spoke on a very interesting problem, inscribing a triangle of minimum perimeter in a given triangle. He showed how this problem could be done by reflection. He said that Schwarz considered this his finest bit of work.

One look at the card catalog in the science library at the 42nd Street

Public Library convinced me that I had to be able to read mathematical German. Consequently, I took two years of German. The first year was just to familiarize myself with the grammar, and the second year was devoted to scientific German. In those days, they still used the Gothic script. At the end of the second year, I had to write a report. I wrote one on the polarization of light, in German of course. This was a fortunate choice since the knowledge I gained came in handy later on in my work on radiative transfer.

The bane of my college existence was chemistry. CCNY had about three and a half years of required courses. They even required four terms of drafting, obviously necessary for a major in mathematics, chemistry, or physics. Brooklyn College had more civilized requirements, about three years. However, a mathematics major, in addition to taking four terms of physics, had to take a year of chemistry or biology. I had taken a good course in elementary and advanced biology in high school. In addition, I wanted to learn something about chemistry.

The first semester of chemistry was quite easy. It was devoted to physical chemistry, about the sophistication of Boyle's law. I had a very good arrangement with two pretty girls in the class. I did the experiments and they washed the test-tubes. The second semester was quite different. It was necessary to memorize some long formulas of various reactions. I was not enthusiastic about this. I had never seen any reason why I should compete with a handbook. Fortunately, the chemistry department at Brooklyn College prided itself on keeping grades very low. This made it impossible to distinguish between an average student and somebody like myself who wanted just a D to graduate. I had a firm average of twenty during the semester. I figured I could get another twenty on the final, and thus earn a D.

Unfortunately, on the last day of the semester, the instructor decided to give a quiz. In addition, this was a quiz on organic chemistry, a subject about which I knew nothing. I was aghast. A zero on this quiz would ruin my average. Obviously, strong measures were called for.

Next to me was a good student who carefully shielded her paper. I waited until the instructor was not watching and hit her hand hard with mine. When she moved her hand away, I copied the required two answers and got my twenty that way.

Actually, I think I passed because that semester we won the William Lowell Putnam competition. This is a mathematical competition for the colleges in the United States and Canada which was held every year. It had started when I was a sophomore. There were competitions for places on the three-man team. Hillman and Sherman won two places easily. I won the third, but nobody believed the result. Consequently, Toronto won the competition the first year. If the scores of Hillman and Sherman were added to mine, we would have won. We won it the second and third years.

The second time the team consisted of Hillman, Sherman and myself. The third time, the team consisted of Pete Chiarulli, Hyman Zimmerberg, and myself.

In those days, the winning school made up the questions. Later, the questions were made up by a committee. Several years later, I served on this committee for three years. It is amazingly difficult to make up good questions.

I stayed in school for four and a half years so I could take the competition the third year. It made me feel like a football player. Anyway, in those days graduate school only began in September.

When the instructor saw my picture in the school paper, he was dumbfounded. He thought I was an amiable idiot. Whenever he asked me a question, I would smile and say I didn't know the answer. I have observed myself when teaching that students that don't know the answer get very sullen.

I got my D or D-, in chemistry and graduated.

When I graduated from Brooklyn College, I did not win the mathematics medal since I had already won it as a sophomore. When they wanted to give me a medal, I suggested that they give me a book instead. That is how I got my copy of Whittaker and Watson, suitably inscribed by Harris F. MacNeish. The first book I bought was Titchmarsh's "Theory of Functions". I had that inscribed by my father. The second book I bought was also by Titchmarsh, "Fourier Integrals". I worked through all three books, and then started writing papers.

My college career was clouded by several factors. In the first place, there was the uncertainty. Since we were on relief, I was not supposed to go to day-school. I should have gotten a job during the day and gone to school at night. Every semester the relief investigator would bring up that question. My father would take out my medals and clippings and give the investigator a pep talk. Since the investigator was usually a young graduate student himself, he was very understanding and willing to bend the regulations. However, one never knew. Secondly, there was the political situation which was not good. In Europe, there was Hitler in Germany, Mussolini in Italy, and Stalin in Russia. In Japan, the third member of the Axis, there was Tojo. At home, there were a number of native fascists such as Gerald L.K. Smith, Father Coughlin, Huey Long and others. In addition, there was the Bund headed by Fritz Kuhn, and American Firsters, which had well-meaning people like Taft.

Since 1939, I was firmly convinced that we would get into the European war sooner or later. Consequently, all academic study seemed a waste of time, since I was prime cannon fodder.

There was also the poverty. We lived in a basement apartment at 630 Banner Ave. on relief, surrounded by Persian rugs, jade lamps, fine furniture, fine books and other attributes of wealth. My grandfather gave us forty dollars a month and my Aunt Peg gave us a like sum. The relief investigators constantly said that we must be getting money from somewhere else because it was impossible to live on the money they gave us.

Usually, poverty didn't bother me since many of my friends were as poor or poorer than I was. Occasionally, however, the resentment would break out. I had two ways of expressing this resentment. Next to Brighton Beach was a very expensive neighborhood, Manhattan Beach. When I came home late at night I would pick a bouquet of flowers in some garden there. I carried a pair of scissors so that I didn't have to destroy the entire flower bed.

Secondly, I enjoyed throwing bricks through windows. In Manhattan Beach lived Samuel Leibowitz. He had been a very famous criminal lawyer and then became a judge. Since he knew criminals and their ways well, he was an excellent judge. He had a large house in

Manhattan Beach, with a large picture window. Every couple of months, I would throw a brick through this window. He probably thought it was the mob getting even with him. It wasn't the mob, just an angry teenager.

Finally, there was the illness of my parents. When I was eighteen, my mother died. She had been ill for some time. It was never determined what it was. Lou assured us it was not cancer. Her death was expected. I remember reproaching myself that I was not more touched by her death.

Her death caused a schism in my family. My grandfather had never liked my father. When my mother died he felt that this was a good excuse to severe relations. Naturally, this made things awkward for me. One of the minor consequences of this schism was that I had to eat two huge Thanksgiving and Christmas dinners. This was a strain even for me.

On the other hand, my grandmother had always liked my father. She visited him regularly in the hospital.

A well-meaning friend arranged for me to be nature counselor at a camp that summer. I was not enthusiastic about leaving the city since it interfered with my social life, but I was curious as to summer camps, and I always wanted to make money.

I had many amusing experiences at this camp, and I will restrain myself to just telling a few of them. Incidentally, this camp like about five others, was on the edge of a lake. I learned later on that this lake was used by Murder, Inc. to get rid of their victims. The camp was located about ten miles from Monticello. Since the members of Murder, Inc. were often good boys as far as their mothers were concerned, they would get rid of the victims in the lake and then visit their mothers in Monticello.

As a nature counselor, a subject which I have always disliked, I also had the responsibility for the six-year old group. It was forbidden to touch these little brats. I solved that problem very neatly. I taught them a game where they hit each other with ping-pong paddles when they lost. It gave me great pleasure to stand by and watch as they whacked each other.

Counselors were not fed very much. However, the children could have as much as they wanted. They were all feeding problems, being used to parents who pleaded with them to eat. I handled that problem very easily. The first few times I passed the plate around and gave them a chance to take a portion. When they did not eat I took all the rest.

When their parents came up on the weekend, they were delighted to see how voraciously the children ate. They asked me what method I used. I replied, "Applied psychology."

The boys and the girls swimming was carefully segregated.

The girl in charge of the girls swimming was very ugly. Consequently, she reported all infringements of the girls' area and got a lot of us in trouble. We decided to retaliate, commando style. We prepared a bucket of slime. We knew the bungalow in which she slept and the bed. The operation was carefully planned. One boy was to hold the door, one was to hold the flashlight, one was to pull back the covers and I was to pour the slime. As soon as she felt the slime she started screaming. Her girls started screaming too. The boy holding the door got scared and ran away as did the one with the flashlight and the one holding the covers. There I was in pitch darkness surrounded by screaming girls. Somehow, I found the door. I am sure that I broke all the Olympic records in running. My memory is that I came down to earth every fifteen feet.

One of the boys had a reputation for pranks of that type. Consequently, we left him carefully surrounded by witnesses. Sure enough, she hired a lawyer and sued him.

When I was about eighteen, I started taking girls out. There were several reasons for that. In the first place I was old enough. In the second place, girls were available at college. In the third place, my financial situation had improved. I didn't have to spend as much money on carfare and I made some tutoring.

For years, I wouldn't look in a mirror because of a mild case of acne. I went to Lou and asked him what to do. He gave me good advice as usual. Stay away from candy. It was bad for the skin, bad for the stomach, and bad for the teeth.

I had several minor girlfriends and four major ones. They were Thelma Austern, Sylvia Korman, Evelyn Eisenberg, and Betty Jo Kates.

This was remarkable since I was quite moody and melancholy. I was very depressed by the illness of my parents, culminating in the death of my mother and I was convinced by political events in Europe and Asia that I would never have a chance to be a mathematician. Long walks and talks with these girls did a lot to alleviate my unhappiness. I shall be forever grateful.

Thelma and Sylvia lived in Brighton Beach which was quite convenient. Evelyn lived near King's Highway which was two express stops away from Brighton Beach. Betty Jo lived in Borough Park, about one-half hour away by subway but within walking distance of the college. These girlfriends were a great help to me. We would go for long walks and talk about many things.

All were highly intelligent, very attractive, very charming girls. It is interesting to speculate why I didn't marry any of the first three.

Thelma was too young for serious decision. Sylvia got involved with somebody else. By the time she had changed her mind it was too late. Evelyn's mother didn't like me. Why I don't know. I feel sure if Evelyn's mother had liked me as much as Betty Jo's mother did, I would have married Evelyn. Usually, I got along quite well with mothers. For example, Sylvia could get out during the week by saying she had a date with me. I would pick her up and deliver her to her boyfriend.

I enjoyed female companionship greatly. With them, I could relax and be myself. With boys, I had to be on my guard for various reasons. It was only when I reached Princeton that I felt I could afford to be natural.

I was horrified when I read history to find how badly women were treated in most cultures. I became a feminist at an early age. I swore that if I had a chance, I would give women their chance. Fortunately, I had this opportunity at RAND and USC.

I had a very simple technique with girls. I treated them as people. I no more thought of giving a girl a line than giving a boy a line. A girlfriend was to be a friend who was a girl.

I met Evelyn in one of my first year German classes. I made repeated overtures and was repeatedly rebuffed. She had plenty of boyfriends and spent a great deal of time going out. As a matter of fact, she went out so much that she neglected her work at school.

Evelyn looked almost exactly like Jean Simmons, and thus it was no wonder that she had lots of beaus.

When the final in German came, it was obvious that she knew very little. Fortunately, I was sitting next to her, separated by one seat as was the custom in final examinations. After I had finished my examination, we exchanged booklets and I wrote hers in pencil. The proctor was quite suspicious and watched us very closely. Fortunately, someone near the front of the room had a question. He hurried down, answered the question, and hurried back. But, while he was doing that we exchanged booklets again. She rewrote my penciled answers in ink, and handed in her booklet. She got a B for the course, and I got a C. After that we became friends.

It is difficult in a city like New York to find privacy. Every place one goes there are people. Even when we went to the park and sat on the grass, there were people constantly walking back and forth.

In Central Park there is a children's playground. This has a fence around it and is locked up at night. Evelyn and I found a part of the fence which was easy to climb over. Inside the playground there was a mound with a granite rock which was very convenient to sit on. One night, while I was giving her a lecture on projective geometry using the stars, I noticed a pair of eyes. It was a Peeping Tom, waiting for something interesting to occur. Instinctively, I jumped up and started chasing him. Suddenly, I thought, "What will I do if I catch him?" So I slowed down and let him escape. I returned and finished the lecture.

Evelyn was an art major but had quite a flair for mathematics. She discovered many interesting results herself. In particular, she found how easy it was to trisect an angle using a marked ruler. It is amazing how often people forget to say, "unmarked".

Evelyn came to a tragic end. I kept in touch with her and we saw her after the war. About 1952, she developed breast cancer. She had a mastectomy, but it did not arrest the cancer. She died of cancer in about 1955.

She was a fine person and a good friend.

I met Betty Jo on the steps of Boylan Hall. She was engaged in a hot political debate. I liked what she said, and she was a very pretty girl.

The boyfriend she had at the time was a frat boy. He often

complained to Betty Jo that I looked at him in a very menacing fashion, as if I wanted to hit him. It wasn't jealousy, it was just the attitude I had towards frat boys and fraternities. Brooklyn College had a few fraternities who tried to introduce a rah rah spirit. Most students, who had more serious things on their minds just laughed at them. Many stories can be told about these fraternities. My favorite is the following.

Near the campus was a whorehouse. One of the frat boys patronized this house regularly and fell madly in love with one of the girls. He wanted to bring her to the annual dance. The other members of the fraternity were aghast, thinking of what their parents and the parents of their girlfriends would say. They tried to dissuade him, but he was adamant. They threatened that if he brought her they would make her life miserable. A couple of hours before the dance his best friend convinced him to bring a neighborhood girl who was not known to the other members of the fraternity. They kept their promise. When they danced with her they whispered all the indecencies they could think of into her ears and pinched all the taboo areas. The girl had a wonderful evening and went home thinking she was irresistible. I hope no one ever told her the whole story.

Our first "date" was taking her home and making some hot tea for her when she had her usual menstrual cramps. After that, we had more usual dates.

Betty Jo was the first girl that I went out with in the day-time. Both my parents had a very good skin, and I had the mildest form of adolescent acne. However, I was very sensitive about this.

I became an expert in interesting and inexpensive dates. In the summer time I usually went to either Central Park or Prospect Park. On Friday nights, the Goldman Band gave a concert in Prospect Park, and on Saturday nights the concerts were given in Central Park. What I would usually do is rent a rowboat at twenty-five cents an hour, and listen to the band from the middle of the lake. Incidentally, a rowboat is a bad place for necking because of ribs in the boat.

After the concert the conductor would ask for requests from the audience. There always was a request for Ravel's Bolero, and sometimes he would oblige. There always was a request for the William Tell overture. This was used as the theme music for "The Lone Ranger". Someone would always yell out, "Heighho, Silver."

About that time, I felt that I was too parochial in dating only American girls. It was not easy at Brooklyn College to find a European girl. Finally, I found one. She was Dutch. Her father was a diamond merchant. She wasn't very attractive but she was non-American. So I took her out. We were sitting on the grass in Prospect Park talking about this and that. Suddenly, she took out a giant hat-pin and stuck it on the grass between us. "Now," she said, "nobody will get fresh." That put a damper on the evening. I did not take her out again and I gave up on European girls.

In the winter time we went to movies. There was a movie, the Apollo on 42nd Street, which showed good French films. These films had stars like Jean Gabin, Harry Bauer, and others, but, the chief attraction was that the admission was only twenty-five cents. My taste for foreign films was far more economic than artistic.

Around Christmas time, we all went to midnight Mass at St. Patrick's. Admission was only twenty-five cents. We knelt when others knelt, and thus were inconspicuous. It was quite a show.

Another attraction was the ferry-boat. For five cents one could go to Staten Island and then for another five cents, one could come back. It was great fun to take these rides and be on the water.

There was also a ride along Fifth Avenue in the double-decker bus. Oddly enough I never did that when I lived in New York. When I lived in Los Angeles and visited New York, I made up for several opportunities which I had not taken at the time.

When I visited New York with Nina, we took the double-decker bus up Fifth Ave. to the Cloisters. The Cloisters is a medieval monastary which was brought over stone by stone from Europe. It is run by the Metropolitan Museum of Art. We heard a program of medieval music there, including Gregorian chants. We enjoyed it hugely.

When I was engaged to Betty Jo, I was more flush. I think I made as much as fifteen dollars a week tutoring. It was hard work but I enjoyed having the money. Having so much money, I was able to go to a real Broadway theatre with Betty Jo. We saw, "The Wizard of Oz" at the late show starting at eleven o'clock, admission was sixty cents a person.

Also, in that way, we saw "Fantasia".

Also, in the winter time one could go to concerts. The New York City Symphony Orchestra had very good guest conductors, like Sir Thomas Beecham. If one bought tickets far in advance, at twenty-five cents a seat, one could sit in the first row of the fifth balcony and hear the concert. Actually, for various acoustic reasons, it is better to sit there than in the orchestra, where the seats are much more expensive. I can never hear certain pieces without thinking where I heard them first. I forget the girl I was with but I well remember the other setting.

CHAPTER 3

GRADUATE SCHOOL, MARRIAGE AND WAR

I graduated from Brooklyn College in June of 1941 and began graduate school at Johns Hopkins in September of 1941, not a good time to begin anything.

When I told people I was going to Johns Hopkins, the immediate reaction was, "So you're going to be a doctor." At first I would patiently explain that Johns Hopkins was a university with many departments and that I wanted to become a mathematician. After a while I just said, "Yes."

I was brought up by my father to be an individual. In many discussions, he pointed out that children had no obligation to their parents. Rather the parents had an obligation to their children. After all parents had brought children into the world. Then and now, I have no patience with people who say they have sacrificed themselves for their children or their parents. I believe very strongly that one's first obligation is to one's self.

When, however, I wanted to go away to Johns Hopkins, my father wanted me to stay in New York so that I could take care of him. He suggested that I go to graduate school in the evening at Brooklyn College. I had taken some of their courses, sitting in, and found them uniformly poor. They served two useful purposes. In the first place they gave useful credits for high school teachers who wanted promotion. In the second place they gave some additional money to the instructors. But they were not for professional mathematicians.

Johns Hopkins, on the other hand, at that time, had a very strong department of mathematics. They had Wintner, Zariski, and Van Kampen, who died at a young age from a brain tumor. In addition, they had very good younger men, such as Kershner and Dowker.

Furthermore, they had a number of strong graduate students. I had applied to several other graduate schools, but predictably had been turned down. I didn't think that D's in physics and chemistry helped. I didn't even apply to Princeton.

I was able to go to Johns Hopkins because one of the professors at Brooklyn College, Moore, had gotten his degree there and was able to recommend me.

I told my father that he had his chance and that I deserved mine, and took off for Baltimore.

I roomed with two other students, one in mathematics, Bernie Sherman and one in physics, Elmer Eisner. Our apartment was one-half of the second floor of an old southern mansion. One of the bedrooms had been converted into a "kitchen" by the simple expedient of putting a range in. However, this "kitchen" had no sink, nor did the bathroom. We had to wash our hands and the dishes in the bathtub. As a matter of fact, I got so used to using the bathtub that even when I went to New York I automatically used the bathtub to wash my hands.

As I said, we used the bathtub with a spray for the dishes. Since this spray was unreliable, and since each of us possessed only one suit anyway, as soon as we came home we changed into pajamas. We had exactly three dishes, three knives, three forks, and three spoons. Consequently, anybody who came to dinner had to bring his own plate and cutlery.

We lived very cheaply according to my calculations. It took about twenty-six cents a day. This was a little misleading, since Helen regularly sent food packages. In particular, she would send a giant salami which lasted for weeks. Among other things, I would use the salami for spaghetti. I became an expert at making spaghetti. Since I was used to living alone, because my father was in the hospital so often, living in graduate school caused no difficulty. Back in Brooklyn my usual dinner was, as I have said, a can of hash and a can of green peas.

Life settled down to a very pleasant routine. During the day, we went to the University, which was a pleasant walk away. During the evening we would study mathematics.

Wintner felt that every graduate student in analysis should read the entire Borel series. At first, I was surprised that a mathematician of

Borel's stature would busy himself with editorial duties. After reading these volumes, I understood how important it was to the progress of mathematics that research results be widely available. When I started my series for Academic Press, these volumes were an inspiration.

Wintner also highly recommended the book by Zygmund, "Trigonometric Series". I duly bought a copy and spent a great deal of time reading it. I learnt a great deal of analysis from this book and from the reprints that Zygmund was kind enough to send me.

Wintner had married the daughter of Lichtenstein, a mathematician. This was a quite common practice. When one mathematician was asked why he had married the daughter of another mathematician, he replied, "because Weirstrass had no daughters."

Elmer was a very good violinist and was always preparing for some concert. He would practice a piece by Bach or Beethoven and this made good background music for studying mathematics.

In Baltimore, I saw my first color movie. It was a short, "Gaiete Parisienne". I have always been very fond of the music and use it to change my mood.

In those days, it was quite an adventure to go from Baltimore to New York by car. In the first place there was no freeway. In the second place, a ferry ride was involved. In the third place, many of the small towns on the way were well-known traffic traps and one had to go through them at about twenty mph. We made the trip once. Dowker had a car, which we loaded up with graduate students and set out. It was a fun trip, but, as I say, once was enough.

Occasionally, other graduate students would drop over and we would have animated political discussions. One of the graduate students was very pro-communist. As a matter of fact, he had wanted to join the party. But knowing that he wanted to become a teacher, he was not allowed to so that he could, without fear of perjury, say that he was not a member of the Communist Party. We had many arguments. When I pointed out some of the fallacies in his argument, he would say, "These are not for intellectuals. We have different arguments for intellectuals."

When several graduate students came over, we would occasionally play Red Dog. This is a deceptively simple gambling game, which any number can play. When the kitty has no money, each player antes one penny. Then, each player is dealt four cards. They play in turn. They have the prerogative of betting up to the amount in the kitty that they can beat with the cards in their hand the next card turned up by the dealer.

Many years later, with Dave Blackwell, I was able to analyse this game mathematically. As a matter of fact, we wrote an expository article for the *Scientific American,* and even made the cover. The title of the article was "Red Dog, Blackjack and Poker". I will say more about this in Chapter 11. At the moment let me merely state that a mathematical analysis shows that you bet the maximum or don't bet at all. Most people play this game incorrectly. They bet a small amount on a hand that is not very good. This is a sure way to lose.

Every two weeks, I would go in to New York and see Betty Jo. I would stay over at her house. On alternate weeks, I visited my Aunt Peg in Washington.

One weekend, Betty Jo came down to visit me. We had a bed in the "kitchen" for such events. From time to time fellow graduate students who ran out of money would stay there.

At the time, Betty Jo suffered very severely from menstrual cramps. I was studying some mathematics while she was taking a nap on one of the beds in the living room. To take this nap she had taken off her dress and was wearing her slip. Suddenly, there was a knock on the door. It was my Aunt Peg who had driven down from Washington to pay me a surprise visit. I introduced her to Betty Jo, saying, "Aunt Peg I would like you to meet a friend from New York."

Aunt Peg said, "Tell your friend to put on her clothes and we will go out to dinner."

I felt very affluent at that time. I had a scholarship which gave free tuition and $700 a year. The chairman of the department was Murnaghan, a good mathematician but a very difficult character. He had the custom of disliking everybody he knew. Consequently, the good fellowships always went to the freshmen class. Graduate students who had been there one year got free tuition and $300 a year.

My duties were minimal. I had to teach one course in trigonometry on Thursday night from seven to nine.

Thanksgiving was a long vacation. Originally, Betty Jo and I had planned to get married after I got my Ph. D. However, the uncertainties of the world situation was such that we decided to get married then and there. Consequently on November 22 of 1941, I married Betty Jo. She was eighteen and I was twenty-one. Clearly, we were both too young.

The marriage ceremony was short, conducted in a study. My Aunt Sylvia and grandmother were there as was my father. Also, of course, Betty Jo's mother was there. My only reaction during the ceremony was that I was receiving a Boy Scout's lecture again.

Some weeks later, there was a wedding reception. I was dismayed by the horde of obscure relatives, whom I didn't want to see and who certainly I would never see again. As a matter of fact, I had a running battle with Helen seeing her close relatives. Consequently, I sneaked out to a nearby candy store and read magazines until I judged the reception was over.

The next weekend, I visited my Aunt Peg in Washington as usual. We took a drive to Maryland. During the drive I said, "Aunt Peg, do you remember the girl you met in my apartment, I married her." My Aunt Peg said, "Oh," and that was the end of the conversation.

I was rather unfortunate. Up to the year that I came, it was the custom for the senior mathematicians to teach the freshmen class, and have junior mathematicians teach second year students. When I came they reversed that. Nevertheless, I sought out Wintner and got friendly with him. Wintner was a very good mathematician and very erudite. He had read everything that had ever been published on every topic. Whenever someone spoke, Wintner always had additional references. Once, Rainich gave a talk on relativity. At the end of the talk, Wintner asked if Rainich was aware of the work of Rabinowitz. Rainich replied very simply, "I am Rabinowitz."

For many reasons, it was convenient for many people to change their names. In the first place there was a great deal of anti-Semitism. In the second place, it was often awkward to have a foreign sounding name. The simplest procedure was to translate into the native language. Thus, Battenberg became Mountbatten, and Weiss became Fejer.

There is an amusing story about Fejer, a great mathematician.

When he was proposed for a professorship, someone asked, "Is he related to the theologician?" One of his supporters said, "Illegitimately."

There was a famous feud between Wintner and Zariski. What the origin of the feud was I don't know. But, whenever one spoke at the weekly seminar where attendance was so compulsory, the other would turn his back to the board and just smoke. Another famous feud was between Vandiver and Moore at the University of Texas. Finally, the situation got so bad that a separate department, a department of applied mathematics was created for Vandiver. What makes it particularly amusing was that Vandiver's field was number theory. Such feuds are very common in academic life.

They are very amusing at a distance in time and space, but quite distressing to those in the middle who like both parties, or don't want to take sides. When Wilson who was president at Princeton was elected Governor of New Jersey, someone asked him if he would have any difficulties with the politics of the state house. He replied that after being president of Princeton, everything else would be easy.

As Charlie Chaplin has written, "Comedy is tragedy at a distance."

Murnaghan was not happy that I was married. He felt that graduate students should not be married. He was probably right.

The next weekend I went to New York. On Sunday, December 7, Betty Jo and I went to visit my father. As usual, he had the radio tuned to the music station WQXR. Suddenly, we heard the familiar voice of H.V. Kaltenborn, "The Japanese have attacked at Pearl Harbor. . ." War!

Actually, the Japanese did us a great favor in attacking. Overnight, we became a united nation. The American firsters disappeared. Within hours, Germany and Italy also declared war on us. England, France, and Russia were delighted.

There are many interesting questions about the Japanese attack which have never been answered. For example, why was there "business as usual" attitude in the face of repeated warnings from Washington? In the second place, radar had just been installed. The Japanese planes were clearly spotted by the radar. However, the officer-in-charge, pooh-poohed this and did nothing. As far as I know, no action was ever taken against him.

A garbled version of the Japanese attack appeared in movie form a few years ago. It was called "Tora-Tora", the Japanese code name for the attack on Pearl Harbor. We called the movie "Terrible-Terrible".

At the time, I thought that victory was inevitable. However, it was clear that I would be drafted now and I seriously doubted that I would survive the war in one piece. I didn't worry so much about death as about mutilation. During the pacifist days of 1935 and following, many pictures had been passed around. I was very familar with what war could do.

I made some attempts to find a war job. Norman and I went to the Aberdeen Proving Grounds. However, they would not think of hiring somebody who would be drafted soon. I could hardly blame them.

My Aunt Peg tried in Washington with no success for the same reason.

My Aunt Sylvia saved the day. She saw an advertisement for instructors in electronics. I protested that I knew no electronics. However, it was worth a chance.

I went to see Murnaghan and told him that I was going to Belleville. He was very indignant. "How could I leave him in the lurch?" he asked. That did not seem reasonable to me, considering that I only taught one class two hours a week.

I asked him whether I could take the examinations in June so that I could have credit for one year of graduate school. He replied in his usual frosty manner, "Mr. Bellman, you are by no means at the head of your class." In other words, the answer was definitely no.

This was meant to be insulting. However, I had a great deal of difficulty in concealing a smile. We had a very peculiar graduate class which I will not try to describe. It requires the talents of a Somerset Maugham to do it justice. I learned from this a very valuable lesson. An all-purpose insult is rarely effective. One has to know a great deal about a person to insult him effectively.

I was sure that my mathematical career was over. I remember walking through the stacks of the mathematics library, looking at the various volumes, and felt sure that I would never see them again. I was very sad.

CHAPTER 4

BELLEVILLE 1942; I LEARN ELECTRONICS

I arrived in Belleville carrying a heavy suitcase, a tennis racket which was given to me by Uncle Arthur, and my copy of Whittaker and Watson. I strongly recommend this book to anyone interested in analysis. Particularly valuable are the exercises at the end of the chapters which are quite difficult.

The first task was to find a place to stay. This was not difficult, since the office to which I reported had a list of places. I picked a room at eight dollars a week.

This room was in an old house run by an old lady. She was very glad to have company, and invited me into the parlor at night. There she told me the same story every night. Some sixteen years before, she had been part of one of the two exciting events that had ever happened in Belleville. Her sister's fiancé murdered her sister. She visited him in jail and made cookies for him until he was hung. The other exciting event was that Lincoln had stopped in Belleville on his way to his inauguration.

Scott Field was a few miles outside the city. We were taken there every morning by bus.

The same bus took us back to town at about four o'clock in the afternoon. One day, I got a lift from two young men. It turned out that they were Mormon missionaries. To be a Mormon missionary you first had to work and save up money to support yourself. I asked them many questions about the Mormon church. They were delighted to answer them.

Midway between Belleville and Scott Field was a railroad track. As I was talking to the young men, I noted a train approaching. The young missionaries were so eager to answer my questions that they drove looking towards the back seat. Finally, when we were about 100 yards away from the track, I pointed out the approaching train. We barely stopped in time.

I always felt that I came close to going to a Mormon heaven. I would have been well escorted.

At Scott Field, we were given the rudiments of radio and electronics. In particular, we were given the various circuits which are used in radar. Soon, I was quite familiar with the multivibrator and flip-flop circuits. What was astonishing to me was that such simple circuits could be used. Years later, I found that a very simple differential equation, the equation of Van der Pol, could describe the output very accurately.

I enjoyed electronics. The subject had a clearness and elegance about it that appealed to my mathematical soul. In studying electronics, I learned that various laws were only approximate. This was a new idea. Presumably, my instructors in high school and college had pointed this out, but I had certainly not heard it.

Someone had the bright idea that since we were to teach radio and electronics, we should be familiar with the Morse code. This was no strain on me since I had been familiar with the Morse code since my Boy Scout days. As a matter of fact, Eddie Kanner and I won a gold medal in Morse signaling at a rally. These rallies were held once a year in an armory. They consisted of competitions in such areas as knot tying, fire making by flint and steel, fire making by bow and spindle, semaphore signaling, Morse signaling, etc.

The year before, Marty Klein and I had entered semaphore signaling. Unfortunately, Marty forgot to bring his glasses. We did not win a gold medal.

The requirement for the Morse code was something like twenty words per minute. "A word" consisted of a group of four letters. Without difficulty, I got up to thirty words a minute, and then stopped. I could see no reason for going any further.

Sending was a different matter. As usual, the sending sets were made for right-handed people. When I pointed this out to the sergeant in charge, his comment was typically Army. "You'll learn." He was right. I did learn and to this day I can send Morse code with my right arm but not with my left.

While I was a student, my pay was $1,600 a year. When I graduated, I became a P-1 at $2,000 a year. It was a pleasure to have enough money for the first time. The teaching was not onerous, three and half hours a day of actual teaching, and three and half hours for preparation. At the time, this was five days a week.

As I said above the rent on my room was eight dollars a week payable in advance. One week I paid two weeks in advance. As soon as I did that, I knew it was a mistake. I was too young to ask for a receipt, and the landlady was a bit senile. Sure enough she asked for the rent the next week, and refused to believe that I had paid for two weeks in advance. I had to move.

For about a week, I lived in a boarding house. I didn't particularly enjoy this experience but I had read a good deal about such places and I was curious to see what they were like.

Then I moved in with Al Nadel. I had known him slightly at Brooklyn College where he was a physics major. He was one month ahead of me and really knew electronics and radio. His father had been in the signal corps in the First World War and Al had grown up knowing about radio and electronics. I learned a great deal from him.

Our landlady was a typical midwestern type. She felt that a bath once a week was enough. Although it was only about May it was hot. Al and I pleaded with her in vain. She refused to make hot water available during the week.

As I said, Belleville was hot. Indeed Betty Jo who took a course in geography at the University of Wisconsin said that St. Louis had the same climate as equatorial Africa. The geographical conditions were the same. The Army, with its usual sensitivity made the students, soldiers, wear coveralls. You could tell where the doors to the classrooms were by the smell. Probably the most difficult part of teaching was coming close to the students and adjusting the circuits. They smelled.

As the summer came closer, it got hotter and hotter. Belleville would stay hot until twelve o'clock at night. Then there was a thundershower. It was quite dramatic. The entire sky would open up with a lightning flash and the thunder was very loud. I was used to heat lightning from

New York but nothing like this.

This is how I became part of the first Jane Russell fan club. Al was vice-president. The full title was, "The Jane Russell Fan Club Number One of Belleville, Swansea, and East St. Louis". We decided to retaliate against our landlady. At that time the only source of cheese-cake photos was Esquire. This magazine regularly had difficulty with the post office. The post office would claim they were using the mails for obscene matter. It is quite amusing to think of Esquire of thirty years ago with Playboy or Penthouse today.

In Esquire, we found some photographs of Jane Russell. I had the inspiration of writing to her and asking in the name of the club for some additional photos. Sure enough her press agent was glad to send them. When we received these, we asked for some more. Each time we wrote a letter, it was a masterpiece. I wish I ad copies of them now.

When we got all these photos, we hung them around the room. Across various parts of her anatomy, we wrote fond messages to Al and to myself. We never had any reaction from the landlady.

Belleville was a small town, and had very few attractions. However, I discovered while walking the tree-lined streets, a Carnegie library. Not only did they have a good collection of books, but it was delightfully cool. I spent many pleasant hours there.

The library was one of the two elegant buildings in town. The other was the undertaking parlor.

Walking the tree-lined streets, feeling the peace and serenity, I understood isolationism for the first time.

One of the neophyte instructors with whom I became quite friendly was John A. He was quite an interesting fellow. He had worked his way through the University of Michigan as a pool hustler. By the time he had graduated he was working in small towns 100 miles away. It was through him that I developed my liking for snooker. Snooker is intermediate between pool and billiards.

He was also a master poker player. On the square, there was a candy store which had a nightly poker game in the back room. I was not a good poker player then, but I would occasionally play because Belleville had few diversions. John said he would make a killing a few days before he left town and he did.

During the Depression he was really down and out. He became a bum and wandered about the country. Whenever he wanted a meal, he would go to a restaurant and wash dishes. When this failed, he would go to the local whorehouse. He said that it was true that whores had hearts of gold. He always got a meal there.

He married a wealthy girl, and we, unfortunately, lost contact.

In June, Betty Jo's semester at Brooklyn College ended and she joined me. We found a very pleasant apartment on Emma Street named after the landlady as she told us repeatedly.

The air force was building up at the time. The big news was that Scott Field was going to expand to Chicago, Madison, Wisconsin, and Sioux Falls, South Dakota. We were given a choice of where we would like to go.

Madison, Wisconsin, seemed highly desirable. Not only would I have the benefits of a real university, the University of Wisconsin, but Betty Jo could finish her senior year there. I didn't want to go to Chicago. I had gotten quite fond of small towns. When I left New York for Baltimore, I thought I was leaving the hub of the Universe. By the time I had spent six months in Belleville, I had no desire either to return to New York or Chicago.

To our great joy, we were able to go to Madison, Wisconsin.

CHAPTER 5

MADISON, WISCONSIN, 1942–43; MY HORATIO ALGER PHASE

We arrived in Madison, Wisconsin at one o'clock in the morning.

I had checked the distance and time at which we were to take the train, and it seemed clear to me that we would arrive at this time. However, the ticket agent was adamant. He insisted that we would arrive at one o'clock in the afternoon. I finally gave in. I figured that he knew more about the vagaries of trains in wartime than I did.

A few telephone calls ascertained that all the hotels were full. In addition the Y's were filled up too. Some thoughtful person had put in arms on the benches in the waiting rooms so that it was impossible to stretch out. We resigned ourselves to a very uncomfortable night.

At about three o'clock in the morning, a trainman saw our plight. He had to spend two nights a week in Madison at the end of a run. He recommended a rooming house where he stayed. The difficulty was that the rooming house was run by an old lady who was very deaf, Mrs. Trumpf. Consequently, there would be a little difficulty in raising her. However, at this point, we were willing to try anything. We trudged over, carrying our suitcases. Fortunately, Madison is a small town and the rooming house was not far from the terminal. We rang the doorbell repeatedly, and got no response. Finally, carefully, I threw pebbles against the window where she slept. At last she woke up and came down to the door. We had a place to spend the night.

We decided to rent a room in her house. She was not enthusiastic about renting this room, but it was wartime and she took a fancy to Betty Jo.

Years later, Betty Jo told me why she was so reluctant to rent this room. It seems that her house overlooked a whore house and she could sit in this room and look right into the house to observe what went on.

This furnished a good deal of entertainment.

The Field had not only expanded but the activity had increased. Truax Field was in operation seven days a week, twenty-four hours a day. This meant that one-third of the instructors had to teach from eleven at night to seven in the morning. To make this fair we rotated. We taught one month from seven to three, one month from three to eleven, and one month from eleven to seven. Naturally, the eleven to seven shift took some adjusting to. What, for example, do you call a meal which you eat at three o'clock in the morning?

As luck would have it, I had drawn the eleven to seven shift first. Consequently, I was quite sleepy most of the time. When I got to the rooming house all I wanted to do was sleep. Mrs. Trumpf, on the other hand was quite garrulous. This, combined with the fact that she was almost totally deaf did not make her a good conversationalist.

One morning I fell sound asleep, as usual, after using the old plumbing. There was a loud pounding on the door which I ignored. It seems minutes after, actually it was about four or five hours later, that I was woken up by Betty Jo with tears streaming down her face, "What have you done?" Naturally I was quite curious what I had done. It seems that the toilet bowl had overflowed, from generations of trainmen. Not only was the entire second floor soaked but the wallpaper on the ceiling of the first floor was quite discolored.

We paid for the wallpaper and I promised faithfully that I would not eat prunes, and we were allowed to stay. However, I refused to use the facilities at the rooming house after that and would save my business for Traux Field. However, I would shave at the rooming house. Mrs. Trumpf had an old-fashioned water heater. First one lit the pilot, then one turned on the gas for the water. That seemed very uneconomical in time. One evening I turned on both gas lights and threw in a match.

There was a loud explosion, and I was hurled against one side of the bathroom. Meanwhile there was a big hole in the ceiling where the gas heater had disappeared. I had launched the first space missile.

We paid for the water heater and the ceiling and henceforth I shaved at the Field. However, this was an absurd situation. I told Betty Jo that we had to find other quarters. Accordingly, she combed the city. Madison is not only a university town, but also the state capitol. In addition Traux Field at that time had a population of about 20,000. Housing was difficult.

She looked everywhere. Finally, after the last possibility and the last rejection, she leaned against a nearby wall and burst into tears. The window was opened and a very sympathetic woman asked her in to have some tea and tell her why she was crying. Betty Jo poured out her heart. Well, it seemed that this was the landlady of the apartment house and she had been saving an apartment for her maiden aunt. However, after hearing Betty Jo's story she figured that we could make better use of it and that is how we got our first apartment at 444 Hawthorne Court.

It was a nice apartment, consisting of a living room, a breakfast nook, a kitchen and a bathroom. The living room had a bed in the wall. The breakfast nook had a built-in table. All this meant that we didn't have to buy much furniture.

We did need a couch. We had the usual difficulty which a call to the Better Business Bureau cleared up. Throughout the war the great majority of the American people could not do enough for soldiers and sailors. They staffed the USOs and made food for them. The churches and the synagogues had regular programs. Many people had Sunday dinners for homesick soldiers and sailors.

However, there were a few who felt that men in uniform and their dependents were fair game. There were many complaints about merchants like this. Some even had two price tags, one for natives, and one for soldiers or sailors. A call to the Better Business Bureau or the mayor usually took care of them.

The apartment was very convenient. About 100 yards away was the main street of Madison, State Street. About two blocks down State Street, the University began. On the other side of Hawthorne Court, about one-half block away, was an A&P where I did my shopping.

Shopping was very easy in those days. In the first place, thanks to OPA, prices were low. In the second place, we had the point system, a very effective form of rationing. As a result, we ate lots of Spam, one point a can. When cold, Spam is not very tasty. If, however, it is cut into thin slices and cooked on both sides, it is quite palatable. Like apple butter in Baltimore it served the purpose at the time. Like apple butter, I have never eaten it since.

When I came to Madison, I was made a P2, at $2,600 a year. With all this money I bought a cheap phonograph and my first record, Beethoven's Ninth Symphony. A friend, Paul Brock, sat on the record album by accident and broke two of the records. It took a little care to play the symphony. Fortunately, the vocal movement, which I was particularly fond of was not damaged. When he realized the damage, he went out and bought us an album of Shostakovich. I repeatedly played this album, but never developed a taste for Shostakovich.

Sometime in 1944, I was promoted to P3 at $3,700 per year. According to my estimates, it was about fifteen years before I made an equivalent amount of money. I bought my first insurance policy, a Metropolitan policy for $5,000, double indemnity, with a premium of $92 a year. At the time, both the amount and the premium seemed very large. By today's standards, they are negligible. The dividend today is $88 per year. How I wished that I had gotten more insurance of that type back in 1944.

Teaching at the Field was not onerous. We taught three and half hours a day and had the other three and half hours for preparation and reading. The Field was in the charge of a retired CPC. Presumably, his experience as a radio man in the navy qualified him for this position. He was not very intellectual, and would always frown when he saw me reading electronics or mathematics. For many reasons, I didn't want to displease him. Consequently, I solve the problem in the following way. I got some comic books and covered all my electronics and mathematics books with comic books as covers. When he saw me reading a comic book he would smile happily and approvingly.

The problem soon took care of itself because we were required to teach two classes, seven hours a day.

After the oppressive heat and humidity of Belleville, Madison was delightful. On my day off, while Betty Jo studied, I learned how to canoe. I delighted in canoeing across Lake Mendota. If one does not know how to paddle, or if one does and very carefully tilts the oar, one can drench the person behind.

On Sunday, I saw Al Nadel. He was always a fastidious dresser, and this day since he had a date he was dressed with even more care. I, on the other hand, since it was my day off, was dressed in old clothes. I was never a strong swimmer and if the canoe capsized I was prepared to hang on to it until rescued.

Al wanted a lift across the lake. He knew my sense of humor and made me promise not to wet him. He got into the canoe carefully, and I paddled carefully across the lake. When we reached the dock, he was a little careless about getting out. It was a clear manifestation of Newton's third law, every action has an equal and opposite reaction. The canoe started to tilt. I suppose that if I had taken appropriate action I could have righted the canoe. But I had not promised to do so. Consequently, within a few seconds we were both in about five feet of water, up to our necks. Al was furious. I could not contain myself. After a few seconds, he saw the absurdity of the situation and began to laugh himself.

When school began in September, I decided to be Horatio Alger. I would teach on the night shift from eleven to seven, so that I could go to graduate school during the day. My friends thought I was crazy. They pointed out that I was sure to be drafted anyway and I might as well enjoy life now. I was not happy with myself either. I looked in the mirror and promised myself that I would not drive myself as hard again. This is a promise which I have faithfully kept.

It was a wise decision. Several times in my life I have had to make major decisions. Looking back, I think that I was very fortunate in that every one of these has been correct, or at least I think so.

As you may imagine, I had no difficulty in arranging exchanges so that I stay on the night shift. Staying on the night shift had some advantages. My system got used to this peculiar arrangement, especially my stomach. However, there were also disadvantages. For example, what did one do on one's day off? Sometimes, I just stayed up. This procedure is not recommended.

This activity broke my health down. I thought it would be a good idea to go to the University hospital and get a few nights good sleep. As I have found out many times, a hospital is no place for rest. Apart from the usual nuisances of blood tests and so on, they were conducting a big experiment on blood there. Consequently, they wanted a large contribution from every patient. I hardly thought that it was a good idea to take so much blood from someone already run down. Thus, I refused. The nurse argued with me, and the doctor tried to use psychology on me. However, I had laryngitis and could not argue back. When he asked whether I was a man or a mouse, all I could do was hold my fingers up to show I was a mouse.

Finally, the doctor said that if I refused to give, I could not stay there. I should have appealed to the head of the hospital, but I was disgusted by them. I put on my clothes and walked home in below zero temperature, with a fever of about 102°. Miraculously, I did not get pneumonia.

It was a very good experience to teach. In every class, there were those who were very resentful about my being a civilian. In every class there were those who said, "Stay out of the Army as long as you can." It was quite a challenge to be a civilian teaching a class of soldiers.

At this time I built up my repertoire of jokes. Theoretically the soldiers who went to class during the night should have slept during the day. The Army, however, was not very considerate. Indeed, some of the barrack walls were used for target practice. In the second place, it was very natural that the students would want to go out when they were in Madison. During the winter it gets rather cold in Madison. Often, it was 30° below zero outside.

As soon as the soldiers got to a warm classroom, they would start to fall asleep. After a while, what I would do is give some electronics until I noticed that a considerable number of students were dozing off. Then I would tell some stories to wake them up. When they were awake, I would give some more electronics and so on. Naturally, I soon exhausted my stock of stories. To remedy this situation, I had various volunteers tell stories of their own. Since I had a class every two weeks I soon had a large supply of stories.

What I found very effective in keeping the students awake was having an undertaking assistant describe the embalming process. I imagine that listeners after hearing this were afraid to fall asleep for fear of waking up embalmed.

I soon had a regular schedule. I would be at the Field from eleven to seven. When we came back from Truax Field, I would have breakfast and then go to a listening room in the student union. In these rooms, one could listen to classical music. Graduate school began at nine and lasted until twelve. Then I would do some shopping for dinner, and then go to bed. I would sleep until five or six so that I could have dinner with Betty Jo.

This didn't leave much time for sleep, and I slowly broke my health down. I had the flu repeatedly and had laryngitis several times. One time, I even caught the mumps. Fortunately, I had a very mild case. However, I was quarantined for three weeks. I was delighted and had an orgy of mathematics. I sent Betty Jo to the library regularly and read and read. I even wrote a short paper during this period.

Surprisingly this paper, "Almost-Orthogonal Series",[1] plays a role in the giant sieve method of analytic number theory.

I enjoyed going to graduate school greatly. After leaving Johns Hopkins, when I thought I would never see a mathematics book again, it was so wonderful to be at the University of Wisconsin. I took a course in differential equations from Langer, and a course, which I don't remember from a very nice fellow named Leon Cohen. My real good fortune, however, was in meeting a first rate mathematician, Stan Ulam. He was very generous with his time and we would spend hours in conversation. I learned a great deal from him, particularly about scientific philosophy and model making.

In Madison, I did my first piece of good mathematics. My procedure for doing mathematical work was simple. I would thumb through the latest issue of the *Duke Mathematical Journal* or the *Bulletin of the American Mathematical Society* and see whether there was something which interested me and was something I wanted to do. I found a little paper on stability. During the hour intermission for a meal, I still don't know what to call it, I tried to establish this result. I was able very easily to convert the problem into a problem involving an inequality. At this point, I was very discouraged. All my previous experience with inequalities had been that they produce nothing useful. You can imagine how surprised I was to find that this one actually yielded something worthwhile and the desired result.

Naturally, I checked the result over and over again. I knew from sad

[1] *Bulletin of the American Mathematical Society*, Vol. 50, 517-519 (1944).

experience how often I had invoked the principle of wishful thinking. But, it was correct.

This inequality, the Bellman-Gronwall inequality was destined to play a large part in my life.

Having access to a mathematics library, I read voraciously. In particular, I read the classic paper by F. Riesz on integral equations in *Acta Mathematica.* The idea that simple geometric arguments could yield very powerful analytic results was quite intriguing.

We have gone much too far in the use of arithmetic in digital computers. For this reason we find it very difficult to communicate with the computer, either to give it instructions or to interpret its results. The computers of the future will be much more geometric, using pictures to aid in this communication.

June came with the end of the school year. I obtained a Masters Degree from the University, taking an oral examination. I even wrote a Ph. D. thesis on double orthogonal series, stimulated by the book by Kacmarz and Steinhaus. It was a very trite thesis and I had the sense to write it and throw it away. Also, stimulated by the book, I wrote probably the worst paper I ever wrote. There are a few papers in my bibliography which I would gladly withdraw. I console myself philosophically with the thought that "even Homer occasionally nods" and that Shakespeare and Beethoven wrote some stinkers.

In the meanwhile, Betty Jo had finished her senior year at the University, majoring in history. Every week, there was a seminar with an invited speaker. One week, a lawyer spoke about a famous financier. Betty Jo knew the name well. Her father had died at the age of twenty-eight of leukemia. However, he had left Helen well provided for — so he thought. This financier had embezzled most of Helen's money. Consequently, during the Depression she went to work making hats at fifteen cents per hat.

At the end of the talk, there was the usual question period. Betty Jo raised her hand. "That was a very interesting talk," she said, "but, I noticed that you omitted two years of his life. What was he doing during that time?"

The lawyer said that he had retired. Betty Jo said that it was very curious that so important a man would retire for two years.

Again, the lawyer hedged. Again, Betty Jo repeated the question.

Finally, the lawyer admitted that the financier was in jail during this period.

That brought down the house.

With the end of the school year, life returned to normal and we settled down to enjoy the Madison summer. In about July, I received a telephone call from Lefschetz, "Did I want to be a graduate student at Princeton?" I explained that I couldn't. If I left Truax Field to be a graduate student at Princeton, I would be drafted immediately.

I was very depressed after the call. It seemed to me that fate was playing a cruel joke on me. I had always dreamt of being a graduate student at Princeton. Here I was offered the chance, and I couldn't accept it.

About two weeks later, I received another phone call from Lefschetz, ASTP, Army Specialized Training Program, had started. Did I want to be an instructor in this program and come to Princeton?

I accepted on the phone. My friends again thought I was crazy. They warned me that as soon as I went to Princeton I would be drafted. But, I was firm. Here was my chance and I would take it. I realized full well that it was a gamble. However, it was not the last time that I was wrong to gamble for high stakes. Incidentally, as I have said, I never regarded my card playing as gambling. It was really a way of making money. Before going to Princeton there were two things I had to do. In the first place, I didn't think it would be wise to leave a civil service position abruptly. I might survive the war, I might want to work for civil service again. Consequently, I wrote a letter to the Civil Service Commission telling them about all the illness I had on the job.

Secondly, I had to tell the officer in charge of instructors at the Field about my leaving. He was a very nice young man, "Why," he asked "did I want to go to Princeton? After all teaching is teaching."

I repeated that the climate was obviously unhealthy for me.

In September, we took off for Princeton.

CHAPTER 6

PRINCETON 1943–44

Princeton is a charming small town.

It has two main streets, Nassau Street, the old route 1, and right angles to this, Witherspoon Street. On one side of Nassau Street are various shops and restaurants, as along Witherspoon Street. On the other side of Nassau Street is the University. Princeton University is built in Gothic style, like CCNY. The setting, however, is much more attractive.

It is impossible to describe adequately my emotions when I walked across the campus of Princeton. I had always dreamt of going to Princeton and knew that it was unattainable. Yet, here I was. The war was forgotten, the past was forgotten, I had my chance to be a mathematician.

The mathematics department was in a separate building, Fine Hall. This was named after a dean who unfortunately got killed riding a bicycle. It was a very luxurious three-story building. The first floor had classrooms and offices. The second floor had some more offices and two large rooms for receptions. One of these rooms was called the Commons, where tea and cookies were served every weekday at four. In addition, there were two kitchens for making tea and coffee.

The third floor was devoted to the library. In addition, it had a reading room and two offices, one of which was assigned to me. That was wonderfully convenient.

The librarian, Miss Shields was an excellent librarian. As a new journal came in, she checked all the references. In some ways she was a typical librarian, she only felt happy when all the volumes were on the shelves.

There were many interesting people at the University. But,

certainly, one of the most interesting was Solomon Lefschetz. He had been born in Iran, raised in Moscow, went to school in Paris, and then came to United States as an engineer. While working as an engineer, a wire fell across his hands severing both.

After coming out of the hospital, he returned to mathematics. He had spent about ten years in Kansas and then had come to Princeton in 1933. He was very proud of the fact that he was the first Jewish professor to have a permanent appointment at Princeton. He often spoke with amusement that certain people still refused to recognize him. When they passed him on a walk they would look straight through him.

Despite his handicap Lefschetz did extensive writing and travelling. He had wooden hands in which one could tuck a pen or piece of chalk. He founded the American school of topology and was responsible for making Princeton a center of topology. He and Birkhoff turned out most of the American Ph.D.s in mathematics.

He had quite a flair for language. He spoke French and Russian fluently and English without an accent. No doubt, he also spoke German, but I never heard him use this language. Well in his 60's he learned Spanish and gave lectures in Mexico City in Spanish.

He had a very quick wit and a very sharp tongue. He heckled at seminars unmercifully. However, being very independent himself, he appreciated this quality in others. Consequently, when I stood up to him, he liked it.

He had become friendly with Tucker in that way. At a seminar, he started heckling Tucker in his usual fashion. After a few minutes of this, Tucker put down the chalk and said, "Mr. Lefschetz, you will let me proceed in my own fashion." Lefschetz subsided and he and Tucker became very close friends. Lefschetz took care of the graduate courses, and Tucker handled undergraduate courses.

When I came to Princeton, I naturally saw Lefschetz first. Then, I went to see Bochner. Bochner is a great mathematician. Not only does he know a great deal of mathematics, but he is very erudite in general. It was always a pleasure to hear him talk and I learned a great deal of mathematics that way.

Bochner was very generous with his time and we spent many hours in conversation. We became good friends.

After I had seen Lefschetz and Bochner and we got settled in a rooming house for a few days, I went to see my father. He was in the Veterans Hospital at Kingsbridge Road in the Bronx. When I saw him, I told him about Princeton and some of the episodes in Madison. We had a nice conversation.

After seeing him, I returned to Princeton. The next day I received a telegram. My father was dead. This was a shock, since I had not been prepared for this either by him or by any doctor there.

Although by this time, my father and I were not very close, I was saddened. I was saddened not so much by the loss, as by the waste. I knew well what my father could have been, what a great potential he had.

After staying in the rooming house for a few days, we found an apartment in the Prospect Apartments on Prospect Avenue within easy walking distance of the University. We had to buy some furniture but the majority I got from Sears Roebuck disassembled. Theoretically, there were instructions. After trying to read these, I threw them away and looked upon the disassembled furniture as a large jigsaw puzzle. The people downstairs were very patient.

My duties at Princeton were not very great. I had to teach five sections in calculus, with each section meeting three times a week. The pay for this was $2,600 a year. Naturally, this was never a consideration. Tucker, who was in charge of the calculus section, was very apologetic. It was wartime, and that was why I had to teach fifteen hours. I consoled him with the observation that I had been teaching forty-two hours a week in Madison.

I even took some graduate courses, one in differential geometry from Eisenhart and one in point set topology from Tucker. The course in differential geometry was a disappointment. Eisenhart, a very nice man personally, came into class and read each day from his book. Since I could read English too, I hardly considered this a good way to teach.

I, naturally, wanted to do well in the course in point set topology, although I have never liked the subject. Tucker gave some lectures and then some topics which we could choose for lectures. I used a trick which I had often used in college. I chose the most difficult topic, the Urysohn imbedding theorem. I could have done a standard text for this, but I thought it would be more fun to read the original paper. I gave the lecture which took two hours. At the end, Tucker made some scathing remarks and said it could be done much better, and he would do it next time to show how it should be done. I had no doubt that he was right. The next time, he gave the result up to the final point. When he was about to make the concluding argument, he suddenly realized what had taken me another hour. I didn't say a word, and we became good friends.

Our next door neighbors at the Prospect Apartments were the Bailey's. Betty Bailey and Betty Jo became very good friends. Herb, the husband, was a naval officer taking a course in electronics. He had been a Princeton undergraduate, and looked like a Princeton undergraduate. We took an instant dislike to each other. He appeared to be everything that I disliked and conversely. However, our wives were persistent. We discovered that we had tennis in common, and then in the course of conversation, realized that we had misjudged each other completely. Not only was he highly intelligent, but very sensitive. For example, he had been class poet. We had many interesting conversations and we became firm friends.

There were several interesting fellow instructors. One of them was Milton Babbitt, the expert in electronic music. He showed me how mathematics could be used to produce electronic music. Also, Abe Hillman was there. He was writing his thesis under Ritt at Columbia.

Then in about March of 1944, the blow fell. ASTP was dissolved. I learned later that at this time the army was losing more men by discharge than it was getting by induction. The several hundred thousand soldiers in ASTP were sent to basic training and then to the European theatre. The casualties were very high. With the end of ASTP, came the end of my deferment. I felt that fate again was playing tricks. I was even more dejected than at Baltimore. I gave up and played Go with Abe Hillman.

I tried to get a commission in the navy. All seemed favorable until the letter at Madison was produced. Looking back, it was probably fortunate that I didn't receive the commission.

In about April, Glen Camp and Borne Eaton came to New York. I went to meet them at their hotel and Glen offered me a position in San Diego. I thought that I might as well be drafted from California as New York, and we had never been to California. So I accepted, and off we went.

CHAPTER 7

SAN DIEGO AND SONAR 1944

We arrived in San Diego by plane, our first flight.

I expected to be airsick since I was seasick on the ferry in rough weather. I was very seasick on that unfortunate voyage to Bermuda. However, much to my joy, I was not airsick, nor have I ever been airsick on a plane even in bumpy weather.

At that time, a cross-country flight took thirteen hours. This was far superior to the train which took three and half days.

Our first task was to find a place to stay. This was a constant problem in wartime. In any city used by the military, housing was always tight. We found a room way out in the country, and I discovered that I had allergic asthma. I had never had asthma before and I thought at first that I had pneumonia. I realize now that what I thought was a summer cold in New York City was really an allergy and I knew that I had an allergy to wool. Nowadays a simple immunization technique can take care of this allergy. We had to move.

In that way, we met our first western confidence man. Since then, in Los Angeles, I have met many. Growing up in New York City, I was very familiar with eastern confidence men, and could recognize them immediately. The western confidence man is different. He has clear eyes and looks you straight in the face. His handshake is firm. Let us call the one I met Smith, because that is not his name. What was remarkable about Smith is that he was versatile. He would steal anything, large or small. He would even cheat at chess, a game he loved to play.

I could tell a great deal about his peccadillos, but one will suffice. At the time I met him, his wife worked at a nearby beach and tennis club. He was a Lieutenant Junior Grade in the Navy. He would wait until the seamen had sea duty and then rifle their lockers. His wife sold these sneakers at the club. Then he made the mistake of rifling the lockers of officers. At this point the BNI stepped in, and easily tracked him down. A few months later, there was a little item in the paper saying that he had resigned.

After many vicissitudes, we got an apartment in town, 1337 A Street, right in the shadow of the U.S. Grant Hotel.

The second task was to get Betty Jo's fare back. I had received two forms before the trip. In my innocence, I assumed that the second form was just in case I lost the first one. When I arrived, I found that people had whole households shipped to San Diego at the cost of thousands of dollars.

All that was required was a letter from the airline saying that Betty Jo had been a passenger on flight number ... on the specified day. It seemed easy. I wrote to the airline, explaining carefully what I wanted. I received a prompt reply. "Yes, I had been a passenger on that flight." I wrote again. Again, I received a prompt reply. "Yes, flight number ... had left on that day." I explained again what I wanted, and again received a prompt reply to a question that I had not asked. I began to get desperate. If this communication was so difficult, obviously a three-way communication between myself in some Army camp, the airline and the laboratory would be impossible. I decided to write directly to the president of the airline. The letter went something as follows:

Dear Sir:

I realize that the members of your organization are illiterate and you probably are too.

Let me make it easy for you. If you cannot sign your name, please put an x next to the following statement and have it witnessed by two people who can read.

Then I put down the information I required. I received a nasty letter from the president, but also the information I need. $175 was a lot of money in those days.

I was quite dejected at the turn of events. However, the book, "Yankee from Olympus", a biography of Holmes was quite inspiring. I read and reread it. Holmes is one of my heroes.

The laboratory, the Naval Radio and Sound Laboratory, was located at Point Loma. One part of it was devoted to sonar. Sonar works on the piezoelectric effect. If a suitable crystal has an electric current sent through it, its dimensions will change according to the magnitude of current. Thus, with a suitable crystal a pulse of sound can be sent through the water. Conversely, if one receives a pulse of sound, one can determine the source. Thus, sonar can be used both for military and peacetime detection. Naturally, there are some details.

Since I was working on sonar, I had veteran sonar operators let me listen to actual recordings. In the first place, I realized how noisy the sea was. Schools of fish caused a lot of trouble and shrimps are particularly troublesome. An experienced sonar operator could tell from the sound what kind of ship was passing overhead. I never could. It all sounded the same to me.

Glen Camp was in charge of the theoretical unit at the laboratory. I was to be his assistant. He was a superb mathematical physicist and taught me a great deal. He had been a pupil of Oppenheimer of Berkeley and told me many stories about his brilliance and kindness. Oppenheimer came from a very wealthy background, and his pet trick was to borrow a book from a graduate student, and slip a $10 bill in the book when he returned it.

Glen, himself, had not had a very pleasant life. His first wife had died of cancer at about the age of twenty-three. While she was dying the utility company turned off the gas and lights. Glen remembered this and spent a great deal of time devising methods for circumventing meters.

He had had one child with his first wife. When she died he became an alcoholic. His present wife, Nile, was a social worker who had heard of this man who was drunk in the gutter with a small infant. She reformed him and they got married.

Glen had a quick mind and a good sense of humor. He was also very impatient. But, one soon learned to let the storm pass over and did not take his outbursts seriously. I well remember how outraged he was when he found out I didn't know how to use a slide rule. This was not from lack of opportunity because Norman had a very expensive slide rule which he delighted in. At the time, I could see no use for it. Today, a pocket computer would do far better.

The principle thing that Glen was working on was how the dimensions of the crystal effected its frequency. In solving that problem he used many methods of approximations which I learned. He also gave some lectures in the evening and again indicated how approximations could be used. I also learned from him that Maxwell's equations were phenomenological, based on the experiments of Faraday. Up until that time, I thought that all equations had a simple mechanical interpretation. I didn't know then that Maxwell had looked in vain for this interpretation for many years.

Glen was very glad to have me around. Not only did I do all kinds of mathematical chores for him, but I was even clumsier than he was. Before I came, he was the most clumsy person at the laboratory. I well remember one day when the new crystals came, ADP. We had waited for these for several weeks because we wanted to test various properties. Glen and I went out in the dock, and Glen warned me to treat them very carefully because they were irreplaceable. There was a gross of them, a dozen dozen. Glen went on and on with injunctions. Then he very carefully dropped them into the ocean. I just walked away and didn't say a word.

The fellow who ran the experimental laboratory was Glen's boss. Like many experimental physicists, he had no sympathy with theoretical work. Consequently, he insisted that I worked in the laboratory. I was willing since I had never done any experimental physics before.

I ruined several thousand dollars of equipment. I tried very hard not to ruin myself, although I had several near misses.

In particular, they tried to teach me how to attach leads to crystals by soldering iron. This requires a very delicate touch and is quite an art. Needless to say, although I tried, I never learnt it.

I became an expert on castor oil. The castor oil is needed to provide an impedance match between the crystals and the sea water. The concept of "impedance match" is very important, not only in engineering but in many social situations. Unfortunately, the castor oil freezes as the sea water gets colder at lower levels. When the castor oil freezes, its electrical properties change. I had to determine what these electrical properties were.

I even got a patent that way. I devised a circular slide rule for impedance matching.

I also became an expert on glue. The crystals have to be held together, and the properties of the glue are critical.

Norman came to Los Angeles. I learned of the existence of Los Alamos for the first time. Although, naturally, he didn't tell me what they were working on there. He was in the Army by then, and assured me that when I was drafted I would end up at Los Alamos.

I kept in contact with Al, who had gone to Purdue. There had been a general exodus from Traux Field once it was found I could leave safely. Al was delighted to find that I was going to Los Alamos. He wrote back saying, "You are going to Shangri La." Only when I arrived at Los Alamos did I understand why it was called Shangri La.

I took my physical examination in Los Angeles. I imagine that if I had tried hard I could have gotten a deferment because of allergic asthma. I didn't try to get this deferment for at least two reasons. In the first place, I didn't know how long the allergic asthma would last. It may have been just a temporary situation and the position at Los Alamos would not necessarily stay open. Secondly, I was tired of being a civilian in wartime. It was particularly hard in San Diego.

Finally, in December of 1944 I was drafted. I remember that Gene Kelly was drafted at the same time, and gave us a demonstration of dancing using several tables.

I was inducted at Fort MacArthur, outside of Los Angeles. I spent a week there, receiving shots, taking the DCT, and doing KP. At the end of that time, I was given a choice of going into the Army or the Navy. The Navy officer looked at my feet, which I had rather foolishly broken down at Madison, and remarked that I couldn't hike on these. I knew that if I was going to Los Alamos the only hiking I would do would be between my office and the barracks. However, I could not resist a grandstand play. I drew myself up to my full height and said, "Sir, I will do whatever my country requires."

CHAPTER 8

LOS ALAMOS 1945-46

My entry into Los Alamos was not auspicious.

First, I was sent by slow train to Camp Claiborne, Louisiana. Why I was sent by circuitous route, I don't know. Presumably, it was to fool the enemy.

At Camp Claiborne, I was put in a company of men who were waiting for medical discharge. It was rather depressing. However, we didn't have much time to sit around. Those who could work, were put to work doing various menial tasks. I even had guard duty one night, with an unloaded gun, of course.

One of the great advantages of going to Los Alamos was that I didn't have to undergo basic training. Consequently, I never had a loaded weapon in my hands during the war. The only time I shot a rifle was when I went to Boy Scout camp. Since I sighted the wrong way, I peppered the target of the person next to me. By mutual consent I didn't shoot any more. Remarkably, Marty Klein, who had very bad eyesight was an excellent marksman.

Being at Camp Claiborne was very interesting from the sociological point of view. With the protective colorations of an Army uniform I was able to observe the common man. Of course, I had to be careful not to whistle any classical music or to use a cultivated speech. However, I had grown up in New York City and knew how to conceal these qualities very well. I put on my New York accent and talked about sex and sports and had no trouble.

Finally, I received my orders to go to Los Alamos. On Christmas Day of 1944, Betty Jo and I were reunited in Albuquerque. Then I took the bus and reported to the appropriate office in Santa Fe. Then I took a bus for Los Alamos. Los Alamos is about twenty miles from Santa Fe.

The road up to Los Alamos was very winding in spots. When I looked over the edge I saw the drop of several thousand feet, I made a vow that I would never take this road again until the war was over. Of course, I didn't keep that vow.

One of the drivers of a bus had an amusing line. When he reached a dangerous turn, he would say, "Don't worry fellows, I close my eyes too."

The accidents never took place at the dangerous spots. They always occurred on level ground.

When I came to Los Alamos, there was the further difficulty that I needed clearance before I could do any theoretical work. While getting this clearance, I was put to work for the supply sergeant. In addition to doing various menial chores around the camp, we had to go to Albuquerque once a week to have shoes of the soldiers repaired. The sergeant who drove the truck reserved the cab for his friends. I rode in the back of the truck on the shoes. Sitting there, I remember thinking, "Here is a fine place for a mathematician."

Actually, I didn't mind at all going to Albuquerque since it gave me a chance to see Betty Jo.

Finally, the desired clearance came through. I was ready to begin work. I was now a member of the SED, Special Engineering Division. I was overjoyed to find that Stan Ulam was there. We had a very happy reunion. He knew David Hawkins, the Director of Personnel. Thanks to this, I was able to go to the theoretical division instead of to the electronics division headed by Alvarez. Alvarez was the one who had requested me as an expert on mathematics and electronics, thanks to Norman. I repaid Alvarez as best I could by baby sitting for him several times.

All the people who were to do technical work were given several pages describing what Los Alamos was about. Naturally, I was horrified when I read about the strength of the atomic bomb. I discussed this with Stan Ulam who agreed that it always was a shock.

The atomic bomb was always called "the gadget" for security reasons. For psychological reasons some euphemism would have been used.

I reported to the theoretical division where I was sent to see "Moll"

Flanders. He was the head of the numerical section. He was a very nice man, with a Ph. D. in mathematics from NYU. He was the younger brother of the senator from Vermont. Later, he came to a tragic end. In 1952 when Flanders opposed McCarthy, McCarthy tried to get at Flanders through "Moll" who had been mixed up with communist activities when young. "Moll" found out about this and removed himself by committing suicide.

In those days, differential equations were solved by using desk calculators. A great deal of arithmetic is involved. This was done on large sheets of paper with various self correcting results. In addition, at least two people would do the same calculation and compare results every fifteen minutes or so.

There was at Los Alamos a digital computer, which was reputed to be able to solve ten simultaneous differential equations. However, it broke down all the time, and, in addition, probably had very little storage. Consequently, it was not used much and I never even saw it.

Moll Flanders wanted me to go to work as a computer. I pointed out that I had used people of this type in San Diego and that I could do much better work. He said that there was no opening at the present, but if I familiarize myself with what was being done maybe there would be an opportunity later. At the end of the day, I went up to him and told him that now I knew what was being done. Consequently, I wanted more challenging problems.

He sent me to see Bethe. I told Bethe I knew Whittaker and Watson by heart, and I felt sure I could be of help. He countered by telling of mathematicians at Cornell who ask, "How can Galois theory help the war effort?"

It was not a very satisfactory interview. "However," he added, "Marshak needs a mathematician. Why don't you see him in the morning?"

In the morning, I reported to Marshak. He didn't need a mathematician, he merely wanted his own computer. He had a nonlinear differential equation, probably connected with shock waves, and wanted me to integrate it at intervals of one ten-millionth. Again, there was the familiar long sheet of paper. He left, saying that he would come back at noon to see what the results were.

When he came back I told him I had done nothing, and that I was ready to go to the electronics division where I thought I could be of more use. Naturally, he was furious. Why he, Bethe, and Flanders bothered with me I will never understand. Whenever I lose patience with a graduate student, I think of how patient they were in the middle of a war with lots of more important things to do.

Finally, he wrote down an equation and said, "Solve that, and don't come back until you have." Afterwards, he told me that he hoped he would not see me again until the war was over.

I wish I could say that the problem was difficult. Actually, it involved something that every novice on the mathematics team at Abraham Lincoln High School was expected to know. All that was necessary to do was to rationalize the denominator. Why Marshak, Weisskopf, and Bethe didn't know this, I cannot understand. All are brilliant mathematical physicists.

I saw the solution instantly. However, I wanted to be sure. Consequently, I went off by myself for fifteen minutes and checked and rechecked my solution. It seemed airtight. After fifteen minutes, I came back to Marshak and told him that I had the solution.

He was incredulous. Like a true physicist, he refused to check the mathematics, but examined some extreme uses where he knew the solution. They agreed. Then he took me to Weisskopf in a state of high excitement. He showed the solution to Weisskopf who was equally excited. Then all of us went to Bethe, and again the solution was shown.

The reason for the excitement was that this was the only theoretical method for estimating the yield of the first test at Almagordo.

My reputation was made. I was given my own office, and given problems of great interest. I solved the next two problems that were given to me, and then solved no others. They were too hard.

Before I reported to Moll Flanders, I was given a few pages describing what the project was about, as I have said above. At last I knew what they were trying to do at Los Alamos. It seemed they were trying to build a bomb based on nuclear fission. The yield of this bomb was to be about ten thousand tons of TNT. The biggest bomb used up to that date was the "Blockbuster", one thousand pounds of TNT.

There was no moral question involved since the bomb was to be used against the Germans. In all minds, Germans were synonymous with Nazis. Certainly, at that time if a vote had been taken among the Germans, Hitler would have won overwhelmingly.

There was an anti-Nazi underground, and the Nazis had killed or put into concentration camps hundreds of thousands of Germans. Only later did I learn that they had killed thousands of ministers and priests who did not join them.

We had read of the concentration camps and the extermination program for Jews, Russians, Poles, gypsies and others, and we knew what an evil thing Nazism was. We also knew that the Nazis were working on a bomb like this with the aid of several eminent scientists such as Heisenberg. It was a race against the Nazis.

Only the British commando raid at Bergen, Norway, which destroyed the heavy water plants with the aid of the Norwegian underground, set back the Nazi timetable.

The office was our headquarters. We had a very close-knit group: Norman, an electronics expert, Berderson, a physicist, Peshkin, another physicist, and several others who came from time to time. In general, the technical area, tech-area, was our haven. Oppenheimer had decreed that there was no rank in the technical area. Consequently, as soon as we entered the technical area, we relaxed. We were safe from the Army.

We pooled our record albums and had a collection of well over 100. In addition, we pooled our food, cheese and wine. The cheese was kept with the secret documents, in our safe. Consequently, one could tell the secret documents by smell.

We had a very intellectual mess hall. It was considered bad form to inquire what a person was working on. Consequently, at mealtime we discussed art, music, literature and generally anything but work.

I never knew what Peter Lax or Peshkin did. I knew Berderson had something to do with the physical construction of the bomb. I knew that Norman was an electronics troubleshooter. The only reason why I knew what Milt did was that we worked on the same problems.

After some months, I got an office mate, Milt Wing. When I heard the name, I took it for granted that the office mate would be Chinese.

Milt had had that trouble all his life. When he taught at UCLA, he regularly got invitations from various Tongs. He comes from the English Wings not from the Chinese Wings.

Milt was very neat. He always cleaned up his desk every evening. Consequently, we cooked on his desk. We had a hot plate and we supplemented our army meals almost every evening.

Teller was also up at Los Alamos. He wanted to build an H-bomb called the "super", at a time when it was uncertain if an A-bomb could be built. Consequently, Oppenheimer and Bethe put him in a building with several cohorts so he wouldn't bother anybody. I never even saw him.

Theoretically, I was in the Army. Fortunately, the interactions were very slight, but they existed.

To begin with, there was the question of uniform. I had known, because of my wool allergy, that I would have trouble with my O.D. Consequently, I used a trick I had used in college. I wore a complete suit of pajamas under my uniform. It was rather warm, but it prevented the intolerable itching.

Also, in that climate it made me a walking Van de Graff generator.

In those days, I slept nude. Consequently, each night I would take off my uniform, take off my pajamas and go to bed. In the morning I would put on my pajamas, put on my uniform and sally forth.

Each morning, the audience got larger and larger. I am sure that if I had kept it up I could have gotten a Section-8 discharge. However, miraculously I got permission to wear khakis because of the allergy. There were, however, two difficulties. In the summertime, it was alright. In the wintertime, however, I was always out of uniform. Because there were some Navy officers up at Los Alamos, the MPs never stopped me. I always carried a letter with me just in case. Secondly, in the wintertime khaki is rather cold. As a matter of fact, it is like wearing a sheet of ice. However, all of this was preferable to itching.

Furthermore, I could not wear army shoes. The box effectively crippled me. Even an army Sergeant could see that. Consequently, I got permission to buy a pair of shoes in Albuquerque. That, together with the khakis, made me look even more like a navy officer.

During the week I slept in the barracks. There was no trouble about reveille. I worked late at the tech area and just had to sign in. Consequently, I didn't have to stumble out into the darkness at 6:30. Those who did were not very considerate. They would bang their foot lockers and turn on the radio. In that part of the country there was a lot of religious advertising on the radio. In particular, they advertised a statue of Jesus Christ which shone in the dark. I abbreviated this, and my pet comment was, "Jesus Christ, it shines in the dark."

The barracks were quite interesting since we had several kinds of people. Graduate students in science, machinists, and experts in explosives, who I called "Jersey Bounces". At the time, there was a very popular tune called "The Jersey Bounce". Consequently, it was very amusing to look at the book shelves. One would see a shelf of books containing texts of quantum mechanics, then a shelf of comic books and so on.

The Jersey Bounces discovered chess. When they played chess they would make a move and add several four-letter words. It was great fun to watch them play.

There was also the matter of inspection every Saturday morning. One was supposed to arrange the foot locker in a certain way. I thought about this and realized that I would never make it. Consequently, I solved the problem by not having a foot locker. I used one-half of my desk for shorts and socks. Norman had a fetish about these. In some way, they reminded him of home and mother. Consequently, every morning after awhile I went through the same ritual. I would go over to Norman's barracks and borrow a pair of socks and a pair of shorts from him. This took about fifteen minutes.

I estimate that I owe Norman about thirty pairs of socks and thirty shorts. Someday, when I pass an Army Navy store, I will buy these and ship them to him.

One week, Norman made the mistake of sending a pair of wool socks to the laundry. They came back clean, and in perfect condition, except shrunk. They were now the size of baby booties. Norman, with me accompanying, went to the supply sergeant to get a new pair of socks. The sergeant looked at the shrunken socks very carefully and said he could not issue a new pair since these were in perfect condition.

This infuriated Norman. Seizing a pair of shears which the supply sergeant had on the desk, he started cutting up the socks, yelling at the top of his voice, "Perfect condition." After he had cut the socks to shreds, he gave them to the supply sergeant who had cowered behind the desk during this outburst, and asked whether he could now have a new pair of socks. The supply sergeant agreed he could now issue a new pair.

Incidentally, Norman had antagonized his sergeant. Therefore, he had been transferred to the noisemakers barracks. In a usual camp, this individual would have spent some time in the brig. Up at Los Alamos they were needed. Hence, the army had solved the problem by putting them all together.

One morning, I was surprised to find Norman on the upper part of the bunk. It seems that the other members of the barracks would come in drunk, and amuse themselves by urinating on their friends. However, when they were drunk, and especially in the darkness, they often made a mistake.

The latrine and the showers were in a separate building connected with the barracks by some wooden planks to avoid the mud. This meant that one had to take a shower, shave, etc., and then return to the barracks. Nobody ever got pneumonia, why, I don't know.

The latrine had to be cleaned every day. We would gladly have paid somebody to do it. After all, at Los Alamos there was no KP because the personnel could not be spared. However, the Army was adamant. We had to clean the latrine. At first, the ranks below sergeant were liable to this duty. As the war went on and our ranks increased, gradually it was staff sergeant and below. I think I had put on fatigues and cleaned the latrine about two or three times. Each time I thought, "Wait until I get back to Fine Hall, then I will put up a sign saying, 'Everybody below the rank of assistant professor has to clean the john.' "

In addition, one had to be on CQ once in a while. This meant that one had to stay up all night at the company headquarters in case of an emergency. It was easy to stay up all night because one had a choice of asphyxiating or freezing. If one stayed inside, one asphyxiated because of the smoke from the stove. If one went outside, one froze.

Consequently, one took turns asphyxiating and freezing. The only satisfaction was that if one was on CQ, one had the pleasure of waking people up at 6:30 a.m.

Then, there was the matter of food. Occasionally, we ate at the mess hall because it was free and we were out of money. What I had noticed both at Madison and Los Alamos was that the Army bought very good food and cooked it abominably. Since there was little to do in the evening at Los Alamos, our principal entertainment was eating. After payday, we ate in restaurants. Towards the end of the month, we ate in the mess hall. There was no trouble about meat rationing because we were so close to Texas.

We discovered a very good situation. About ten miles from the camp was the site where they worked on explosives. This site was put at that distance in case it blew up. This was a real hazard in that climate. Because of the dryness, static electricity was very common.

The use of explosives involved TNT. This is a fine powder which is a poison. Despite every precaution, it eventually gets into the body and causes the individual to become ill. The only way of keeping the individual healthy as long as possible is by feeding him a good diet. Consequently, the mess hall served a very good meal. We found out about this.

Norman who was an electronics troubleshooter had access to a jeep. Every lunch, then, we would file into the jeep and go out to this site and have a sumptuous meal. Unfortunately, word of this got about and the lines at the mess hall got longer and longer. Also, outsiders could come early with the result that the men who really needed the food did not have it. After awhile the Army gave out special badges and let it be known that anyone who didn't have a badge would be busted. That ended that.

One lunch time, while this was still going on, we noticed a circle of soldiers as we were leaving. In the center of the circle, one fellow sat on the ground and above him, kicking him to get up was a very tough looking redhead. I and the others were not happy with the situation. However, the others insisted it was none of my business.

We got into the jeep and made preparations to leave. However, the situation nagged at me. I told Norman to stop the jeep and jumped out. As I walked towards the center of the circle of soldiers I thought gloomily that this would cost me a couple of teeth. I rolled down the sleeves of my shirt so that my staff sergeant stripes showed.

I interposed myself between the redhead and the guy on the ground saying, "That's enough of that." The redhead looked at me and said, "What business is it of yours?" He looked me up and down. I made sure that he saw my staff sergeant stripes. There were a few tense seconds. Then, he decided not to do anything about it and in addition the others had crowded around by that time. The crisis was over.

Then there was the big row about security.

We were called together in the mess hall. In strode an immaculate Army colonel followed by flunkies, lieutenants, carrying military law books. He had the improbable name of Peer de Sylva. First, he read the penalty for treason. Death, or as I used to say, death or worse.

It seems that someone had written outside of security, to Vannevar Bush, complaining about the fact that civilian machinists received triple time for working on Sunday, while army machinists just worked. Incidentally, everything sent to Los Alamos was sent to P.O. Box 1663, billions of dollars of equipment. Los Alamos was the only Army camp in continental United States where mail was censored both ways. After the colonel had finished the penalty for treason, he asked for comments.

A tall lanky figure got up. He was going to be a preacher and hated profanity and obscenity. You can imagine the time he had in the Army. He said that the writer was perfectly correct. He had not written the letter but he agreed completely with the writer. Then he sat down.

The colonel decided to use some psychology. He said that if the writer of the letter would come to his office and talk to him man to man — he was interrupted by general laughter.

He asked for further comments. At the end of the room a soldier had been frantically waving his hand to get attention. Finally, the colonel noticed him.

"Why," said the soldier, "aren't there more baseball bats on the baseball field?"

The colonel didn't bother to answer. He strode off, followed by his flunkies.

About two weeks later the whole comedy was played again. This time the would be preacher said nothing. But there was a soldier at the end of the room who frantically waved his hand. The colonel recognized him. "Why," said the soldier, "don't civilians pick soldiers up when they go to town?"

We were not called together again. Years later I met an FBI man who had been at Los Alamos at that period. He told me that there was no difficulty in locating the typewriter that had been used. However the typewriter could have been used by anybody in the tech area. They never did find the man who wrote the letter.

Everybody should spend one year in the army. It gives one a taste of what Fascism must be like. One is definitely a second-class citizen in the army. Theoretically, one cannot even write to one's Congressman without going through his C.O.

Many people were curious as to what was going on at Los Alamos. In our correspondence, we tried politely to discourage them. Those who were persistent received a printed form saying that the work was highly classified and please do not ask questions. This only whetted the curiosity of Marty, who had worked with Norman at Fort Monmouth, before Norman was drafted. He wrote facetiously, "Okay, if you can't tell me what you are doing please send a diagram." He was visited by Army intelligence men and thoroughly scared.

One answer that we gave was that we were building windshield wipers for submarines.

There never was any secret about the A-bomb. It was all a matter of technology. Incredible precision was required, precision which didn't exist in the laboratory at the time, much less in commerical circles. This technology was done by first-rate people like Bethe, Fermi, Bohr and many others who put their research aside for several years. This was their contribution to the war against Fascism.

The same was not true about "the man in space program". Most members of the scientific community were opposed to this boondoggle, or shall we call it a moondoggle. Consequently, they refused to have anything to do with it.

When America landed on the moon in 1970, I remember a Russian friend saying, "What took you so long?"

We had a very nice colonel in charge of the SED (Special Engineering Division). Occasionally he would call us together and say, "Fellows, I don't care if you don't salute me but when you see someone with stars on his collar please salute him, otherwise I get into trouble."

The saying was that the colonel put on his track shoes when he inspected the barracks.

The same was not true about the C.O.'s. They seemed to have been alcoholics who were sent to Los Alamos either to drink themselves to death or to a hospital. They spent all their time at the bar at the La Fonda. One, however, was particularly obnoxious. I remember him calling us together in the mess hall and standing on a table, dead drunk, and shouting, "You Bastards! We can't touch you now but wait until the war is over."

He did not last long.

We had a mathematics and physics club at Los Alamos. With the luminaries there we had some good talks.

In particular, we had a talk by Niels Bohr. Bohr had taken the pseudonym Nicholas Baker to avoid retaliation by the Nazis against his relatives in Denmark. Bohr was not a good speaker. For the first five minutes of his talk, it was difficult to know whether he was talking in Danish, German, or English. The saying was that he stuttered in all languages.

He had, however, a keen sense of humor, and it was always a pleasure to listen to. This time he decided to give a talk on the inadequacies of the Bohr theory of the atom. His talk was billed "Nicholas Baker on the Bohr Theory of the Atom." While he spoke there was great indignation behind me. What was this man doing attacking the Bohr theory of the atom?

We also had a talk by Fermi. He also spoke on the Bohr theory of the atom. Without using calculus, or any equation, he derived all the principal properties. This was a new and exciting thought to me. If one understood the process, one could derive the principal properties. Even Bohr, if one understood the process, one could derive properties of the solutions of the associated equations. I have used this principle many times. If one knows what to look for it is not difficult to find it.

I regretted deeply that I did not get to know Fermi. I am sure that I could have learned a lot from him. Fermi had started out as a mathematician and then turned to physics. He had many powerful methods at his disposal. He was unique because he was a master of both theoretical and experimental techniques.

Because of his scientific stature Fermi was made head of a division. In that capacity he was deluged by paper. He did not want to spend his time as a paper shuffler and complained frequently to no avail. Finally, he side-stepped the difficulty very neatly by giving up his office and using a part of a friend's desk for his papers.

I gave some talks on summability, an elegant subject in which I had gotten interested in through the books by Zygmund and Kacmarz and Steinhaus. There was a penetrating question by a young soldier at the back of the room. At the end of the talk, I invited him to my office and continued the discussion. That was the way I met Peter Lax.

Peter had a keen mind and a great knowledge of mathematics. In addition he knew many other subjects and had a good sense of humor. Moreover, he had one further asset. His parents sent him food parcels. At that time, we had a community post office. All that was necessary to do was to give the number and get the mail. We always scrupulously saved something for Peter.

The post office was run by an amusing character. When I first met him, he was in Flanders group, nominally a computer. However, he had the habit of taking four-day weekends, and when he showed up he would spend his time loading dice in a giant beaker of water. His mother owned a number of whorehouses in Pittsburgh which he invited me to use after the war. The Army used him efficiently by making him postmaster, a job that only required a few hours a day.

I was in the library reading when the news came over the speaker that F.D.R. had died. I felt as if I had lost a friend. I knew very little about Truman then. The more I have found out the greater my admiration. I think most historians agree that Truman was one of our great presidents and that his stature will increase over time.

With V-E Day, came moral problems again. Should the A-bomb be used against the Japanese?

From all that I have read Japan was a defeated nation by then. Its cities were vulnerable to bombers. However, MacArthur wanted an invasion. We had until September 1 to construct the A-bomb and have the Japanese surrender. The estimates are that an invasion would have cause 500 thousand to a million dead, and about ten times as many wounded. The cost in Japanese life would have been far greater, not only in the army but because of the round-the-clock bombing.

Why did we not give the Japanese an example of the destruction that the A-bomb could cause?

The answer is very simple. At the time there were two A-bombs available. The thin man and the fat man. The "thin man" was the name for the implosion bomb and the "fat man" was the name for the bomb where slightly more than one-half a critical mass was fired into slightly more than one-half of a critical mass. The fat man was guaranteed to work but there was no guarantee that the thin man would work.

Consequently, there was a big question as to which bomb should be used first, provided that the thin man worked. It was a gigantic bluff. The Japanese had to be given the idea that their cities could be destroyed systematically one by one. If they had not surrendered after Nagasaki, the invasion would have to have taken place with the additional loss of life. When one thinks that many of the men in the invasion army were married and had children, one has an idea of what effect the decision to drop the bomb had.

We worked around the clock, taking time off only to sleep. There was nothing abstract about what we were doing. We all had friends or relatives in the invasion army.

The temporary buildings we were in shook from explosions ten miles away every fifteen minutes. That was not conducive to calm nerves.

The Army had decreed that no wife of an enlisted man could work at Los Alamos. This was at a time when there was a great shortage of secretaries, school teachers, nurses, computers and many others. All of these positions could have been filled by wives of enlisted men. Why the Army made this decree I never found out.

Not only couldn't wives work at Los Alamos, they couldn't live within 100 miles of Los Alamos. This meant. for all practical purposes, Albuquerque. We got an apartment in Albuquerque by staying up for the morning edition of the newspaper. The people who owned the apartment were not eager to rent it to a soldier. However, we used my Princeton connection to good avail and got the apartment. Betty Jo was not happy staying in the apartment alone during the week. After several months she got a job as a school teacher in an Indian village, San Felipe. The chief of this village did not like progress. Hence, there was no electricity.

San Felipe is about halfway between Santa Fe and Albuquerque. I used to hitch a ride to Albuquerque, and asked to be let off in the middle of nowhere. Then, I would trudge to the village of San Felipe. I remember telling myself that I was taking basic training this way. It is not easy to enter an Indian village because of the dogs. They have a nasty habit of nipping at your heels. Consequently, when I visited Betty Jo I made sure I had a stick which I constantly swung behind me.

It is quite an experience to stay in a place where there are no switches of electric lights. When one wants to go from one room to another in the evening, one has to take a lamp. In addition, it was bitterly cold. Fortunately, Betty Jo did not stay there long.

Hitching a ride from Santa Fe to Albuquerque was quite an experience because of the great prejudice against Spanish Americans. When I got sun burnt, I look very Spanish American. Consequently, I usually had Norman stand out on the road while I hid behind a tree. When a car stopped for Norman I would get in too.

Betty Jo had heard that they were forming a medical WAC contingent at Bruns General Hospital, about three miles outside of Santa Fe. She had always been interested in medicine, and had wanted to join the military. In San Diego, she had wanted to be a WAC. I was not happy about her becoming a WAC for many reasons. In the first place, it meant that she had to take basic training for three months at Fort Oglethorpe in Georgia. Secondly, I didn't want Betty Jo to be under Army control. Thirdly, the WACs did not enjoy a good reputation during the war. The Army had not been careful as to who they had taken in and many stories of the misbehavior of the WACs was current. Finally, Bruns was a TB hospital primarily. A New Mexico state regiment had been in the Philippines when the Japanese conquered them. Many died in prison camps, many more died in Bruns.

Betty Jo, however, was determined. I was very unhappy about this and felt deserted. I don't think our marriage ever recovered from this.

While Betty Jo was away, I decided to continue my sociological investigations. I went to a church breakfast. After the food, we sang hymns. The woman in charge went around the table and asked for one's favorite hymn. When she came to me I said, "Rock of Ages". "Oh," she said, "Lutheran." "Not quite," I said.

After taking basic training at Fort Oglethorpe Betty Jo returned to Bruns. Once she had returned, we gave up our apartment in Albuquerque. Unfortunately, that was not the last we were to hear about this apartment.

For some reason, her C.O. refused her weekend passes. Consequently, for the only time, I went to the chaplain and explained the situation to him. A conversation between the chaplain and the C.O. took care of the situation.

It was much more convenient to see Betty Jo now. On weekends, we went to various small hotels. Some of them tried to blackmail us.

The Red Cross did not behave well. The Red Cross volunteers refused to enter the TB wards. They were more interested in marrying officers.

I have had many conversations about the Red Cross with the men who served in various parts of the world. No good word was ever said about the Red Cross.

The Salvation Army, on the other hand, behaved admirably. The Salvation Army lassies put on masks and gowns and entered the TB wards. They always had a cheery word and a gift for the men.

The Red Cross office was open from nine to five. If an emergency developed at five after five, it was too bad. Frequently Betty Jo used her own money to telephone a family to see a son or brother for the last time.

Consequently, I have never given a penny to the Red Cross. I give generously to the Salvation Army about which many good things can be said.

Erdös came to Santa Fe. He was always strongly anti-Fascist and wanted to work at Los Alamos where his great talents would have been very useful. Unfortunately, he refused to sign a paper saying that he would not talk about the A-bomb after the war. Considering all the foreign scientists at Los Alamos such a paper was a farce.

We took him to dinner at the La Fonda, Betty Jo, I, Peter Lax and John Kemeny, another young soldier of Hungarian background. Erdös spoke in Hungarian about the relatives of Peter and John back in Hungary. Then, in loud English he asked, "How is work going on the A-bomb?"

In the beginning of August, there was the test at Almagordo. Naturally, entrance to the test site was possible only if one had a specific task to perform. Consequently, a large number of hunting expeditions were formed.

The test was to take place at about four o'clock in the morning. I had never understood why crucial tests are done on such ungodly hours. In any case, I decided that I would see the test on film in a comfortable fashion.

The test was a success. There is an interesting postscript to this. The man in charge of the experiments had no confidence in the bomb. He thought the yield would be about 600 pounds of TNT. Various people like Oppenheimer, Fermi, Bethe and others warned him that all his instruments would be incinerated. He paid no attention and put all of the instruments much too close. They were incinerated, and all the work that Milt and I and others had done was for naught. Fortunately, Fermi had put up some tin cans at intervals and released some scraps of paper when the atomic wind went past. From this evidence, he was able to estimate the strength of the bomb. It was probably as good an estimate as would have been furnished by our results.

The cover story for Almagordo was that an ammunition dump had exploded. When I saw Betty Jo that evening, she mentioned that. She also expressed concern about a cousin who had fought through the European campaign and was now in the Japanese invasion army. I told her not to worry, the war would be over in a week. Naturally, she wanted to know how I was so sure. I told her I could not tell her, but that I was certain.

Sure enough, the bluff worked. First, Hiroshima, then Nagasaki, then we held our breath. Fortunately, the Japanese surrendered. From all that I have read, it was nip and tuck.

There were three types of badges in the tech area: red, white, and blue. Those who did technical work had white badges. Every week the white badge holders were called together in the auditorium and told about the latest progress. When the Japanese surrendered, Oppenheimer called us together. He told us we now had a responsibility to see that the bomb was never used again.

There was also time for mathematical research. I found an elegant way of using the representation of a group and integration to generate invariance. Later, I found that I had been anticipated by Hurwitz. I never minded being anticipated by a famous mathematician since it showed I was working on the right problems. I always felt it was a matter of time before I found new results.

With the war over, there was time for other things. Many now wrote up various results for publication.

For some months, I had looked at the cartoons by Thurber on Unnatural History. It seemed to me that they were pretty silly. I wrote to the editor and said that they were published only because they had the name of Thurber attached. As I had expected, he wrote back and said that if I thought I could do better to do so. I had expected that and was ready for him. I sent him back about six cartoons. I never received an answer.

One of the cartoons I liked very much. It showed a devil-may-care in a field of lackadaisies.

In particular, I was able to go on leave now. But, this posed a quandary. My grandmother had a very weak heart. If I suddenly appeared, it would certainly kill her. If, on the other hand she knew that I was going to come at a certain time the excitement might very well kill her. I decided to tell her when I would come. Unfortunately, one-half hours before I came she died and I never see her again alive.

It was a bitter blow. That I was the cause of her death was even more distressing.

My Uncle Arthur took us to the opera where we saw the "Bartered Bride" by Smetana for the first time. I like this opera very much and have seen it frequently, although, I don't like opera in general.

We returned to Los Alamos by taking a train to St. Louis, a train to Boulder, Colorado and then a Greyhound bus to Santa Fe.

It was easy to hitch in to New York by plane, but impossible to hitch out. To get in, all we had to do was to go to Kirtland Field and pay a dollar a piece for the rental of a parachute. Then we waited. We did not have to wait long. Pretty soon, an admiral flew in with his private plane. He was delighted to give us a lift to the next naval base, Olathe, Kansas. He was a very nice person, and had his steward serve us steak from his private supply.

I have found that colonels and generals and their navy equivalents captains and admirals are generally nice people. It is the junior officers that one must steer clear of.

At Olathe, several remarks were made about Betty Jo being a WAC. I almost got into a fight with the whole Navy. Fortunately, there was a plane out, going to New York. There was a hurricane that day and this was the only plane in the air. We landed at Floyd Bennett Field in a driving rain. Fortunately, the field was not far from Helen's house.

On the way back, in St. Louis, I almost got into a fight with mountain troops. This would have been much more serious because they were bigger and tougher. Fortunately, one of them was a New Yorker, and we turned the conversation to talk about Manhattan.

Upon our return there were several unusual incidents. First of all there was the forest fire, which threatened something vital. I had never seen a forest fire close up before and volunteered for fire fighting. I suspected that the SED would be called upon anyway, and I was right. A forest fire close up is an awesome spectacle. Fortunately, we were able to contain it. Then there was the great water shortage. The army engineers had been warned that if they put the water pipes above ground, they might freeze if it got too cold. Fortunately, during the war we had mild winters. This was not true in 1945. The water pipes froze and the supply of water to Los Alamos was reduced to a trickle. Those soldiers on leave were sent telegrams to stay on leave. All the water that was available was sent to the army barracks. The civilians suffered dreadfully. In the tech area one could tell where the johns were by smell. Finally, the weather got warmer and the pipes unfroze and water was available again.

We had tough tackle teams, two SED teams, two officer teams, two MP teams, and two civilian teams. They were supposed to generate goodwill. They generated goodwill like international soccer teams do.

I had forgotten about my wool allergy. I wore wool socks when I played quarterback on one of the SED teams. When red spots started appearing on my feet, I took it for granted it was athlete's foot, and I made the mistake of going to the Army Hospital. There I was treated with camphor and phenol, a "cure" recently recommended in Reader's Digest by Paul de Kruif. Phenol and water form carbolic acid. Within a week I had a beautiful infection on both feet. The hospital at Los Alamos had two wards. One ward was for influenza and pneumonia, the other ward was for VD. Since I obviously didn't have influenza or pneumonia, I was put in the VD ward. The conversations there were most interesting, and I wished at the time that I had a tape recorder.

Every three hours, a nurse came around to give everyone a shot of penicillin. I constantly had to say, "Look at the instructions." The nurse would come back and say, "A shot of penicillin wouldn't hurt you anyway." As usual, breakfast was served at a very early hour. Consequently, I had my friends bring me some sandwiches which I saved for breakfast and would just pull the sheet over my head.

Every day, the surgeon came around to look at my feet. The memory still gives me the shudders. Fortunately, sulfur worked, and I was able to hobble out of the hospital. During the remainder of my stay at Los Alamos I wore moccasins which were much too big. Consequently, I was always looking for them and being forced to walk barefoot in the snow to retrieve them.

Every Sunday the chaplain came around. When he saw the word "atheist" on my bed, he carefully circled it.

At some army camps, one was not allowed to call oneself an atheist or an agnostic. Men doing so were put down as Protestants. In the navy, it was necessary to go to some services on Sunday. A friend of mine who was half Jewish and half Italian was informed of this. In indignation he went to Protestant services.

Rumors were ripe. At that time a discharge from the Army was on the basis of points. One received a certain number of points for combat duty overseas. Obviously, service at Los Alamos did not generate many points. I resigned myself to being in the occupation army in Japan for two years at least. One rumor was particularly attractive. It went that the Army would discharge a soldier if there was an invitation for him to go back to a university. Bochner had arranged that I have a National Research Predoctoral Fellowship waiting for me at Princeton. Much to my surprise the rumor was true.

It was necessary to fill out an application, which, naturally, was lost. The Army clerks would not let me fill out another application and insisted on finding this one which they did, after several weeks of anguish. Everything went through and I landed up at El Paso waiting for my discharge. Finally, after one week, the great day came. I was number seven.

A young lieutenant gave out the honorable discharges, 1, 2, 3, 4, 5, 6, 8. I exploded. In my moccasins I certainly looked like a wounded veteran. The papers were full of stories of how dangerous the returning veterans were. The young lieutenant was petrified. I have never seen such fear in a person's eyes. Obviously, he expected me to take out a knife and rip him up the middle. He would be carted off on a stretcher and I would be reprimanded.

He tried to soothe me, and promised me that the whole proceedings would be stopped until they found my discharge. It had fallen behind the desk and after two hours or so they found it.

When I stood on the train station at El Paso, I noticed the rest rooms which read, "White Men" and "Colored Men". "Shades of Nazism," I thought.

CHAPTER 9

PRINCETON 1946-48

I was discharged from the Army on March 1, 1946, a date I celebrated for ten years. I went immediately to Princeton. I should have taken a vacation for at least three months, but I was anxious to make up for lost time.

The married couples lived in Hill Dormitory. Before the war, this dormitory had been inhabited by rich students. They brought whores from Trenton, a practice which the University closed its eyes to. But far more serious, they had a habit of getting drunk, going to the roof and tossing empty beer bottles on the passers-by. Finally, the University and the town passed an ordinance which said that any property which was surrounded on three of its four sides by University property could be bought by the University. Mrs. Hill knew her geometry too. She ceded the walk of the dormitory to her brother, and thus kept the property.

Living in Hill Dormitory was fun. We shared a community kitchen and a community bathroom. This bathroom was used by all the truck drivers on the Philadelphia to New York route, because it had a reputation for being clean. In the dormitory were many foreign couples, Japanese, Indian, Egyptian, and others.

Upper class Egyptians spoke French to irritate the British.

It even had an Army colonel and his wife. I, naturally, was rather allergic to Army officers after Los Alamos. Colonel Si Sinnreich was the senior member of a team which the Army had decided should learn nuclear physics. We had a unique method of learning calculus. He would put a bottle of whiskey on the table between us and as the lesson progressed we both took drinks. Somehow, he learned calculus.

Incidentally, Trenton is the center of the American contraceptive industry. The reader who is familiar with the manufacturing process can imagine how many patients the psychiatrists must have gotten.

When a car was available, we had lunch at a diner on the highway where truckers ate. This day, Peter Lax was down from New York. In the car were Peter, Hal Shapiro, Bernie Sherman, who was now a graduate student at Princeton, myself, and of course the driver of the car. Hal Shapiro asked me, "Do you think you will be a better mathematician then Erdös?"

"Far better," I said. Immediately, four pairs of incredulous eyes fastened upon me. I explained. "Erdös has great talent, even genius, but he has no judgement. He does not match the problems he works on with his ability."

I doubt whether at the time those listening got the point. I think they understand now.

I had met Hal Shapiro in Albuquerque. He was working on the proximity fuse, but naturally couldn't tell me about it. Nor could I tell him about the A-bomb. We were both sure that we were working on the most important weapon of the war.

In Princeton, I learned how to make omelets. Down Witherspoon Street there was a little restaurant run by an old Frenchman about ninety years old. It was a typical French restaurant, unsanitary. The waitress was an old crone with stringy grey hair and cockroaches ran merrily over the tables. However, he did make good omelets and was willing to show anyone interested how he did it. The secret was to use a very hot skillet, well greased. If one wishes to make eggs and onions, it is important to cook the onions first. I even learned how to flip an omelet. This skill as a short order cook came in handy later.

Finally, the Veteran's Housing Development was available. These were quite nice. Three apartments to a building. We were fortunate in having an end apartment so that we had maximum privacy. We were overjoyed to find that our next door neighbors were the Baileys. The neighbors on the other side were the Stevensons, Pete and Barbara, with whom we also became very friendly.

One of Pete's aunts was Emily Post. Whenever Pete had a question of etiquette he would say, "Let me call up my Aunt Emily and ask."

My first task was to get my Ph.D. Thanks to Bochner, I had a

National Research Council Predoctoral Fellowship good for one year and automatically renewable for another. In addition, I taught one class making $1,200 a year. Thus, as a graduate student I was making $3,000 a year, quite a lot of money for those days. However, I was tired of being a peon. I wanted to be my own master.

Consequently, I wanted to get my degree as soon as possible. I had saved several results as a nucleus for my thesis, and had intended to work with Bochner. However, Lefschetz urged me to write up my results on stability theory. If I did this, I could get my degree very soon.

I took a good course in analysis given by Bochner. He was interested in ergodic theory at that time and explained it very lucidly. It is a fine example of a beautiful result which can seldom be used. It is virtually impossible to establish the necessary conditions.

Consequently, I set about studying for my qualifying exams and writing my thesis. My thesis was on stability theory. Stability theory is the study of systems under various perturbing influences. Since there are many systems, many types of influences, and many equations describing systems, this is an open-ended problem. A system is designed so that it will be stable under external influences. However, one cannot predict all external influences, nor predict the magnitude of those that occur. Consequently, we need control theory. If one is interested in stability theory, a natural result is a theory of control.

The National Research Council was very anxious to show that its judgement was sound. All fellowship holders were supposed to take the SAT, Scholastic Aptitude Test. I was not anxious to take this test, feeling that at my qualifying examination I had taken my last test. However, Church was in charge of the program and asked me as a personal favor to take the test. Since I wanted to do him a favor, I agreed.

The test was interesting, except for the part on mathematics. This went as far as calculus and began with public school arithmetic. Consequently, I did the test backwards. I answered the questions until they became insulting.

When the results came back, my highest score was in history and my lowest was in mathematics. This was after I had a Ph.D. from Princeton.

My plan was very simple. I wanted to get my Ph.D., the "union card", and then work on analytic number theory with Siegel. Fate had other plans.

The first step was simple. I got my Ph.D. in June of 1946. The second step was not so simple.

Meanwhile, however, I spent the summer of 1946 learning about stability theory. I wrote in this way my first monograph, "A Survey of the Roundedness Stability and Asymptotic Behavior of Solutions of Nonlinear Differential and Difference Equations", put out by ONR, and gathered the material for my first book.[1] The method I used was the following. There is a German review journal, *Zentralblatt für Mathematik.* I read all the reviews on differential equations. If the review seemed interesting, I read the original. The American counterpart, *Mathematical Reviews,* was started in 1941 when it was recognized that it was impossible to depend on a German journal.

The thesis was good because it opened the way to much further research. The work on time lag processes led to a book[2]. The work on partial differential equations led to a chapter in another book[3], and was a responsible for my interest in quasilinearization.

I even had a section using fixed point theorems. I had been intrigued by the paper by Birkhoff and Kellogg. Again, I was impressed by the power of a simple geometric idea in analysis.

Lefschetz had gone to Washington and had gotten money for research in differential equations and the support of both graduate and post-doctorate students from Mina Rees who was head of the mathematics section of the ONR, Office of Naval Research. She deserves a lot of credit for doing this since occasionally, she had to stretch the regulations.

Hitler also deserves credit, although that was not what he had in mind. Hitler drove European mathematicians to our shores and Mina

[1] Bellman, R., *Stability Theory of Differential Equations* (McGraw-Hill Book Company, 1953).

[2] R. Bellman and K.L. Cooke, *Differential-Difference Equations* (Academic Press, Inc., New York, 1963).

[3] E.F. Beckenbach and R. Bellman, *Inequalities* (Springer-Verlag, Berlin, 1961).

supported them and their students. Between them, they built up American mathematics.

As a post-doctoral student, I was supported by this money. As a graduate student, Peter also was supported by this money.

One of my jobs was to organize small symposia by invitation only, on differential equations and applications. Usually, I had no trouble. One time however, I tangled with a well-known difficult character, also a student of Lefschetz. The more I wrote letters of sweet reasons, the more unreasonable he became. Finally, I lost patience and wrote back a very sarcastic letter. I only remember the sentence with "tears streaming down my face, I read about your inability to attend." At this point, he wrote a long letter to Lefschetz about the way he was being treated. Lefschetz reviewed all the correspondence. He said all my letters were correct, except for the last one. He said that once he had written a letter like this and paid very dearly for it. He advised me in the future to say what I wanted in person or over the phone, but never in a letter.

This was good advise, and I have followed it ever since. Occasionally, I have composed some scorching letters but I never sent them. I have said some choice things over the phone.

When I had come to Princeton in March, I had gone to Siegel at the Institute and asked him to give some lectures on transcendental numbers. He agreed if I would guarantee an audience of at least six. When he started lecturing I understood why he asked for this guarantee.

Princeton University Press was very anxious to get a book from Siegel who had not written one up to this time. Shiffman and I were to take notes, these notes were to be sent to Gordon Pall, who was to work them over and then send them on to Siegel for the final polishing. First, Shiffman dropped out, then Pall wrote that he was too busy, then Siegel decided to take a European trip. Since I was busily writing my thesis, I should have taken heed of all this and postponed the whole thing. However, I was anxious to please, and, therefore, I undertook the publication myself.

The press insisted that it be a joint work, Bellman and Siegel. Fortunately, Shapiro read over the manuscript and caught many mistakes.

It was not easy to take notes of Siegel's lectures. He had the habit of lecturing for two or two and half hours at a time. I found out, however, that he was following various papers word for word. Consequently, I was able just to listen to the lectures and write up the material later. Siegel is very shy. He memorizes his lectures. When someone would point out a better way for doing something he would listen politely and go on as before. This antagonized a few people and they did not attend subsequent lectures.

It was a beautiful October day. I remember well looking at the sky and thinking what a wonderful fall day it was. My first premonition of disaster was Lefschetz waggling a wooden finger at me and saying, "Dickie boy, you're really in the soup now." He went off chuckling merrily. Then Tucker looked at me sorrowfully. I wondered what I had done. I had not long to wait.

Artin pulled me into his office. Siegel didn't like my notation! As a matter of fact, he disliked it so much that he demanded that the press suppress the edition. Artin demanded that we go over to Siegel's house and that I apologize. I, of course, was quite willing. Siegel was not at home.

I offered to pay for the edition, about $300. The press, however, decided to absorb the loss. Copies had already been sent out to the major libraries. For years afterwards one of my hobbies was seeing if a university library had this edition. Siegel rewrote the book, Number 18 of the Annals of Mathematics Studies. In my bibliography, I list it as "Limited Edition".

That ended any idea of working with Siegel. Naturally, Lefschetz was delighted.

Courant, a skiing companion of Siegel, was very angry with me because of the incident. In general, mathematicians took one side or the other. However, I will never forget Neugebauer saying to me, "Let Siegel write his own books."

I did a lot of number theory with Hal Shapiro. One joint paper led to a great deal of difficulty.

The background was the following. Shapiro wrote many papers himself. Erdös was the referee for these papers. Each time that Shapiro wrote a paper Erdös would improve the result a little. Consequently, Shapiro would withdraw the paper.

I thought this was not fair to Shapiro.

Shapiro and I worked on a very interesting problem: What is the probability that two numbers are relatively prime? Incidentally, one is often asked: What do mathematicians do? This is not an easy question to answer. However, one good reply is that mathematicians make natural questions precise.

Shapiro and I treated this problem, wrote it up and submitted our manuscript to the *Transactions of the American Mathematical Society*. Unfortunately, the editor, A.A. Albert, had gone off to Brazil for six months and left the journal in the hands of Kaplansky. Our paper was refereed by Erdös who accepted it. Kaplansky, however, asked Erdös whether he couldn't get a better proof than ours. Erdös supplied one, and Kaplansky transmitted it to us. We wrote back, pointing out if Erdös' proof were written up in the same detail as ours it would be just as long. Kaplansky persisted, and Erdös supplied a very elegant shorter proof. Kaplansky suggested then a joint paper. I refused, saying that we would add Erdös' proof as an appendix if he desired.

And that was the way matters stood.

About a month later Shapiro came to me very disturbed. He had gone to various parties and it seems that Erdös had gone around the country saying that we were stealing our result from him. Shapiro wanted to withdraw the paper. I didn't think that was a good thing to do but one paper more or less meant little to me, and I was in this for Shapiro's sake anyway. I wrote to Kaplansky telling him we wanted to withdraw the paper if possible.

We heard nothing for several weeks. Then we received a letter from Kaplansky saying that the type was destroyed and the bill would be sent to us.

I wrote back, saying that he had misinterpreted my letter and that we had no intention of paying the bill, about $300. By this time Albert had returned, and heard Kaplansky's version of the story. We received a vitriolic letter from Albert telling us that either we pay the bill or face expulsion from the American Mathematical Society. I have often thought of the expulsion ceremony. I think our pencils would be broken in front of us.

At this point, I went to Lefschetz. I felt that the function of the referee was not to improve a paper. Lefschetz handled the problem in a characteristic fashion. He didn't waste any time on the problem. Rather, he wrote a letter to Albert pointing out various indiscretions which Albert had committed in his youth.

Thereupon we received a very nice letter from Albert and the matter was ended. However, we never published the paper nor did Erdös publish his proof. That is a great shame since Erdös really had an elegant method.

Lefschetz loved to taunt Shapiro because Shapiro reacted so strongly. As a matter of fact, most of the graduate students were terrified of Lefschetz. When they saw him coming they would hide. Shapiro used to retaliate by telling Lefschetz that I was doing number theory. One day, Lefschetz stopped me and said, "Which end is turning out the papers on number theory?" "The same end that is turning out the papers on differential equations," I said.

The ONR grant also supported my office mate, Joe LaSalle. He had started out in topology, but had turned to differential equations. Above other things he was an expert in the equation describing the multivibrator, Van de Pol's equation. At last, I understood the mathematics of the multivibrator. He also asked a fundamental question in control theory which had much to do with its development, the "bang bang" control problem.

There was a mathematics colloquium once a week at which a talk was given. I gave a very complicated talk in which I proved a long standing conjecture concerning the Riemann hypothesis. Namely, under the Riemann hypothesis there are no double roots. It was a good talk, but had one slight defect — it was incorrect. On the way home, I discovered the flaw. I had engaged in the principle of wishful thinking.

At tea, I was introduced by Chevalley to Weyl as the young man who had proved this conjecture. I had to tell Chevalley and Weyl that the proof was wrong. Weyl was very nice. He pointed out that if the world knew the mistakes that famous mathematicians made at their desks their reputations would not be as high.

Weyl was not as nice when it came to the inequality which I had discovered in Madison. He and Levinson had become interested in the result which had generated this inequality and in 1946 published papers in the *American Journal of Mathematics* on this subject. I went to Weyl very diffidently and showed him my paper of 1943. He said casually that he had known the result for many years, back in Zurich.

I vowed then and there that I would never treat a young mathematician this way. I complained about this to Lefschetz. His name for Weyl was "Holy Herman". He had pet names for most people, many of which are unprintable. I warned him time and time again he would forget and introduce someone by this name. He said that Weyl had done the same thing to him.

Lefschetz had the happy idea of translating several Russian papers on nonlinear oscillations. He did a free translation of several papers by Krylov and Bogolubov and had the book by Andoronov and Chaikin translated. The translator, a very charming woman of French origin, knew Russian perfectly but no mathematics. Consequently her translation had to be looked at very carefully. For example, we were quite puzzled by the word "mustache". When we looked at the text we found that a proper translation was "graph".

Lefschetz was a very dynamic individual, always full of projects and plans. This meant that he was always stubbing his toes against rules and regulations. Whenever this occurred, he would say, "Why are there more horses' asses than horses?"

He said this so often that I decided to name it Lefschetz's Theorem. It is the only theorem in the form of a question.

The Russians have a very strong tradition in mathematics going back to Euler. When the Communists came into power they at first outlawed probability theory. They felt that in a well run society there was no chance. But, the needs of science and industry gradually took over.

The Russian interest in chess is easy to understand. The Russian interest in ballet, a Czarist interest, is not so easy to understand. I have never heard their rationalization of this.

I decided to learn to read mathematical Russian. Before the war, a Russian paper had a complete translation in French, German, or English with an abstract in one of these languages. After the war, the translations disappeared. Then the abstract disappeared to be replaced by an abstract in Ukrainian or Georgian. It was clear that I learn how to read Russian or else I would be cut off from a very important source.

I sat in on a Russian class for several weeks to get familiar with the alphabet and the structure of the language. As I had expected the Cyrillic alphabet caused no difficulty. Russian has a very complicated grammar, but, fortunately, the word order is practically that of English. Although Russian is an Indo-European language, the vocabulary is quite different. Consequently, practically every word has to be learned. I use the Shleimann technique. I took a book which I knew well, Bernstein, "Lecons sur Meilleure Approximation" which had a Russian translation. Using the Russian translation, the French original, and a dictionary, I went through the text word by word. It was not easy, much like using a bilingual. Many mathematical words are quite specialized. The ordinary dictionary definition does not give their mathematical meaning. However, by using the context and my knowledge of mathematics I was able to figure out their meaning.

Some years later, I even made money, $6.00 a page, translating into English various Russian articles.

Every afternoon at four o'clock during the week, tea and coffee and cookies were served. No classes or seminars were scheduled for that time. It was essential to be on time, and even a few minutes early because hungry graduate students would soon devour all the cookies. At the tea, one had an opportunity to see fellow graduate students and faculty. Most of the discussion was mathematical, but other subjects were discussed too.

It was well known that the tea was held which meant that any mathematician in the vicinity would drop in. In this way, one met many people.

I met Norbert Wiener in this way, but did not become friendly with him until years later. I did become friendly with Van de Pol who was very interested in analytic number theory. His hobby was to make tablecloths by means of the Gaussian primes and give them to various people. He gave me one which I passed on to the department of mathematics.

The Princeton bicentennial was in 1946 and also gave me an

opportunity to meet many mathematicians. One of my treasured possessions is a photograph taken outside of the Princeton Inn showing the visitors.

I became good friends with Lefschetz. He lived in a three-story Victorian fire trap which the University saved for chairmen of departments. It was a block off Prospect Avenue and in a direction of Harrison where the Veteran Housing Development was. Every afternoon after tea, about five o'clock, I would walk home with him. He would tell me about the various difficulties he had in the department, knowing that I was very discreet. Lefschetz ran the department in an autocratic fashion. If it voted with him, fine; if not, he did what he wanted anyway. Many members of the department didn't even bother to attend faculty meetings. Lefschetz taught me a great deal about how to handle committees. For example, he would often put very trivial material at the top of the agenda and discuss it in detail. After several hours, he would say, "I will handle the rest of the material." I have often used this trick myself.

I learned a great deal from Lefschetz. None of it mathematical since we were in quite different fields.

One day, on one of our walks home after tea, I was inveighing against the military as usual. He stopped me and asked, "Have you ever tried to help these people?" This put a new perspective on matters, and I am sure had a great deal to do with my going to RAND.

He also urged me to write books. He said that one could write a large number of papers and no one would see the themes. If I wanted to make things clear, I had to write books.

He and James Alexander, a topologist at the Institute started to write their first book at the same time. Every few days Lefschetz would see Alexander and say, "Well, Jimmy, how is it going?" Alexander would respond that he had finished a draft of the first chapter, didn't like it, and had torn it up and started over. Needless to say, Alexander never finished his book while Lefschetz finished seven.

Alexander had acquired a taste for mountain climbing while at Cambridge. To keep in trim for this activity he would play a game called, "point to point". One took a city map, picked two points and went in a straight line from one to the other. This necessitated going over houses, churches and the like. I imagine the householders weren't enthusiastic about this game. However, being in a University town they were used to students.

Alexander always entered his office on the second floor of the Institute by an outside window.

I saw Lefschetz very clearly, and often used to be amused by his foibles. However, his virtues far outweighed any minor faults. He was a great man as well as a great mathematician.

We often went out to dinner with visiting mathematicians. My job was to cut Lefschetz' meat.

We very seldom spoke about mathematics since we were in different fields. However, when we did, in a few sentences he would explain ideas. He had a reputation of never publishing an incorrect theorem or a correct proof.

Lefschetz occasionally grumbled about the way Bochner spelled his first name, Salomon. "Why doesn't he spell it correctly like mine, Solomon?" I always pointed out it was Bochner's name and he had the right to spell it as he pleased.

During these talks Lefschetz often expressed strong views. As one friend described to me, he was occasionally wrong but never in doubt. Probably, it is because our temperaments were so similar that we became such close friends. In particular, he was very down on Banach spaces. He had expected a great deal when these first came out, but was very disappointed that it was no better than a good notation. This gave me an idea.

Lefschetz had invited Hurewicz, a fellow topologist who was also interested in differential equations, to spend a semester at Princeton. Hurewicz decided to give some lectures on differential equations. He began his lecture, "Consider the following Banach space ..."

I raised my hand, "Professor Hurewicz, Professor Lefschetz has given orders that the words Banach space never be used in Fine Hall."

Hurewicz was startled. Lefschetz was dumbfounded. However, Lefschetz could not say anything because he thought I might have taken various words seriously. Hurewicz knew that Lefschetz was capable of this. Hence, he just shrugged and whenever he came to a point where he wanted to use the words Banach space, said, "Normed, linear space."

I never told Lefschetz or Hurewicz it was a joke. The best jokes are often private jokes. Occasionally, one can share them with another person.

Hurewicz had a tragic and improbable end. He fell off a pyramid. He was climbing a steep pyramid in the Yucatan peninsula when this happened.

Tucker also played a joke on Lefschetz. Lefschetz had to give a talk in Brooklyn on Pearl Street. He knew that Tucker had spoken there previously and asked directions. Tucker told him the subway stop to get off and said the simplest thing was to ask directions from there. However, he added with a straight face, the natives of Brooklyn don't speak good English. Instead of asking for Pearl Street ask for Poil Street.

Lefschetz came back and complained to Tucker. He had asked several people where Poil Street was. Finally one person said, "Poil Street, you mean Pearl Street," and gave him directions.

I don't think Lefschetz ever realized it was a joke.

Lefschetz had a keen sense of humor. Once, many years before, when G.D. Birkhoff was studying esthetics, Lefschetz, with a straight face asked whether Birkhoff had ever looked into the vase de nuit. Birkhoff said he would.

I also became friendly with Fox. He had a house on Prospect Avenue, and often joined Lefschetz and me on the way home. Our relationship didn't start out well.

When I came back to Princeton, Fox had learned in some way that I was an excellent table tennis player. Consequently, he offered to play me. I declined, saying, rather undiplomatically that it was a waste of time, that I would beat him easily. But he persisted. Finally, we went down to the student union, along with a number of graduate students, and played. Even though I was still wearing moccasins and had not played seriously in about five years, I beat him 21-6. As I suspected, he could not take a chop. To return a chop requires that one puts on a top spin, a spin in the other direction. If one tries to return it the way amateurs play table tennis the ball falls off the racquet immediately. I try not to play table tennis, but when I have to I usually play with my right hand. Even so, I can beat most people.

Then, I committed a gaucherie. Fox had a party. The subject of pacifism came up. I said this was a nice theory, but not for this world, and I went on to say something about people who believed in pacifism.

Fox listened while I sounded off, then said, "I am a Quaker."

When I went to RAND I went out to lunch with Ted Youngs and Dave Widder, and told the story. On the way back, Ted burst into gales of laughter, "Didn't you know that Dave's wife is a Quaker?"

I never told the story again.

Ralph Fox was an equally enthusiastic tennis player and just as bad. Fortunately, he was a good Go player. Go is a unique game because the handicap can be adjusted to make two players equal. This is virtually impossible in chess. Under Fox's tutelage I learnt how to play Go.

There is a wonderful story about Go which I heard from Edward Lasker. It seems that Emanuel Lasker, the chess champion, no relation, decided to learn Go. He spent two or three years in study of the game. The Japanese Go champion was touring Europe at that time and Lasker asked the young Lasker to arrange a match between them. The Japanese Go champion had an initial question, "How long has he been studying the game?" Edward Lasker replied that Emanuel Lasker had studied the game for three years. "Then," said the Japanese Go champion, "I will give him the maximum handicap." Edward Lasker pointed out that Emanuel Lasker was chess champion, and Emanuel Lasker was equally outraged. Edward Lasker, however, had a good compromise. Take the handicap, win the first game, and the Japanese Go champion will give you a suitable handicap.

Of course, the Japanese Go champion demolished Emanuel Lasker. Go is a very difficult game which takes years to master. It is impossible to understand the moves without explanation.

I also played Chevalley and Bohnenblust. Playing with Chevalley one never won a game. If one had a winning position Chevalley would sweep the pieces off and start a new game. If one had a losing position Chevalley insisted that the game be played out.

Chevalley was a very good mathematician and fun to talk to on any topic. He gave a course on integral equations which was quite abstract. Very often, he would stop his lecture, draw a little triangle to see how things went, erase the triangle and continue with the abstract presentation. Also, he had the habit of saying, "It is obvious." Then, he would dash off to the library for about ten minutes, come back, and say, "It is obvious."

At Princeton, the language examinations were given by the department. Chevalley gave the French examination and Bochner the German. I had no trouble with the French, either in translation or in reading. With German it was a different story. I had no trouble when it came to translating, and then Bochner had me read.

I read terribly. Finally, he said, "Stop, stop! Anything! But stop reading."

Bohnenblust was also a very good mathematician. He knew many fields of mathematics and could produce very elegant proofs of many results. He was a fine teacher. However, he was not a creator, a "self-starter" in Lefschetz' words. His notes on real variables were a bible for the graduate students. They had been compiled by Boas and concluded with a mathematical paraphrase of a very well known obscene limerick.

These notes would have made a fine book and it is a shame that Bohnenblust never did this.

For the qualifying exam one had to present five topics. Three were standard: algebra, analysis, and topology. Two were optional and at the choice of the person being examined.

For algebra, one was responsible for the book by Van de Waerden. For analysis, one was responsible for the notes by Bohnenblust mentioned above. For topology one usually gave point set topology, a course given by Fox. For my two optional topics, I presented Fourier series and stability.

The subject of point set topology has always bored me. I had had enough of that in 1943. In addition, I have never liked to go to class and it was particularly difficult after five years away from the classroom. Consequently, I dropped out of Fox' class after a few weeks.

He was quite disturbed by that and asked me what I would offer for qualifying, I replied that God would provide.

When I took my qualifying exams, Lefschetz, Tukey, and Shiffman were the examiners. Lefschetz asked me some questions about real variables, and Shiffman double-crossed me. I had sat in on Shiffman's course, calculus of variations in the large and we had agreed he would ask me some questions about the material he had covered in the first few weeks. Instead, I spent a very uncomfortable hour. Whenever Tukey and Shiffman saw that I knew the answer to a question, they stopped me. They only persisted if they saw I didn't know the answer.

When it was over, Lefschetz took me aside and said, "You didn't do very well." I merely snarled.

After I got my degree, Lefschetz used me for many final exams. One day, a student of Artin was being examined on ideal theory. I waited until the technical material was over and asked what was the origin of ideal theory. Artin was furious. I was quite surprised by this, since I have always felt that anyone writing a thesis should know something about the origin of the topic.

Incidentally, ideal theory arose from Fermat's last theorem. Fortunately, unique factorization does not hold in most algebraic number fields. This is an excellent example of how a particular problem gave rise to a very important domain of mathematics.

Manny Singer wrote his Ph.D. thesis in chemical engineering and decided to give a party to celebrate. His father-in-law was very wealthy, and would bring all the food and drink and be the bartender. I decided to do some experimentation. I wanted to see how much I could drink.

Along about the fifth old-fashioned, I decided Manny had never been baptized. The room divided into two teams. One team tried to baptize Manny and the other tried to prevent this. After each baptism, Manny would change his shirt. We reduced him to sports shirts.

After the thirteenth old-fashioned, the room started spinning and I got violently sick on the door step, a fact I attributed to the shrimp I had eaten. Some friends helped me back to our apartment where they tried to sober me up. I remember taking a cold shower and the water felt lukewarm. When I woke up in the morning, I had coffee grinds in my mouth. Obviously, someone thought that they would help sober me. The next morning at about eight o'clock, there was a knocking on the door. It was Herb Bailey. "You haven't forgotten about our tennis date," he said. I replied that I had not and struggled into my tennis equipment.

For the first few games I saw three balls, and decided to hit the middle one. The activity sobered me up as I had expected and kept my record intact of never losing a set to Herb.

It was the custom for mathematics students passing their qualifying to give a beer party at the Nassau Tavern. For economic reasons, several students would wait and then share the cost. Graduate students had amusing experiences. At one tea a professor asked Ted what he had done during the war. Ted replied that he was a weather officer in England. The professor asked what this entailed. Ted replied that he had to predict the weather, which involved thermodynamics. He asked the professor whether he knew anything about thermodynamics. "Tell me," said the professor. Ted gave him the material he had gotten in the nine-month course at Cal Tech. The professor listened intently and politely.

Several days later Ted asked somebody else who the professor was. It was Eugene Wigner. Ted avoided him for several months.

When I came back to Princeton in 1946, I saw a very distinguished man in the corridors. I didn't recognize him at all. Finally, after several days, I inquired as to who it was. It was the janitor.

Wigner was saved from the Nazis by von Neumann who went to the Princeton authorities and had his salary cut in half so that Wigner could be invited.

We had a strong number theory group with Hal Shapiro, Ernst Straus and myself as a nucleus. We had Selberg give his new sieve method and Hua give several lectures on his extension of the work of Vinogradov.

Hua went back to China when the communists took over and became a top scientific man. He was reported shot in various purges but always survived.

On my walks home with Lefschetz and Fox, I usually arrived in time to hear a radio quiz show, "Winner Take All." Betty Jo and I both felt that if we could get on the show, we would do well. The first step was to get tickets, which was easily done. When Betty Jo and I arrived at the show, we sat in different parts of the auditorium to increase our chances of being selected. I had agreed to be from Princeton and Betty Jo from Madison. We were both selected as possible contestants. When the MC, Bill Cullum, who was just starting out, found out about my Princeton connection, I was sent back to my seat, as I expected. Betty Jo, however, was selected.

The person she competed against had won for twenty-six times. However, Betty Jo easily beat him, and stayed on for five more times. She asked me for typical questions, and I gave her two I was certain they would ask. "Who invented basketball?" Naismith. "What was the last state admitted to the union?" Arizona, 1912. The question that did her in was the origin of "grapes of wrath". She naturally said the Bible and the MC ruled that incorrect. I forget what origin he gave.

Several days later, we received a number of letters stating that she was actually right. The phrase "grapes of wrath" does not appear in the King James version of the Bible. It does, however, contain the phrase "vines of wrath". The phrase "grapes of wrath" comes from the temperance Bible.

Betty Jo won several thousand dollars worth of prizes, much of which we could use. What we didn't use, we gave away.

Eric was born in October of 1947, October 13th. With his birth, we had to develop some theories of child raising. One of our neighbors subscribed to the theory that a crying baby should never be picked up. Consequently, that infant would howl for hours until it fell asleep from exhaustion. I am sure that no one within ear-shot would subscribe to that theory.

I had a very simple technique for stopping Eric from crying. I would hold him up with one hand and let him examine the ceiling. For some reason that always worked.

Lou came down from New York several times to take care of Eric. It gave him a great deal of pleasure to do this. Thanks to Lou, I had gone to a dermatologist in New York who had cleared up my foot condition using X-rays. He gave me a million dollars worth of advise, "Most of his patients were a result of over treatment." I have always remembered that.

However, for years afterwards the skin on the top of both feet was very sensitive, and the first thing I would do is take off my shoes. If I knew the people real well I would take off my stockings as well. I never explained why I did this, preferring to let people think it was a personal idiosyncrasy.

Princeton is quite convenient to New York, about 45 miles away. The Princeton station was on the express route to New York. This is probably because some of the directors of the Pennsylvania Railroad lived in Princeton.

When we went to New York, we stayed with Helen. We had many people to see in New York. First of all there was my Aunt Sylvia and two aunts of Betty Jo's. Then there was Norman, Peter, and Al Nader. Al, as usual, had girl trouble. But he was quite happy when we saw him. It seems that he had picked up a young lady in the subway. A very attractive girl. He was a little disturbed that he had gone to bed with her that night. But when we went out with them the next evening we agreed that she was a very attractive girl.

When we saw Al next, several weeks later, he was very disturbed. In the first place, some private detective had rudely come into his apartment looking for the girl. In the second place, the money he had given her to live on, she had given to an African prince in Greenwich Village and then moved in with the African prince.

It turned out, and I don't remember how we found out, that the girl was the younger sister of a wife that we had become quite friendly with in Belleville, who had run away from home. The couple had been with us in Belleville and we had become quite friendly. When Scott Field divided, they went to Chicago which was their home. The younger sister was boy crazy. The family had moved several times, but it did no good. When we found out about the younger sister, we wrote immediately to this couple and that is how they tracked Al down. We never told him how he had been located, and it must have puzzled him a great deal.

The young girl stayed with the African prince for some time. When we were returning to Princeton one night, some graduate students who had met her at a party at Greenwich Village gave her regards to us.

Norman also had some trouble. He had picked up a girl at the 42nd Street Public Library, Fay. She was a very pretty girl and very intelligent.

One Sunday, she took me aside in a state of great agitation. It seems Norman wanted to go to bed with her and she was running out of excuses. What should she say?

I said, "The next time Norman asks you that, say that Richie Bellman said, "Don't do it."

When I saw Norman next, he was furious. I told him that I knew him very well and that Fay would make a good wife and that he would never marry her if she went to bed with him before marriage.

We also saw Evelyn from time to time. Occasionally, during the week when I was in New York, I also saw Sylvia. She worked in the French book store in Radio City. Unfortunately, she moved to Long Island, after marriage, and we lost touch with her.

In 1970, I was giving some lectures in Buffalo. After one of the lectures, an attractive woman came up to me and said, "Remember me? I'm Naomi, Sylvia's cousin." I had last seen Naomi in 1941. After chatting with her a few minutes, I asked how Sylvia was. "Don't you know," she said. "Sylvia died of breast cancer a few years ago."

Two ex-girlfriends and two deaths from breast cancer. It is no wonder that I am fanatical on the subject. I believe that every woman should learn how to examine herself, and that after thirty-five she should visit her gynecologist twice a year.

Miraculously, none of my friends were killed or wounded in the war. Eddie Kanner was a naval officer and was repeatedly attacked by kamikazes. Fortunately, they were all shot down or missed. Jerry Janoff was a dental officer attached to the "Bastards of Bastogne".

One day I was at the beach with Norman when we spotted a big six foot four inch fellow. When he saw us, he covered his face with his hands and said, "Don't hit me, don't hit me."

It was Murray Katzen. When I had last seen Murray, he was about five feet tall and about twelve and one-half years old. He was quite bratty. Al Harvey had a habit of putting all the bratty fellows in my patrol. To keep Murray under partial control, I used to hit him regularly. From long experience on the streets of New York, I knew how to do this without inflicting any real damage.

Murray had fought in the infantry from Normandy to the Rhine and was a very tough character indeed. He could have demolished Norman and me with one hand behind his back.

Marty Klein worked with Norman at Fort Monmouth and stayed there awhile before getting drafted. He ended up in the occupation army of Japan as an officer. Alex Rosenthal got jungle rot in the Pacific. He wanted to run a beauty shop and be a hairdresser but could not stand on his feet. He ran a pet shop instead.

Paul Brock was working on the Manhattan project when it was so super secret he could not even tell his draft board about it. He ended up in the middle of Tibet. Pete Chiarulli went to the European theatre. He was on his way to Paris to do mathematical work when the Battle of the Bulge started. He manned a machine gun for three days, got a medal and then went to Paris. Bernie Sherman was in ASTP until it collapsed, then he went into the infantry and fought all across Europe. He got a nervous stomach from this, but that was all.

We also got a very good lecture from Atle Selberg on his new method of estimation. Selberg was spending some time at the Institute on the way to Cornell. In the halls of the Institute, Selberg met Erdös. One never knew where Erdös was, not even the country. However, one could be sure that during the year that Erdös was everywhere. He was the nearest thing to an ergodic particle that a human being could be. During the long years of Nazi occupation of Norway, Selberg had managed to push the prime number theorem much further than anybody had done before. This theorem is the most famous in number theory, and one of the most famous in mathematics. It gives the asymptotic density of the primes as may easily be seen from tables, as was done by Legendre and Gauss. However, a rigorous proof was only given in 1899 by Hadamard and de la Vallee Poussin. The proof, however, was always displeasing to a number of mathematicians. The result concerned integers, while the proof used the theory of functions of a complex variable. Furthermore, the result was finite, but all the proofs known use the infinite. It was not an esthetic situation. However, many mathematicians had convinced themselves that this was the only route.

Selberg had made an essential step forward and told this result to Erdös. They went home and were able to push the result through to obtain the complete theorem. The next day Selberg obtained an independent proof, using a different method.

They were supposed to write a joint paper. Somehow this did not happen. Selberg wrote his paper, then Erdös in self defense was forced to write his.

It became a matter of national honor. In the Scandinavian books, it is called Selberg's theorem, in Hungarian, it is called Erdös' theorem.

Who should get the credit? Should it be Selberg who made an essential step or Erdös who pushed it through? I think both can be argued at great length and to no avail. I prefer to call it the Erdös-Selberg theorem. If Norwegian were like Hungarian where the first name is last, I would be glad to call it the Atle-Paul theorem.

It is a fitting memorial to the genius of both mathematicians.

One of the people at Princeton who was very interested in number theory was Ernst Straus. We became very friendly with Ernst and Louise Straus. He had met Louise at Columbia where she had been a graduate student in mathematics. Ernst knew a great deal of mathematics and many other subjects as well. He also had a keen sense of humor. He delighted in telling how Louise used to wake him up at three o'clock in the morning and ask, "Give me a counter example to the following theorem." They were an intermarriage as is very common in academic circles. Ernst came from generations of rabbis, and Louise had a Lutheran background. Both were irreligious. When I hear the term "intermarriage" I always say, "How mixed can a pair be, one male and one female." When they were married, the minister took Ernst aside and said, "When you get angry at her don't call her a stupid Lutheran."

Ernst was Einstein's assistant, and thus I had access to Einstein whenever I wanted. However, I didn't feel it was right to bother him since I was not interested in relativity theory, Zionism, didn't play the violin and spoke execrable German.

I often use to show visitors on Sundays Einstein's office. It was about thirty by forty, with a small office, about eight by ten for Straus. Characteristically, Einstein took the small office and gave the large one to Straus.

I knew, however, that in years to come people would ask me about Einstein. One day, I went to Ernst and said, "How can I see Einstein without disturbing him?" Ernst said it was easy because Einstein used to walk home every day from the Institute with him and Godel. If I joined them at this time, I would not interfere with Einstein's working schedule.

It seemed like a good idea to me and we decided upon a day. On the appointed day I walked over to the Institute, about two miles from the University and went to see a secretary of the mathematics and physics division. It was then about one o'clock. She asked me if I had an appointment. I said that I didn't. She said that Einstein was working at home that day. This seemed quite reasonable to me. There was a shuttle bus from the Institute to the University which left the Institute a little after one each day. When I heard her remarks I caught the bus and then browsed in the library in Fine Hall for about forty-five minutes. When I returned to my office my phone was ringing like mad. It was Betty Jo, "How could you stand him up?" I told her that I had not stood him up at all and recounted the conversation with the secretary.

What had happened was the following. About five minutes after one, Einstein, Godel and Straus came out of the Institute and looked for me. After waiting about fifteen minutes Einstein looked through the whole first floor, Godel looked through the whole second floor, and Straus looked through the whole third floor. Einstein was very disturbed. He kept saying, "Why doesn't he like me? Everybody else wants to see me and here he doesn't."

I tried to explain to Ernst but I'm afraid he never believed me. I never tried to see Einstein again. I saw him at a distance at various lectures, for example, the one by Russell. I called up the secretary and said a thing or two to her. The result was that whenever I wanted a notice posted I had to use a fictitious name.

I wrote to Einstein to get contributions for various liberal causes. I found that a check from him worked wonders. Particularly, Lefschetz was very competitive with Einstein. They had a running debate for many years. Lefschetz insisted that there was difficult mathematics. Einstein said that there was no difficult mathematics, only stupid mathematicians. I think that the history of mathematics is on the side of Einstein.

Ernst told me an amusing story about Godel. Godel decided to become an American citizen. He studied American history and the Constitution and then went to Trenton to take the test, taking Einstein and Ernst along for moral support. The judge asked various questions and at first Godel just gave the answers. Then the logician mind started working. He gave possible alternatives and the judge became more and more angry. Einstein observed this. Finally, he kicked Godel and said, "Kurt, just give the answer."

After I got my Ph.D., I decided to do some political work. I thought that Truman was much too conservative and joined the PCA, Progressive Citizens of America, the Wallace movement, Henry Wallace.

I went to several meetings in New York. I was dismayed, however, to find that communists were infiltrating the movement and gaining positions of control. I wanted the PCA to do what the AVC did, American Veterans Committee, which was to pass a resolution that communists could not join. The American labor movement also removed the communists from positions of control. I warned several liberals that they would pay a high price if that was not done. Unfortunately, in the 1950s when McCarthy was on a rampage, my predictions came true.

In 1948, Ernst went to UCLA. Einstein's next assistant was John Kemeny. Now John is president of Dartmouth.

In November, 1947, Lefschetz took me aside and said that Princeton had the custom of not keeping its graduate students. As a matter of fact, the only graduate student who had been kept on was Tukey, and that was only half time. The other half of his time was employed by Bell Telephone Laboratories. He suggested that I start looking around for a position and named Syracuse and Cornell as possibilities.

Immediately, I went to visit Syracuse and Cornell, giving lectures at each school. Syracuse then had a very strong mathematics department, Loewner, Bers, Gelbart, and Rosenbloom, and Cairns was chairman of the department. I was spoiled by the luxury of Fine Hall and was dismayed by the shabbiness of the mathematics buildings and their offices. Also, the snow drifts that I saw in Syracuse and Ithaca did not make me enthusiastic.

I decided that I had had enough travelling about during the war, and I had no desire to start the academic merry-go-round. Thus, when I returned to Princeton, I went to Washington and got a job in Steinhardt's group. There was no trouble. I had learned about this group through Glen Camp. Then, I went back to Princeton to say goodbye to Lefschetz.

He was indignant, and wrote an outraged letter to Steinhardt accusing him of stealing his graduate students. As a result of this, Lefschetz got together with Tucker and they gave me a permanent position at Princeton as an assistant professor. I had made it. I had always dreamed of a position at Princeton and here I had it.

But, I was not happy. I felt that Princeton was not a good place for a young mathematician. I wanted to work on problems which had a high probability of remaining unsolved. There was too much pressure that came from the Institute where there were many fine mathematicians and the pressure was overwhelming.

Gabor Szego is Peter Lax's uncle by marriage. I had met him on one of his trips east through Peter. We had gone to a Hungarian restaurant where I sampled some chopped lung, and spent several hours in discussion. Szego was a very charming man. A typical European intellectual.

Some weeks later he called me up from Stanford where he was chairman of the department of mathematics. He offered me an assistant professorship at Stanford. I pointed out that I was already an assistant professor at Princeton. The next day he called again and offered me an associate professorship, which I accepted, provided that Princeton did not meet the offer. Princeton, of course, did not want to make me an associate professor, so at twenty-eight I was associate professor at Stanford at $5,000 per year.

Lefschetz, Tucker, Wigner, and others thought that my leaving Princeton to go to Stanford was a serious mistake. But, I was firm, and we took off.

I knew that this would hurt Lefschetz a great deal, and I was very unhappy about this. However, I felt it was the right thing to do.

In Princeton I was still deeply wounded by Betty Jo's action in joining the WAC. I hoped that at Stanford we would begin a new life.

CHAPTER 10

RAND, SUMMER OF 1948

Since I knew Lefschetz was angry and hurt at my leaving Princeton, I was not surprised when he refused to support me through the summer. Alger of General Electric near Boston was interviewing graduate students for summer employment. He was not happy with my idea of a summer salary, $100 a week. He pointed out one could get veteran engineers for that sum. He suggested that I come to the General Electric plant in Lynn, Massachusetts, and prove that I was worth this amount. Naturally I did not go. A few weeks later, I received a call from Alger asking me why I had not come. I replied it was expensive to go to Boston. He replied, that "Of course General Electric would cover all expenses."

When I came they were probably working on the forerunner of the jet engine. Not only did they have complicated problems involving gases which meant highly nonlinear partial differential equations, but in addition they had to worry about the metal container melting. I may have made a contribution to their problems in three years but not in three months. Consequently, I turned down their offer. The more I refused the more insistent they were. But, I was firm. I looked forward to a summer staying with Helen in New York, a very unattractive prospect. However, when one has no money, one has no choice.

As a last resort, I wrote to Ted Harris, who I knew had taken a position at RAND at some phenomenal salary. I was overjoyed when he wrote back that RAND would be glad to have me for the summer at $25 a day and $12 a day for expenses. I did a quick calculation, $209 a week, affluence.

We were met at Burbank, where the airport used to be, by a cousin of Betty Jo's, Harvey Kates, and driven to a motel, the Fox Motel, on

Santa Monica Boulevard. In the morning I went to the Douglas plant where a guard told me project RAND was in Santa Monica, 1500 4th Street. This was quite convenient as far as various buses were concerned.

RAND is an acronym, standing for "Research and New Development". A common joke is that it really stands for "Research and No Development".

Project RAND was then administered by the Douglas Aircraft Company. It was the brain child of General "Hap" Arnold, who felt that the Air Force because of its global commitments had to know both the politics as well as the technology.

While I was there, Project RAND became the RAND Corporation. It started the following way: A $300,000 loan was from some San Francisco banks, and allowed RAND to establish a line of credit of $1 million. That established RAND as a responsible entity that could accept contracts, permitting the departure from Douglas. Then, at a later date, RAND obtained a $1 million loan from the Ford Foundation, ostensibly to build a building, which, of course it did, in due course. But after a few years, the Ford Foundation "forgave" the loan on the condition that it would be spent for research in the public interest. It had a very simple charter, "To work in the public interest."

RAND was organized like a university. It had a mathematics division, which covered both mathematical research and numerical analysis, a physics division, engineering division and various social sciences divisions. Naturally, there was as much politics at RAND as at a university, which meant that sometimes there was one engineering division and sometimes three, and the same for the social science division.

For computing RAND had a copy of the machine at the Institute for Advanced Study devised by von Neumann, the Johnniac. Programming was done in machine language.

The head of the mathematics division was John Williams, a very brilliant person. He had started out in astronomy, but had worked for Vannevar Bush during the war. He understood research and particularly mathematical research. The head of RAND was Collbohm. He had been a test pilot for Douglas and they had rewarded him by making him the president of Project RAND. He understood engineering research but I don't think he understood the value of mathematical research. John Williams tried constantly to convince him.

RAND was an exciting place. It had a strong staff. The mathematics division, for example, had George Brown, Abe Girschick, Ted Harris, Olaf Helmer, Alec Mood, Ed Paxson, Lloyd Shapley, and others. The physics division had people like Herman Kahn, Dick Latter, and Jess Marcum; in social sciences there were people like Herb Goldhamer, and many others. It also had a very active summer program. Mathematicians like Beckenbach, Blackwell, Bohnenblust, Dantzig, Karlin, LaSalle, Tukey, Youngs, Widder and others came; mathematical economists like Arrow, Marshak, and Morganstern and Shubik were there; philosophers like Abe Kaplan worked on various problems; psychologists like Bales gave lectures.

George Dantzig was developing linear programming. Here the main problem is the maximization of a linear form subject to linear constraints. This is a classical problem going back to Fourier. It has many algebraic and geometric aspects and strong connection with the theory of games.

Dantzig found an algorithm for treating large problems by means of the digital computer, the simplex method. Thus, this method could be used in many applications and is now a standard part of the techniques used by the operations analyst.

This was my first exposure to effective numerical solution, which subsequently became a central theme of my research.

One interacted with these people several ways. Many interdisciplinary studies were carried on at RAND.

One had discussions which took place over the luncheon table. There were many good restaurants in Santa Monica.

Many of the staff were ardent Kriegspiel players. Kriegspiel may be described as semi-blindfold chess. It requires two players and a referee. Each player sees his own position perfectly but not the others. Information concerning allowable moves and pawn tries is given by the referee. I will not go into the rules in detail since different places use slightly different rules.

John Williams had shields built so that the players could sit comfortably at a table. If no shields are available the players sit back to back.

Kriegspiel is a good game since it combines various features of chess and poker. Like poker, it is reproducible. Strong players win consistently. We had a ladder. The winner would get 10% of the loser's total. Each player was given 100 points initially. A strong player would hover around 200.

Expertise at chess did not necessarily mean expertise at Kriegspiel. As a matter of fact, there usually was a negative correlation. If one were very good at chess, he often hesitated to make good Kriegspiel moves.

We even had major and minor leagues. The mathematics division furnished the major league. Several minor leagues existed in other divisions.

We occasionally went to Los Angeles for lunch. On one of these forays Ted Youngs introduced me to the Cock and Bull.

Many years later, I was having dinner with Ted at the Cock and Bull when we spotted a well-known actress and her secretary at a nearby table. I turned to Ted, "Would you like to meet her?" He thought I was joking. I said I was not, and told him to just do what I did when she went to the buffet table.

I stood behind her and said, "Miss so and so, we have a friend in common."

She was very cool and distant when she said, "Who?"

I said, "Leonard Maccombe."

Immediately she thawed. "How is Leonard," she said, and we had a lively discussion. She invited us to her table after we got our food, and Ted was charming as usual. We had a very pleasant time.

The story is the following. I got friendly with Leonard Maccombe when Life decided to do a story on RAND. I will say more about that below. A few years before, this actress and a well-known black entertainer were having an affair. Harry Cohn, the head of Columbia pictures, felt that this was not good for her image. So, he sent the mob around to the black entertainer warning him to stay away and sent the actress on a personal appearance tour by train. Life magazine heard about this and sent Leonard Maccombe, one of their senior photographers, along. About the second day out, the actress sent for Leonard and propositioned him. Leonard had to think quickly. He had just gotten married and had no desire to make love to her. On the other hand, if he antagonized her that would be the end of his assignment.

He said, "Miss so and so, I like you very much, but women are not my thing." This actress, who was used to the movie industry, was very understanding. She and Leonard became good friends.

Only sometime later did the full implication of what I had said hit me.

Living in Santa Monica, a suburb of Los Angeles, one encounters movie and TV stars everywhere. In restaurants, in the airport, on planes, in the streets of Beverly Hills, in stores, and many other places. Let me mention Jimmy Stewart, Bing Crosby, Gary Cooper, Walter Mattheau, George Burns, Robert Taylor, Elaine May and Mike Nickols, Marlene Dietrich, and Ginger Rogers. Many others of lesser rank could be mentioned. Indeed, it is impossible to go to any large party without meeting actors and actresses, writers, and people, in general, connected with "the industry".

I usually let the stars enjoy their privacy. Occasionally, when I have seen them in a particular performance I will go over and say a few words. I have exchanged some conversation with Elaine May and Mike Nichols, and winks with Bing Crosby.

It was amusing to drive into Hollywood and see where various stars got their names. Peck Street, Mansfield Street, Hayward Street. Naturally, we went into Hollywood to see various landmarks. The first thing we did was go to the intersection of Hollywood and Vine. On one corner is the RKO Pantages, where the Academy Awards presentation was held at that time. Down Vine street, there was the famous Brown Derby. There is another Brown Derby in Beverly Hills, and two others in Los Angeles. Down Hollywood Blvd. was Grauman's Chinese theater with the famous footprints and handprints. Hollywood Blvd. was very much like Broadway. It had movie theaters, bookstores, restaurants, and many small shops. It also had characters. It was great fun just to walk along and watch these.

About one-half block from Grauman's is the best bookstore in Los Angeles, Pickwick Book Store. I enjoyed browsing there and spent many hours in this bookstore.

The main mathematical activity of the mathematics division was the theory of games, under the influence of von Neumann who visited from time to time. This is a mathematical theory of competition and one expected that it would be quite useful for the Air Force. It is a beautiful theory with many uses inside mathematics.

The principal theorem is the min-max theorem due to von Neumann. Borel had worked on the theory earlier, unknown to von Neumann and had a partial proof of the principal result. Unfortunately, he made an arithmetical mistake and thought he had a counter example to the full result.

There are many difficulties in application of this theory to the real world. Let me mention a few of them.

In general, competitors are not in complete opposition. As a matter of fact often they don't even have the same objectives. This difficulty can often be circumvented by using a different objective, "games of survival". Secondly, a decision is seldom made once. This motivated the study of multistage games, which I carried out with Joe LaSalle. Finally, decisions are not usually made simultaneously. Recognition of this fact leads to "games of protocol", work which I did with E. Marchi. Games of protocol can also be used to handle processes involving three or more people.

Of great interest at RAND was the question of target selection in the U.S.S.R. For any efficient selection of targets it is necessary to know a great deal about the economic system of the country. These questions are quite difficult. As a matter of fact, the more one looks at actual decisions the more difficult they are. One generates a great deal of sympathy for people who have to make major decisions.

Ed Paxson gave some lectures on a global model of the interaction between countries. I thought his model was too ambitious but very interesting. It showed very clearly the uses of mathematics for these questions.

I also saw that many qualitative as well as quantitative variables were involved. It would be many years before I possessed tools for handling these questions, the theories of simulation and fuzzy systems, the creation of Lotfi Zadeh.

Mathematical model making is an art. If the model is too small, a great deal of analysis and numerical solution can be done, but the results, in general, can be meaningless. If the model is too large, neither analysis nor numerical solution can be carried out, the interpretation of the results is in any case very difficult, and there is great difficulty in obtaining the numerical values of the parameters needed for numerical results.

It is clear that if we want to keep the model within reasonable bounds, a great deal of aggregation, or "lumping", must be done. However, this must be done carefully as the following classic story illustrates.

During the war, the Air Force was interested in how many planes could be produced. They went to Leontiev, a famous Harvard economist, and asked him to make a model which would predict the number of airplanes. Leontiev agreed and constructed his famous input-output model. At first he used ten industries to represent American economy. The aggregation was clearly too great. He went over to 100 industries, a respectable number in those days.

After the model was constructed it was found that closing down the lead mines in Butte Montana had a serious effect on the production of planes. This was obvious nonsense. The reason was not difficult to find. There are two large categories of metals, ferrous and nonferrous. The two representatives of nonferrous metals are aluminum and lead.

I was eager to work with Ted Harris because I knew of the many interesting analytic problems in his research. I was well acquainted with his work since at Princeton he often used me as a sounding board and I was on his qualifying exam. The problem he was studying was the following. Suppose we have a particle which at some time divides into particles of similar type. The particles then continue independently, a branching process.

In his thesis, Ted considered the case where the particles split at a fixed time, enabling him to use many results of iteration. We considered the more realistic case where there is a distribution of splitting times, and age-dependent branching processes.

We were able to derive a number of fundamental results. We announced these results in the PNAS in 1948 and wrote a full paper for the *Annals of Mathematics*. We had the usual difficulties with referees. The third referee felt he owned one of the fields, and said that we had not given him sufficient credit. Actually, our results were quite different from his. However, when we saw his objections, we added a bit to the effect that this work was based on so-and-so's work and then the paper was accepted.

If one considers the case where one particle gives rise to particles of the same type and particles of a different type, we have a good model of mutation. Ted and I were very much interested in the cancer problem, and we looked into it enough to be aware of the complexity of the physiological processes. As a matter of fact, a considerable motivation for the research was the question of mutation.

If we considered the case where one particle can produce many different types of particles, we have a good model of the fundamental particles of physics. I thought we should write a paper for the *Physical Review* pointing this out. However, Ted demurred, saying he was not a physicist. I replied that one did not have to be much of a physicist to point out this process. However, he was firm. I shrugged, feeling it wasn't my principal field anyway, and we let it go.

These results were discovered independently by Janossy and Bhaba as well as by others, a few years later.

The case where one particle produces particles of many different types is very interesting analytically. In particular, it leads to the theory of positive matrices. We did not investigate these areas since we had given the problem to a graduate student who was supposed to write the results up for his Ph.D. thesis. Unfortunately, he discontinued his work in the middle. Subsequently, these results were investigated by Charles Mode.

Incidentally, positive matrices were introduced by Perron in connection with the three-dimensional continued fractions of Jacobi. These matrices play a significant role in many areas of pure and applied mathematics. They are of particular importance in connection with computing and much fundamental work was done by Garrett Birkhoff.

It is a good illustration of the way the research can produce significant results.

Finally, I had some results of my own in differential equations and number theory to write up. Obviously, I had enough to keep me busy.

I made contact with Al Nadel again. I did this by reading Matt Weinstock. He wrote a column for the newspaper, The Los Angeles Daily News. This was a good counterpart to the New York Daily News, and I greatly enjoyed reading it.

In Matt Weinstock's column he wrote about peculiar food combinations. In particular, he mentioned that onions and ice-cream were a great favorite of Al Nadel. As soon as I read that, I thought that must be the Al Nadel that I knew. I wrote to Matt Weinstock and asked for Al's address. We had a very joyous reunion.

When last I heard from Al he was at Purdue and I was in San Diego. He had written asking whether a certain position was available. I sent him a night letter starting with the two words of importance, "Job available". Then, since it was a night letter, I had thirty-eight more words to squander. I quoted various snatches of poetry. Unfortunately, since it was wartime, the telegram was sent direct wire. It reached Al while he was lecturing in front of a class, and he had to take up a collection from the class to pay for it. He always thought it was a practical joke of mine.

Even when I explained it I am not sure that he believed it.

Al knew Los Angeles very well, and showed us a number of interesting places. In particular, he introduced us to Barney's Beanery, which became a favorite spot of ours.

Since we were going to Stanford, it was necessary to buy a car. We looked around and got a second-hand car in very good condition, a 1936 four-door Chevrolet. It was in good condition since the owner was an auto mechanic.

I got a learner's permit and took driving lessons. I tried very hard to be legal. Usually, I took Al when I wanted to practice driving. Al was a nervous passenger. His nervousness was not lessened to find it was impossible to open the front door on the right from the inside. The car also had a habit of stalling. Something in the engine used to slip. After I had called the AAA about four times the auto mechanic showed me how to fix it. Thereafter, when the car stalled, I would dash out, throw open the hood, fix the slipped part, and start again. Sometimes, the car stalled right in the middle of a busy intersection.

Since it was a second-hand car, I took it for granted that several things would go wrong. In particular, the reverse gear was stuck. Since I have a bad combination of no mechanical ability and strength, I have learned the hard way not to force things. When the reverse gear didn't go easily, I took it for granted it was out of order. I tried to drive in such a way that I didn't have to back up. Occasionally, it was impossible to turn around. Then, I would put the gear into neutral and push the car in a position where I could drive forward. I did this once when Al was in the car. "What are you doing?" he said incredulously. I explained the situation to him. Without difficulty, he showed me how the reverse worked. Thereafter, I had the luxury of a reverse gear.

Occasionally, temptation got too much. Even when Al was not around, Betty Jo and I would try the car. We even drove to the top of the Griffith Park Observatory.

I finally took my driving test, which I failed. I had no difficulty in driving but parking was another matter. I ended up perpendicular to the curb. I had the ignominy of having to ship the car to Stanford, and to take the train.

It had been a very stimulating summer. Not only did I see a great many interesting mathematical problems, but more important, I had been exposed to a number of significant mathematical ideas. Large systems, effective numerical solution, the application of mathematics to the social sciences, mathematical model making, the theory of games and branching processes. I was well aware of the importance of these areas. However, I wanted to study analytic number theory. These problems, important as they were, would have to wait until next summer.

I had been invited back for the following summer. In addition, I could come down at Christmas and Easter. This was a tremendous financial help.

CHAPTER 11

STANFORD 1948-51

El Camino Royale, route 101, separates Palo Alto and Stanford University. Palo Alto lies on the west, Stanford on the east.

Upon arriving at Stanford, we went to the veterans housing. I had been warned by Szego that it was bad, but I didn't realize how bad. Not only were the insides shabby, but the kitchen was dangerous. I thought to myself, "America's heroes deserve better." We had to start looking for a house immediately. I had planned to stay in the veterans housing for several months and look leisurely.

We didn't even bother to take the furniture out of storage. We slept on a mattress on the floor. Bella Shiffman brought over some sheets and blankets.

The first house we saw was about seven miles from the University in the Searsville Lake district. This was seven miles east. This is a redwood belt.

The real estate agent told us the usual stories about a retired couple and a young couple being interested in the house.

The house was around a traffic circle. The whole property had been subdivided from an old Spanish land grant. The house had been built by the architect for himself and his wife but he ran out of money. The builder then continued and also ran out of money.

The house was on a half acre of land with a stream in the back. On this land were about sixty redwood trees, each about fifty feet tall. The house had been carefully designed to avoid cutting down trees.

The house, too, was made of redwood. It was a very elegant house shaped like a U. In the middle was a huge living room, twenty by forty, with a beamed ceiling and a huge fireplace. This fireplace had a large mantle made of a single redwood log. Opposite the fireplace was a picture window. It was an ideal room for listening to music. Often, I would turn on some Mozart while I did mathematical research.

The high beamed ceiling was good for ballet leaps. In Princeton, Leon Henkin, a friend and fellow graduate student, had taken ballet. Since he felt awkward being the only male in the class he asked me to join him in lessons. I had been interested in ballet since high school. A friend, with whom I played tennis, was an expert at ballet and I was impressed by the way he handled his body. Ballet is much more difficult than it looks. It is easy to make the various leaps. It is hard to keep a smile on your face while doing so.

Along one side of the U were two bedrooms, ours and Eric's, and a bathroom. On the other side were the kitchen, the guest bedroom and another bathroom.

We had radiant heat, and thought that our bedroom was heated that way. Actually, it was a leak. Radiant heating is excellent until a leak develops. The difficulty is that one seldom knows where the leak is. I had a brilliant idea. Why not use "Stop Leak?" It was an excellent idea and stopped the leak. However, it also stopped other things as well. One day our water heater blew up. Fortunately, the water heater was outside.

The house had many other features, a fireplace in our bedroom, a large entry hall with tiled paving, a copper hood over the stove, lots of closet and cupboard space, and many others. However, it was only 95% complete. I had to finish it myself. The first thing was the roof. Obviously, that had to be done before the rainy season.

We had two fireplaces, and a chimney from the kitchen. I proceeded like a mountain climber. Tying myself very securely to this chimney and to the one from the fireplace in the living room. Some of the neighbors laughed at me but I was determined not to fall off the roof while shingling. In this fashion, I shingled the roof.

The next objective was to build a brick path. The first step was easy. I got some cement mix from the hardware store and had no difficulty adding water. However, brick laying is much more difficult than it looks. It is impossible without extensive practice to make a path level. Since it was a rustic setting, I didn't worry too much about this.

We had three lawns, a front lawn, a rear one, and a side one. I decided to do the front one first. It took a lot of work with the scythe to clear the weeds. Then, it was continual battle against the moles. Every morning, I would get up to see little brown hills where they had dug their holes. Finally, I resorted to poison, but I never won that battle.

There were also many weeds in the rear. I decided to burn them down. Fortunately, there were not too many because I made the mistake of standing in the middle of the weeds while burning them down. I understood for the first time "brush fire". I will never forget the moment of panic that I had when I saw the flame travel toward me.

Incidentally, there are many interesting mathematical questions connected with the propagation of flame.

One afternoon in November of 1949, there was a torrential downpour. In this downpour Stanford was playing Army football. Football has the tradition that the game is played despite the weather. Baseball is more civilized. If it rains too hard the game is either postponed or discontinued.

We were laughing at the people in the stands being drenched by the rain. We watched this on TV. At half time there was a knock on the door. Two friends dropped by with tickets to the game. We could not resist. We took umbrellas and shower curtains and joined those in the stands who were being drenched.

It was impossible to run because of the mud. Each team played with a ten-man line. It was almost impossible to pass because the ball was so slippery. The Army quarterback, the son of the coach, managed to pass for ten yards. This was the margin of victory. Army beat Stanford 7 to 0.

We got our first TV set for $25, a seven-inch set. Every Sunday when we were at RAND in the summer, we scanned the ads in the paper. One Sunday, we saw a set advertised for $25.00. We drove all the way to the store in south Los Angeles. When we got there, the salesman pointed out that the $25.00 did not refer to the TV set although it appeared to. When I looked at the ad carefully I could see that he was legally right.

The next Sunday there was a similar ad. I looked this over very carefully, but there was no question, the $25.00 referred to the TV set.

We drove to the store again. At first, the salesman denied everything. Then we produced the ad. Very ungraciously, he took us into the back where a few of these TV sets were available. That is how we got our first TV set.

To get reception from San Francisco we had to erect a tall antenna. Pete Stevenson knew how to do this.

When Kirstie was born, July 20, of 1950, we added a bedroom next to ours.

Next to Eric's and our bedroom, there was an estate, and there seemed little probability that there ever would be building there. At that time, we had no neighbor on the right. Sometime later, a house was built there. A very nice couple, with a five-year old child, moved in. It turned out that they had been hounded out of Palo Alto because the child was an idiot. They had adopted a beautiful baby of one year of age, and at two he developed brain trouble. He was now a hopeless idiot.

We trained Eric to play nicely with him, and we became good friends with the parents. It was just as well, because in the process of subdivision the property lines had not been drawn carefully. It turned out that we owned a half of their back yard and they owned the access to our house. Since we were friends we had the property lines redrawn and shared the expense.

Theoretically, the title search takes care of this. But, if one reads the contract carefully one finds that the title search is worth very little.

On the left, however, we had neighbors. They had a teenaged son who was a peeping Tom. I decided, therefore, to build a fence. Since we would have to look at the fence, it seemed reasonable to put the studs out. After I had built it, I found out this was illegal, and had to do the whole thing over with the studs in. Then, I bought some little fencing so that Eric would have a playground. In order to mow this lawn, either I had to lift the lawn mower over one of the fences or take it through the house. Taking it through the house left a trail of grass. Consequently, I lifted it over.

One Sunday, in the process of lifting it over, I heard something snap. "Oh, oh," I said to myself, "I ruptured myself."

We drove to the hospital where I was examined by a cheerful doctor.

"It is nothing to worry about," he said, "it is only a twisted testicle cord."

That was good news. However, I wanted to know what happened if the twisted testicle cord didn't untwist.

"Oh," he said, quite cheerfully, "then we will make a little incision." The room got very low, I walked out the front door and fainted dead away. When I came to, my head was cradled on the lap of a very pretty nurse. I promptly closed my eyes again.

Meanwhile, Betty Jo had been chatting with the doctor. His only reaction was, "Oh, my God, not in front of all the visitors."

I revived and we drove home. The twisted testicle cord untwisted but I did no more lifting of the lawn mower. From then on it was through the house.

As soon as the car arrived, I drove to the DMV to take my driving test. The examiner asked, "How did you get here?" When I said I had driven over myself, he refused to give me an exam. I drove to the University to get Max Shiffman. When we arrived at the DMV, the examiner asked to look at his license. Naturally, it had expired. However, the examiner relented. I passed my test without difficulty and was now legal.

I drove the car for the next five months until it literally fell apart. When the rear end fell off, I called the AAA. The mechanic looked at the car and said, "I could swear this car has never been lubricated."

"What's lubrication?" I said.

It was clearly necessary to get a new car. It was now two-thirty in the afternoon. I went to the bank and in addition to borrowing the money for car payments I was able to borrow the money for a down payment. As soon as I mentioned my connection with Stanford University there was no difficulty. The only question that the bank official asked was whether I knew Bacon with whom he had taken calculus.

It was quite a thrill to drive a new car, a four-door, Ford sedan.

When I had a new car, we built a garage, also of redwood.

I was horrified to see the genteel poverty in which many faculty people lived. Here were people who had devoted over twenty years to training and they made less than a checker in a supermarket. I promised myself that I would never live like that.

As Russell said, "Poverty is alright for artists and poets, but mathematicians need luxury."

We had a plumber who loved to come to academic homes. He would loudly proclaim that he had never graduated from high school and would bet that he made more than three times what the man of the house did. The wager was never taken up, because the ratio was more like five to 1.

Max Shiffman and I came to Stanford at the same time and we had great plans. On many long walks, we discussed these plans and much mathematics. Max was a powerful mathematician. He was a RAND consultant too, and we did some work together there. This involved the use of the Neyman-Pearson lemma, a very important technique in analysis.

Max also derived a proof of the min-max theorem using an important technique. His proof should be better known, and some day I intend to include it in a book.

Szego regarded Max and me as troublemakers, because we wanted to introduce modern courses. When we were recommended for the editorial board for the newly formed *Pacific Journal of Mathematics,* he blackballed us. He had a very simple technique for running the department. He did nothing for six months, and then went to Europe for six months, leaving orders that nothing was to be done.

Max and I were aghast at the graduate offering. By comparison with what was available at Princeton or NYU, Stanford seemed like an elementary school. We set about remedying this. Max gave some courses on the calculus of variations, and I gave courses on the functions of mathematical physics and algebra.

I wanted to give a course in number theory but Szego was saving it for one of his friends, Van der Corput. I ended up giving a course on stability theory, which was quite unsuccessful. I was not prepared for the low level of students.

I gave a course on the theory of equations, using the excellent book by Uspensky. I was full of admiration for the ingenuity of 17th and 18th century mathematicians.

We had the usual difficulties in getting good graduate students. Fortunately, a number had come to Stanford. Let me mention my only

Ph.D. student from Stanford, Ken Cooke, Howard Osborn who had followed me from Princeton, Hal Royden, Joel Franklin and a very good undergraduate student, Sherman Lehman.

I gave Ken as a thesis topic a question in differential-difference equations. This became the basis for our book on differential difference equations. We had worked together extensively since then. We have written these books together and numerous papers.

As usual, I had a program. I had an important problem, the squarefree problem, and I wanted to study the Siegel theory of matrix automorphic functions.

I believe very strongly in research programs and have always followed them. I tell the following true story to my classes. A friend got a summer position at an aircraft factory on Long Island in 1946 for the then magnificent sum of $35.00 a day. He reported bright and early on Monday and received a problem from the head of the section. Anxious to please, he stayed up all night Monday night and found a solution. On Tuesday morning, he came in, bleary eyed but triumphant, and showed his solution. The head of the section looked at the solution and groaned, "You have solved our summer problem."

One of the attractive and aggravating features of number theory is that it is possible to derive heuristically many formulas. These formulas agree with very high accuracy with the tables. For example, consider the prime number theorem.

It is another matter for primes in a polynomial sequence. It is relatively easy to derive a formula heuristically, but no one has been able to establish this formula rigorously. The problem that interested me was nothing as ambitious. I wanted to derive the asymptotic density of squarefree numbers in a polynomial sequence. Again, it is easy to derive the formula heuristically.

I had hoped that the solution to this problem lay in algebraic number theory, and maybe it does. I tried very hard to find an elementary proof, but did not succeed.

The Siegel theory was very attractive aesthetically. In addition, it gave me motivation for learning a great deal of 19th century analysis. Finally, there were great opportunities for original work.

I began writing my first book on stability theory. I was very hesitant after the experience with Siegel at Princeton, but I decided to go ahead. I wrote the book for several reasons. In the first place, the work I had done at Princeton and the summer at RAND had convinced me of the importance of stability theory. Secondly, I had two advantages. I had a very powerful analytic tool, the inequality I had discovered in Madison, and I had a good notation, using vectors and matrices.

I was also struck by how much could be obtained by a simple physical hypothesis. It goes both ways. As Galileo remarked, mathematics is the language of science, but, important clues about the behavior of various equations can be obtained by looking at physical processes. This is a technique which I have used repeatedly since.

I enjoy writing, but recognize it involves work. I once read, "If you cannot stand the sight of your own blood on the page, don't write." Writing is like playing the piano or tennis, it involves constant practice.

I received a letter from Arthur saying that he wasn't well. I called him up to see what was wrong. He had stomach cramps and nausea. In view of his temperament he went to a psychiatrist.

While the psychiatrist probed his past, Arthur was dying of stomach cancer. However, Lou assured me that nothing could have been done anyway.

One day I received a long form from Jacques Cattelle, the editor of "American Men of Science". During the war, I had filled out many similar forms in triplicate and quadruplicate. I was heartily sick of this.

I wrote back to Jacques Cattelle, that filling out forms was not a hobby of mine.

After several weeks I received a letter from Jacques Cattelle, which read, "Dear Dr. Bellman, It is not necessary for you to fill out the forms. We know all we need to know about you."

"Touche," I said to myself. Score one for Jacques Cattelle.

I combined social life with mathematical life as far as possible.

We saw a lot of Max and Bella Shiffman, Ken and Selma Arrow, Abe and Mary Girschick, and Al and Betty Bowker. Max and I had met at Princeton, Ken and Abe at RAND.

Al Bowker was Chairman of the Department of Mathematical Statistics. Abe was a professor in that department. He knew a great deal of mathematical statistics and was an expert in the theory of games. We did some work together on duels. Unfortunately, Abe contracted an abdominal infection and died in 1951. Al had built up the department from nothing to a point where it was one of the leading departments of Stanford. He was a very able administrator, going on to become head of the City University of New York; CUNY, and then head of the University of California system. Al had come to Stanford as an assistant professor in the Department of Mathematics. Szego, a quite old-fashioned mathematician refused to see him. This went on for several months until Al complained to Dean Terman, the father of the psychologist. Terman solved the problem by creating a separate department.

We were also on friendly terms with the other members of the department, Bacon, Herriot, and Weinstock.

Hal Bacon had an amusing hobby. He collected brochures from departments of education around the country and delighted in reading me choice parts. We agreed a department of education was a blight on a university. We often quoted to each other the well-known modification of the aphorism of G.B. Shaw, "Those who can, do; those who can't, teach; those who can't teach, teach teaching."

Bob Weinstock often came to visit and we had long political discussions, mainly about China. We agreed that communism was bad but Chiang Kai Shek was worse. It was fortunate that we had an ocean between us and the Chinese, not just a line on the map.

Nicholas Minorsky was at Stanford continuing his work on nonlinear oscillation. His book on this subject is probably the best book to read. I had met him at the David Taylor Model Basin through Lefschetz. His knowledge and experience had saved the Navy many an embarrassment. His wife, Madam Minorsky, was equally charming. She was a retired opera singer of French origin. She looked like an opera singer.

Minorsky had befriended a young mathematician and had gotten him a job at Berkeley. Unfortunately, this young mathematician was a fascist and an anti-Semite. Since Madam Minorsky was a practicing Catholic with many crucifixes around the house, he thought it safe to spout his anti-Semitism to her. She was very indignant, and thereafter gave his name the French pronunciation which made it quite obscene.

Minorsky and I had many mathematical discussions. We felt that the fundamental equations of physics were nonlinear, but that this nonlinearity was an unobservable. Our thoughts were guided by the Van der Pol equation where the slightest amount of nonlinearity quantizes.

Minorsky's successors were two German mathematicians, Flugge-Lotz and a man whose name I don't remember. He was by far the lesser mathematician. They had worked at Peenemunde for the Nazis on the V2. Naturally, I had nothing to do with them.

When Lefschetz came out to visit, because of his connections with ONR, he had to see them. He always referred to her as Lugge-Flotz. I warned him that some day he would forget and call her that. But, he never did.

Someone at the Pentagon thought that they were saving the talents of these German mathematicians from the Russians. I didn't think so, and felt it would be good punishment if they had to live under the Russians, rather than the luxurious life at Stanford.

Flugge-Lotz wrote a very bad book on control theory for Princeton which I had to review. Since Herb Bailey had just become assistant director of the Press, I didn't want to greet him with a bad review. I was in quite a quandry, until I remembered a trick that Alfred used. I wrote a review saying what the book should have contained.

Alfred had reached the retirement age and so had his pinochle cronies. Some of them were very wealthy, wealthy enough to publish their memoirs at their own expense. These memoirs were uniformly awful, but naturally Alfred didn't want to hurt any feelings, particularly of pinochle cronies. He would write to them, "How you must have enjoyed writing this."

I learned a lot from Alfred on my Washington visits. For example, Alfred was a teetotaler. He had found that if he said this he always got an argument. Consequently, he used the following device. When offered a drink he said he never drank before dinner. During dinner when offered wine, he said he never drank during dinner. After dinner, when offered an after dinner drink, he said he never drank after dinner. He found that nobody ever put these together.

Also, whenever he was asked to do something he didn't want to do he would say it was against his principles. One day I asked him where he had gotten so many principles. He replied that he made them up as necessary. He had found that no one ever asked you to break your principles to do something.

Some years later, Herb Bailey became director of the Press. His first book was really a hot potato. A retired Episcopalian minister felt that the Protestants did not grapple with basic issues such as abortions, divorce, suicide, and so on like the Catholics and the orthodox Jews did, right or wrong. Consequently, he wrote a book containing what leading experts said about these subjects. Herb had the book reviewed in the usual fashion, and the reviews were uniformly good.

However, when the book came before the Board it ran into trouble. Hugh Taylor was a member of the Board. He was an excellent chemist who had kept his Canadian citizenship so that he could be knighted. He was also a very fanatical Catholic. Since the book in many ways contradicted Catholic doctrines, he did not want it published by the Press. He threatened to resign from the Board if the book was published. This was a very sticky situation for a new director. Herb went to see the president of Princeton, Dodds, asking him what to do. Dodds asked him if he had followed the standard procedure for the book. Herb replied that he had.

"Well," said President Dodds, "We shall miss Sir Hugh."

The book was published and got bad reviews, predictably only from various Catholic journals. Hugh Taylor did not resign.

On weekends, I frequently had various graduate students visit me so that I could spend a lot of time with them.

When I got settled, I was curious about the Stanford Research Institute, SRI. The Stanford Research Institute has no formal connection with the University, but it does have the same board of trustees. I found that SRI had little in common with RAND. It was industrially oriented and took many short-term contracts. The vice-president of SRI was Don Benedict with whom I became quite friendly. We often visited each others' homes.

Some years later, Don became president of the Oregon Graduate School and I became an advisor. Other advisors at my suggestion were Garrett Birkhoff and Lotfi Zadeh. When Don got into a fight with the board of trustees and was summarily fired, I resigned too.

We frequently drove to Berkeley where we knew several people. In Princeton, we had gotten quite friendly with Rafael and Julia Robinson. When they returned to Berkeley, we visited them and met several other mathematicians through them, notably Dick Lehmer and his wife Emma. Emma had translated the book by Pontryagin for the Princeton University Press.

After the summer of 1949, we often visited Dave and Ann Blackwell.

Let me warn against the advice of friends. It is very easy to ignore the comments of enemies since we know how to discount them suitably. But it is very much more difficult to override the carefully thought out advice of people who are deeply concerned with your future. Oddly, people who themselves were rebels and made their reputations by working in unfashionable fields at the time rarely see the analogy between their past and the present. At the time, dynamic programming was barely known to a few people; control theory was not the fashionable field it is now; differential-difference equations did not occupy the important position that they do now, and so on. Yet it was obvious (to me, at least) that these fields had fantastic intellectual potential, with rich, untapped mathematical veins to prospect. In my own mind, it seemed like a sure thing — which is the only way to gamble professionally.

In addition, Henry Scheffe was now at Berkeley. We had become quite friendly with him and his wife in Princeton. Henry was an expert at mathematical statistics which had had a rough time at Princeton. He often complained about this.

Lefschetz often remarked, "We have the mean and variance. What else do we want?"

One day, Henry said, "Dick, why don't you forget about dynamic programming and go back to traditional mathematics?"

I smiled. It is always amusing to see the rebels of one generation become the orthodox of the next. I vowed that this would never happen to me.

Several of our friends came to California at the same time. Manny Singer took a position with Shell Oil in Emeryville, just outside of Berkeley. Pete Stevenson took a position at Livermore and lived nearby. Ernst Straus took a position at UCLA.

Then there were the neighbors. The ones on the left, with the Peeping Tom son, had sold their house to a nice young couple with whom we became quite friendly. We also were very friendly with the couple down the street. At the time there were only three other houses. It wasn't so easy to stay on good terms with the third couple. We wanted very much to remain on good terms with our neighbors. Not only a matter of general principles, but I had a very practical reason. The man in the third house was a mechanic, and often helped me start the Chevy in the morning.

The fog would come in at night and get the spark plugs wet. It was a very pleasant drive from the University in the day-time. In the night-time it was often foggy. Frequently, I had to drive at five miles per hour with my head out of the window looking for the white line.

The wife was a 200% American. I am sure that she joined the John Birch Society when it started. Two stories will illustrate.

At the time, Berkeley was going through the throes of the loyalty oath controversy. In a discussion at our house, I pointed out that a democracy had no place for loyalty oaths. I knew a little English history and was aware of where loyalty oaths could lead. The Supreme Court agreed with me and sometime later declared loyalty oaths unconstitutional.

In the morning, I discovered a scythe and a hammer which I had left on the front lawn, neatly arranged as a hammer and sickle. A few days later, we received a visit from the FBI. The FBI man strongly hinted that our neighbor had reported us.

A few months later, a Mexican American family started building a home around the circle. She wanted to circulate a petition to stop them. Her argument was that the presence of this family would lower the property value. I asked her how much. She replied that it might be as much as $5,000. Since I planned to stay at Stanford for forty more years, I pointed out that it was only $125 per year, a small price for principle.

The Mexican American family moved in and their house was the showpiece of the circle.

One day when I visited Berkeley, I met a member of the faculty who was a very ardent communist. He wanted to join the party but the party wouldn't let him so that he could swear truthfully that he was not a card-carrying communist. I asked him where the party stood on the loyalty oath. He replied that the instructions were to sign and to urge everybody else not to.

I wanted very much to meet people in other departments. I thought a good way would be to join a faculty group, Los Casados. They had a dance once a month. This necessitated buying a tuxedo. We went to San Jose, fifteen miles away for this. We went to two affairs, which were very boring. I called the group Los Castrados and shelved this approach.

San Francisco was forty miles away, with the airport halfway between. San Francisco is a charming city. It is quite compact, unlike Los Angeles. I was able to walk over the whole city and get to know it quite well. I often showed visitors various landmarks.

We had a few visitors, not as many as at Princeton. Burgers, of the famous equation, and his wife came through. I showed them around San Francisco and took them to dinner at a very well-known Armenian restaurant.

I was very eager to discuss his work with Burgers. I have always been very interested in both hydrodynamics and nonlinear partial differential equations.

Mary Cartwright was also a visitor. She gave a talk on differential equations, a very model of what a talk shouldn't be. I endured this because I knew she had worked with Hardy, one of my mathematical heroes, and I wanted to ask her about Hardy. After the talk, I invited her home for tea so that we would have some time together.

She was then headmistress of Girton College, and looked like it, except for the hat. The hat was very frilly and feminine.

I knew quite a lot about Hardy and remarked that he was quite a rebel. "Oh, yes," she replied. "Let me tell you a story." I wondered whether she would tell about how Hardy had finally brought about the end of the math tripos or how Hardy had been a pacifist in World War I and almost gone to jail.

"We went to a meeting of the London Mathematics Society, and after the meeting, we went to a small restaurant in London Station. It was only a small restaurant, but it was a public restaurant. Hardy took off his jacket, took off his sweater and put on his jacket in public."

I agreed that Hardy was quite a rebel. Privately, I thought, this story tells a lot about Mary Cartwright, not much about Hardy.

Hardy was a great mathematician but became a tragic figure. Pacifism made sense in WW I, but not in WW II, the war against fascism. The essay by C.P. Snow makes this very clear.

I was very eager to go to RAND in the summer of 1949 to continue my work. I did two important things that summer. First of all, I still wanted to find out more about RAND. I had become friendly with Ed Paxson and asked him what RAND was interested in. He suggested that I work on multistage decision processes. I started following that suggestion.

Secondly, I did some work on games with Dave Blackwell. Since my days at Johns Hopkins, I had been interested in red dog. I was curious to see if mathematical analysis could determine optimal play. It did so easily.

Emboldened by this success, Dave and I investigated two-person poker. We were able to determine optimal play, and to identify certain play as bluffing.

The *Scientific American* heard of this work and asked us to write an article, which we did. This article was used for the cover illustration.

Also, the Hearst papers heard about this and asked us to write an article about gambling for them. We liked the money but we didn't want to use our names. Consequently, we wrote the article under an assumed name, using both our middle names. The author was Harold Ernst. As Betty Jo foretold, the article was illustrated by a slinky woman in a low cut gown bending over a gaming table. There was precedent for this investigation of poker. In their classic work, von Neumann and Morganstern had investigated poker in great detail. This precedent was very important because RAND had to be careful. It had powerful enemies in the Air Force, in Congress, and in the universities. In the Air Force, many were not happy at the thought that their actions were scrutinized by a non-Air Force organization. In Congress, many felt that RAND was circumventing civil service as far as salary was concerned. In the universities, there was great jealousy.

Some did not like the salary scale, some did not like the kind of research that was carried on, some did not like the fact that young men and women had options now.

An important principle emerged from the study of poker. Put in non-technical terms what it showed was that one level of uncertainty was enough. In this case, the unknown card was sufficient. It was not necessary to vary one's style of play from hand to hand.

This is why one analyzes a particular problem. One hopes that general principles will emerge. One gets an instinct for a good problem rather than merely a difficult one. Naturally, one makes mistakes. Frequently, no general principle emerges; frequently, a problem is impossible to analyze. This instinct is developed by seeing what great mathematicians have done in the past. Recall Abel's dictum, "Read the masters, not the pupils."

Even great mathematicians have made mistakes. For example, Gauss refused to consider Fermat's last theorem. Yet, this problem had a great influence on the development of algebraic number theory, a very great influence in 19th and 20th century mathematics.

I enjoyed working with Dave, and we did other work as well. We wrote up one little paper and send it to the *Annals of Mathematics*. It came back with the observation that it was too long. Dave said he would handle it. He rewrote the paper in the typical dense style of the *Annals of Mathematics* and it was accepted. The difficulty was that I couldn't read it.

Max had the same difficulty. He handled it by retyping his paper on a pica typewriter and resubmitting it. It was accepted.

Hemingway handled his difficulty with copy editors in a different way. He would put the manuscript in a drawer for three months and then send it back untouched.

Stanford was on the quarter system. I taught three quarters and had the fourth quarter off. Ordinarily, I taught two courses a quarter, hardly a difficult life.

Szego didn't want me to go to RAND. Consequently, in 1950, he asked me to teach a course during the summer. This course was for high school teachers, "Elementary Mathematics from the Higher Point of View". My private name for the course was, "Elementary Mathematics from the Difficult Point of View".

I expounded on my favorite theme: Progress is not due to those who roll up their sleeves and do things the way their fathers did. Progress is due to those who say, "There must be a simpler way."

At the end of the quarter, I gave a choice of books for a book report for the final exam. Everyone else handed in twenty or thirty pages. The young nun handed in a half page, writing that she had taken my precepts to heart.

I gave her an A, and always felt I had seduced a nun.

I spent the fall quarter at RAND. My first task was to find a name for multistage decision processes.

An interesting question is, "Where did the name, dynamic programming, come from?" The 1950's were not good years for mathematical research. We had a very interesting gentleman in Washington named Wilson. He was Secretary of Defence, and he actually had a pathological fear and hatred of the word, research. I'm not using the term lightly; I'm using it precisely. His face would suffuse, he would turn red, and he would get violent if people used the term, research, in his presence. You can imagine how he felt, then, about the term, mathematical. The RAND Corporation was employed by the Air Force, and the Air Force had Wilson as its boss, essentially. Hence, I felt I had to do something to shield Wilson and the Air Force from the fact that I was really doing mathematics inside the RAND Corporation. What title, what name, could I choose? In the first place, I was interested in planning, in decision-making, in thinking. But planning, is not a good word for various reasons. I decided therefore to use the word, "programming". I wanted to get across the idea that this was dynamic, this was multistage, this was time-varying — I thought, let's kill two birds with one stone. Let's take a word which has an absolutely precise meaning, namely dynamic, in the classical physical sense. It also has a very interesting property as an adjective, and that is it's impossible to use the word, dynamic, in the pejorative sense. Try thinking of some combination which will possibly give it a pejorative meaning. It's impossible. Thus, I thought dynamic programming was a good name. It was something not even a Congressman could object to. So I used it as an umbrella for my activities.

The summer of 1951 was old-home-week. Sam Karlin and Hal Shapiro were at RAND.

Hal Shapiro, Ted Harris and I worked on an interesting functional equation which arose in learning processes. Although, we wrote a long paper on this, we never published our results. Sam Karlin obtained some results concerning this equation which he published in the *Pacific Journal of Mathematics*. I had studied a very interesting functional equation which arose in multi-strike analysis, the gold mining equation. The solution was given most easily not in terms of the unknown function, but in terms of an action or a decision. This intrigued me, because I had never seen this phenomenon before.

Hal Shapiro, Sam Karlin and I tried very hard to solve the general case. It was like a problem in number theory, the solution seemed tantalizingly close, but outside one's grasp.

I did manage to handle a continuous version, which showed why the original problem was so difficult.

Hal Shapiro and I took advantage of proximity to do some work on number theory. We greatly enjoyed working together again.

Meanwhile, of course, I kept up the investigation of dynamic programming processes.

Every Easter and Christmas I went down to RAND. Every visit was an adventure. One of them was rather grim.

On one of the two-week trips, Eric got bulbar polio. The doctor said there was no point in sending him to a hospital since they could do nothing for him. He would either live or die. Bulbar polio is about ninety per cent fatal but, in return, if one survives there is little nerve damage. We should have had therapy but were given bad medical advice. After a few days in a coma, Eric got better, and apparently had no bad effects.

Every Christmas, John Williams gave a party for the mathematics division. He lived in Pacific Palisades in one-third of a house which had been owned by an aunt of the McCormick Reapers. In order to sell this white elephant, the house had been divided into three parts, and John Williams bought one of them. He had the kitchen and the game room, as well as various bedrooms upstairs. The three houses had a common heating unit in the basement.

We came to the party with Eric whom we put in one of the upstairs bedrooms, and left at about twelve o'clock. We were staying at that time at the Kensington in Santa Monica. This meant that we had to go down Chautauqua and then drive a short distance along the Pacific Coast Highway. We drove down and on the Pacific Coast Highway I heard a honking behind me. My impulse was not to stop but the Chevy could make only a top speed of thirty-five miles per hour. Consequently, I found a place under a street light, locked Betty Jo in the car, told her to use the horn if any trouble developed and stepped out.

The other car had pulled up in front of me. From this car emerged two men, a gigantic negro, about six feet three inches or six feet four inches and a white man about six feet tall. The negro looked as if he were doped, and the white man looked like a criminal type. I asked what the trouble was. They claimed I had sideswiped them on Chautauqua. Naturally, I wanted to see the damage. The dents were on the wrong side, and I knew I had not come within six feet of any car. However, I felt that it was not wise to point this out. Instead, I said that my insurance company would be glad to cover the damage, and in the process of giving them the address of the insurance company I made sure that they saw I had only a few dollars in my wallet.

They wanted to know my home address, so I gave them the address of RAND. After I had given them all the information they drove off. I heaved a great sigh of relief.

I had expected an attack. Fortunately, I had a pencil in my pocket which I intended to use as a dagger. I had carefully located the jugular of the negro and I intended to use my pencil on that. Then, I would take care of the white man. But, I was not happy.

If I had more money on me I would gladly have given it to them. I see no point in being a hero for fifty or hundred dollars.

Howard Osborn decided to marry Jeanie. He had met Jeanie while playing the violin. Howard was about six feet and three inches, Jean about five feet, and she played the bass fiddle. It was always very amusing to see her wrap herself around that.

They decided to get married in the Stanford chapel and I was to be best man. Unfortunately, I could not come to rehearsal, but I promised to attend the ceremony.

Before the ceremony, I was briefed by the minister as to the functions of the best man. I had to supply the ring, but, more important, I had to make sure that the groom didn't run away.

At the ceremony, I was supposed to walk down the right side, and the maid of honor to walk down the left side. Since I had not gone to the rehearsal, I decided to mirror image what the maid of honor did. The ceremony went off smoothly. After the ceremony I remarked to the maid of honor at what I had done. She laughed and said that she had not been to the rehearsal either, and had just done what I had done.

I got to know the road between Palo Alto and Santa Monica quite well. In December of 1948, I drove down with the Chevy which was quite an experience because the Chevy couldn't go more than thirty-five miles per hour. When I got my new car, it was easier. In Easter time of 1949, I drove down with the new Ford.

Sure enough, while I was waiting for a light to change, with the Whitemans in the back seat, we were rear ended. This had happened to me several times. Often, I have gone through a red light when I thought the person behind me was travelling too fast to stop.

Although it was an open and shut case, and the driver of the other car did not contest it all his brakes had failed, the insurance company was very slow in paying off. I managed to speed it up by telling a representative that if they did not want to have the car fixed in Los Angeles, I would drive it to Palo Alto where prices were higher. That threat worked.

One Christmas, I decided to go down by plane. Kirstie had just been born, and we thought it would be a good idea if we could get to Santa Monica and back quickly. In addition, the airline offered a very low rate to acquaint people with the flight. The flight was at twelve noon. We had intended to get there at eleven, but due to a combination of circumstances it was about eleven-fifty when we arrived. We found about eight people waiting and the plane completely full. The airline had done their usual trick, they had oversold. We asked when the next flight was and were told it was at twelve midnight.

We didn't relish the idea of waiting around in the terminal with two young children for twelve hours. In addition, the Strauses were to pick us up at Burbank.

I decided to take action. I was outraged at the overselling. After all, I had gotten the tickets immediately to make sure we would have seats, and they were supposed to be guaranteed. It was not first come first served.

I stood in front of the propeller so that the plane could not move. The ticket agent threatened me with police action. I told him to go ahead and I would make sure that my friends on the newspapers in San Francisco heard about it too.

After several tense minutes, the airline gave in. We went down to Burbank on a flight one and half hours later.

There was a certain amount of interaction between Berkeley and Stanford. That was the way Ken Arrow, Dave Blackwell and I put on the worst TV show ever.

To begin with, Dave, Ken and I were scared stiff. It was the first TV show for all of us. Although, we practiced our speaking parts, we heaved a sigh of relief when they were finished. This sigh was quite visible.

After we had finished our parts, the last year's quarterback of the Stanford football team was due to speak for five minutes. He was a dramatics major and was quite glad of the opportunity.

Finally, it was his turn. He said, "The way to play football is to find a weak point, and keep hitting them there."

We were horrified. We had carefully explained the idea of strategy. Nobody had taken the trouble to find out what he would say. After his talk we understood why the year before Stanford had one of the worst records ever.

For weeks after people stopped us on the street and asked, "What was the point of that program?"

CHAPTER 12

PRINCETON – PROJECT MATTERHORN 1951-52

I received a long letter from John Wheeler, Professor of Physics at Princeton, which set me thinking furiously.

In this letter, he surveyed the political situation vis-a-vis the Russians and concluded that we had a great need for a strong national defense for security. This security could be guaranteed by a thermonuclear device, a H-bomb. This device would be a maximum contribution to national security, and he asked me to help him do it.

I agreed with John about the political situation and the need for a strong defense. I had hoped that we could cooperate with the Russians, but that didn't seem to be the case. The cold war had begun and the iron curtain had dropped. It was clear that the only thing Stalin understood was force. Only the threat of SAC bombers kept Russian troops out of western Europe and Scandinavia.

A-bombs were sufficient for this deterrent. However, I felt that we certainly should know if an H-bomb was possible, and if it was, it should be in the American arsenal. How many we wanted was another matter.

I didn't want to build bombs. I thought all that was behind me with the war. Now, I wanted to do mathematical research and be a university professor. However, I felt that I owed a debt to society. I knew that my brains had contributed to the war effort, more than my brawn ever could. I was well aware that I had not been in the army until December of 1944, and then I had gone to Los Alamos, where I had only spent sixteen months.

I decided to discuss these matters with other people. I received no help at Stanford. They were not concerned with either the moral questions or national defense. All that concerned them was that I was going away for one year at a time when Stanford was negotiating for a big contract from Washington.

I had more luck in L.A. I had several long discussions with Ernst Straus which clarified my views. Like his friend and mentor, Einstein, Straus was an ardent pacifist, and strongly opposed to my working on the H-bomb.

Ernst had many cogent arguments and it was a painful decision. I knew I would not be happy whatever I did. It was a case of damned if I did and damned if I didn't. I imagine many major decision makers find themselves in this position.

It is ironical that Einstein was responsible for the A-bomb. Szilard had tried repeatedly to interest the military in this but had been repeatedly brushed off. In desperation, he went to see Einstein. Einstein knew that the Nazis, under the leadership of Heisenberg, were actively working on developing an A-bomb. Only the British commando raid on the heavy water plant in Bergen, Norway, set their timetable back. Einstein knew how the Nazis would have used A-bomb if they had developed one. He wrote his famous letter to F.D.R. and the A-bomb project was started.

I only remember one bit of the conversations with Ernst. At one point he said, "Think of the women and children in Moscow."

I retorted that if it were a choice between the women and children in Pittsburgh and the women and children in Moscow, I would do everything I could for the women and children in Pittsburgh.

I called up John Wheeler and told him I would come. He was delighted.

We made all preparations to go. I got a year's leave at Stanford and rented our house. I had a chest built filling in the back seat of the car and put a mattress over this so that Eric and Kirstie could sleep. We bought many coloring books to keep them happy on the trip. Finally, we put a hitch on the car and bought a small trailer. In this trailer, we took the children's cribs and some other things. The trailer was covered by a tarpaulin which was held in place by rope. This tarpaulin would protect the trailer from bad weather and also make sure that thieves would have a tough time.

When the summer was over, we took off for Princeton. The trip was not uneventful.

Near Kansas City, I got a flat tire. Fortunately, this occurred right across the street from a service station. I made the mistake of trying to fix the flat tire without unhitching the trailer. I merely succeeded in stripping the gears from my jack. I decided I needed professional help.

I went into the service station and told my story to the attendant. He was very sympathetic, but said he could not help me now since he was alone in the station. If I waited until lunch time, about an hour off, then his replacement would be there. I waited patiently. At twelve o'clock his replacement came and he took off. The replacement gave me the same story. The three yokels who were hanging around thought this was very funny. I put an end to the game by calling the AAA in Kansas City. The repair truck came out in about half an hour, and after a few minutes we were on our way.

In the Ozarks we were caught in a torrential downpour. The rain was so strong that the windshield wiper was ineffective. I had to pull over and let the storm pass.

Near Dayton, a wheel of the trailer came off. I spent a sleepless night keeping an eye on the trailer. This was just as well, because several cars stopped to investigate and then drove on when they found I was in the car.

Finally, I got on the Pennsylvania Turnpike that night. Since I had not slept the night before, I thought it wise to get off the turnpike and stay the night in some small town. Unfortunately, that was not easy. At the time, the last bit was being built on the Pennsylvania Turnpike and there were detours. I was like a white rat in a maze. I rode past the same service station and got the same instructions three times. Finally, I came to the town of Mononghela. I asked directions to get to a hotel. The hotel I came to was obviously shabby and I didn't like it at all. I asked a garage attendant for a better one. He said that there was one across the street.

When we entered, with Betty Jo and two young children, the woman at the desk gave me a queer look. I soon found out why. There was a great deal of noise in the background and the sound of bottles being thrown across the room. The hotel was a whorehouse.

I decided that the best thing to do was to drive on to Princeton. I was pretty tired by that time. Fortunately, there were few cars on the road.

We arrived in Princeton at about seven in the morning. I had had the forethought to rent a house while in L.A. I slept a little, shaved and went to see John Wheeler at Forrestal.

I was sure that the FBI had bugged the house. I would often amuse myself by repeating various remarks which I thought would be of interest to them.

The H-bomb project was in a one-story temporary building at Forrestal, about three miles from Princeton. I had had my security clearance transferred from RAND so that I could begin work immediately. Also, there was a project headed by Lyman Spitzer, the Stellarator. The Stellarator project was the peacetime use of the fusion process. This has been worked on for some years but has never succeeded. The difficulty is that no one can figure out how to hold the material.

Lyman Spitzer was the treasurer of the project and independently wealthy. This was just as well, because often he would forget to do the necessary paperwork. Then he would pay us by personal check.

The first thing I was interested in was whether an H-bomb was possible. I think that everyone connected with the project hoped that it wasn't.

Up at Los Alamos, Teller had wanted to build a super at a time when it wasn't clear that an A-bomb was possible. He didn't have the faintest idea as to how to do it. Oppenheimer had put him in a special building with a few acolytes under the condition he wouldn't bother people who were trying to build an A-bomb. I never saw Teller at Los Alamos.

Teller was sincere, but paranoid about the Russians. As Eric Fromm described him, "He was a man afraid to take a nap for fear his pet spaniel would bite his ear off."

Ulam, a mathematician, had devised a very ingenious way for building an H-bomb using an A-bomb. The question was whether this was feasible.

It seemed to be an engineering question. I looked over the entire procedure for a question which could be handled by mathematics. Finally, I found a problem of stability. With a young army captain Pennington, I did some work on this question. We found that viscosity and surface tension, as expected, playing a considerable role.

I could not find any other mathematical problems. After one month I went to John Wheeler and told him I wasn't doing anything and would like to go to Los Alamos for the rest of the year. He persuaded me to stay another three months.

I respected John Wheeler enormously. He had a lot of guts to go against Oppenheimer and the liberal establishment in constructing an H-bomb. He had a very vivid scientific imagination and several far out ideas concerning the universe. He spent hours with his graduate students helping them. Furthermore, he was a man of obvious sincerity. With all that we didn't get along. The trouble was he had no sense of humor. There were several points of friction. To begin with, he could never understand why I spent so little time in Forrestal. I preferred to spend my time in the Fine Hall library, reading various books and doing mathematics. One of the advantages of being a mathematician is that mathematics can be done anywhere. It is not necessary to sit in an office.

He called up once and asked, "What can we do to keep you at Forrestal?" I replied, "Move the Fine Hall library to Forrestal."

Another source of friction was that I didn't keep a notebook. We had lectures once a week during which people reported on their progress. All the other members of the project kept notebooks in which they marked the date and the subject of the talk. My attitude was the same as at college. If the material was worthwhile I would remember it. If it was not worthwhile, why take notes.

He called me into his office and said, "Dick, we don't seem to get along." I agreed. He suggested that we keep notebooks in which we would put down all the things we found disagreeable about the other and then once a week we would compare notes. Notebooks again!

I said, "John, during the war I got along with all types of people. I am sure that I can get along with you."

At Forrestal, I heard two good lectures. One was by Bochner on the subject of characteristics. For the first time I understood the important role that characteristics played in physics. Then I heard a lecture by Tukey on machine arithmetic. This stimulated me to do some very interesting work. However, this work was not related to the project or to the work I was doing either at Stanford or at RAND. Consequently, I didn't want to get too involved, and never developed it. However, I saved it for exercises for a later book. I used this technique frequently when I didn't want to spend time on an interesting subject which was unrelated to my directions of research at the moment.

I took advantage of being at Princeton to hear two fine lectures.

The first was by a visiting professor of Italian on Etruscan. He gave all the words in Etruscan which were definitely determined and how they were determined. Then and there, I decided that I would look into the decipherment of Etruscan at some later date.

I also heard a lecture on germanium, the basic substance of transistors. It was clear that transistors would revolutionize electronics. They would eliminate vacuum tubes in many cases and permit miniaturization. Thus, they would make computers faster, smaller and cheaper. I was very pleased by this. Dynamic programming is intimately bound to computers. If computers became faster, smaller and cheaper, dynamic programming would have many more applications.

I was greatly saddened to receive the news that Peg had died. She had a weak heart for many years and finally had a fatal attack. One of my favorite aunts was now dead. She had a tremendous influence on my upbringing. The world seemed much emptier.

Over Christmas time, I thought it would be a good idea to have some money in my account. Consequently, I wanted to borrow $250, and I didn't anticipate any trouble. I was used to western bankers, not eastern bankers.

When I saw the loan officer at the bank, he looked at me with obvious disapproval. Clearly, I must be a very improvident person if I wanted to borrow money. When I mentioned my connection with Princeton University this disapproval increased.

He took out three long forms and said, "If you fill these out, your application for a loan will be considered."

I very carefully tore up the forms, put the shreds in his wastepaper basket and shelved the idea.

Alice Tucker decided to have a New Year's party. I dropped over in the afternoon to see if there was anything I could do. I found her in the process of putting a half bottle of vodka in the punch. I suggested that she put in two bottles.

It was a great party. All sorts of people who said they didn't drink, but who took one glass of punch, got drunk. People who drank freely got very drunk and many passed out, both upstairs in the bedroom and in the kitchen. It was a great party.

Al Tucker was furious with me, but Alice was delighted.

I had a reunion with Herb Bailey. He taught me how to play squash, an ideal winter game. The first game we played, I almost knocked him out with a wild swing. Thereafter, I was more careful.

We often drove in to New York and stayed with Helen. It was very convenient to have the car. With the car, it took only a few minutes to drive over to Sylvia, and using the Westside Highway, we could frequently visit Lou. He lived near the Yankee Stadium and his wife, Milly, and children Martin and Susan were usually there. Milly was Lou's second wife. Lou's first wife, a good friend of Milly, had died in childbirth, together with the baby.

I was not used to driving in Manhattan and frequently had trouble with the one-way streets. Once, I even found myself going up the off ramp of the Westside Highway. Fortunately, I survived without an accident or a ticket.

A very frustrating thing about going into New York on Saturday night was finding a parking place. Even in those days one did not want to park below Fifth Avenue. Finally, I got an inspiration. I knew just where to park. I drove over to St. Patrick's Cathedral and parked in the place reserved for Cardinal Spellman. I didn't think he would have any use for it on Saturday night.

We also decided to learn square dancing which was then all the rage in academic circles. We went several times to the Polish National Hall. One of the girls we danced with had an older brother who had been a Pathfinder during the war. These were men who parachuted in several days before D-day to find good places for the gliders to land. Naturally, the casualties were very high.

After the war, he decided to make some money on the black market. He had a very simple technique. He would sell army equipment to a black marketeer, and then several miles down the road would have a friend retrieve the equipment at gun point. He made a great deal of money that way. He invested this money in Wall Street and lost it all.

The moral of the tale is that big sharks eat little sharks.

Dave and Anne Blackwell came to town and we did a tour of various nightclubs in Greenwich Village. Dave is a jazz aficionado, and he wanted particularly to hear an intermission pianist at a nightclub. During the intermission the conversation was so loud that we couldn't hear the playing. However, Dave and I went to meet the pianist.

They had parked their car in front of our house in Princeton, and taken the train in. After the nightclub tour, they wanted to go to a hotel before going to get their car in the morning, and continue on to Washington. I suggested that they take the four o'clock train and sleep in our house before continuing.

It was a good idea, except there is no four o'clock train. Consequently, they stayed up all night and took the seven o'clock train to Princeton, cursing me all night.

Dave and I went to World Headquarters of IBM to visit. We were both dressed in California style, slacks and a sports shirt. In addition, I had my usual white buckskin shoes, and Dave wore a pair of casual shoes. The elevator operator was typical IBM, crewcut, white shirt, black tie, and well polished black shoes.

When we got out, I said, "Dave, that is what they want and we are what they get."

A friend went to World Headquarters shopping for a computer for his company, an aircraft company based in Los Angeles. He, too, was dressed in typical Los Angeles style. The floor manager refused to let him on the floor, which had a big plate glass window. My friend was not in the image which IBM wanted to spread. My friend pointed out that he was a customer, not an employee, and had a right to dress the way he wanted. The floor manager could see the point of that, but wanted instructions from the appropriate vice-president.

The vice-president probably called up corporate headquarters to get instructions. At last the word came down. My friend *was* a customer, not an employee and had a right to dress the way he pleased but, draw the blinds.

In the spring, John Wheeler finally agreed that there was nothing for me to do. We had a very pleasant lunch during which I tried to tell him what a mathematician did. I had called up Olaf Helmer at RAND, and he was delighted that I could come early.

Helen had two older sisters. One, Clara, with her husband ran a grocery store in the Bronx, and the younger, Anna, with her husband, Irving, ran a knitting mill in Queens. We often dined there, and were on very cordial terms with their children Norman and Joey.

When we drove west, we took Anna with us. She was good company and was a great help with Eric and Kirstie. She would baby-sit them while Betty Jo and I had a quiet meal together.

CHAPTER 13

RAND 1952-65

I had to make a major decision. Should I return to Stanford or stay at RAND. I had thought about this question in Princeton, but it was not an easy decision to make since there were strong arguments on each side.

At Stanford, I had a tenured position, good for another thirty-eight years. The retirement age at Stanford was seventy. I also had a good teaching position, with not too much teaching, and a fine house, which I have described above. But these were not the important considerations. At Stanford, I had a chance to do analytic number theory, which I had wanted to do since I was sixteen.

However, I had to face the fact that I couldn't do what I wanted to do. Possibly the state of mathematics did not allow this. Certainly, my state of knowledge was not up to it.

I had spent enough time in Los Angeles to know that I would enjoy living there. I also knew that Los Angeles had many fine houses. Although it was not until 1968 that I had one that was better than the one up at Stanford.

I was intrigued by dynamic programming. It was clear to me that there was a good deal of good analysis there. Furthermore, I could see many applications. It was a clear choice. I could either be a traditional intellectual, or a modern intellectual using the results of my research for the problems of contemporary society. This was a dangerous path. Either I could do too much research and too little application, or too little research and too much application. I had confidence that I could do this delicate activity, pie à la mode.

At RAND, I would have time for all this without any obligations of teaching, committee work, or contract proposals. The more I thought about it, the more attractive RAND became. I made the decision. I wrote to Stanford and resigned my position and accepted one at RAND. Since RAND had a formula for salary depending upon what you got before, it was a good idea to do this now when I could use the Princeton salary, $10,000 a year rather than the Stanford salary, $5,000 a year.

Also, RAND had a new building, 1700 Main Street right across from City Hall. This was an attractive two-story rectangular building, which was used for many purposes. Because of the proximity to the ocean, there was no air-conditioning. As a matter of fact, the only room which was air-conditioned was the computer room because the IBM cards wrinkled if the humidity became too high.

When RAND wanted to pay back the loan, the Ford Foundation said to keep the money and construct a building.

It was certainly a pleasure to have a spacious, modern office. As RAND got more successful, it needed more office space. Finally, at the north end of the building, another building, six stories high, was constructed.

I decided to investigate three areas, dynamic programming, control theory, and time-lag processes.

My first task in dynamic programming was to put it on a rigorous basis. I found that I was using the same technique over and over to derive a functional equation. I decided to call this technique, "The principle of optimality". Oliver Gross said one day, "The principle is not rigorous." I replied, "Of course not. It's not even precise." A good principle should guide the intuition.

Some of the functional equations could be handled easily using classical techniques. Some required a great deal of work. I wish I then had available the projected metric of Garrett Birkhoff. Many years later, Tom Brown and I wrote a short paper pointing out how useful this was.

Secondly, I turned to the study of the associated functional equations. I was not enthusiastic about doing this. The equations were highly nonlinear and unlike any others that had appeared in analysis. I was delighted when I found that a simple argument could handle most equations.

While doing this, I started work on control theory. I had seen problems in economics and operations research and it was clear that some effort was required. I had a good team, Irving Glicksberg and Oliver Gross. Both were talented and ingenious mathematicians.

The tool we used was the calculus of variations. What we found was that very simple problems required great ingenuity. A small change in the problem caused a great change in the solution.

Clearly, something was wrong. There was an obvious lack of balance. Reluctantly, I was forced to the conclusion that the calculus of variations was not an effective tool for obtaining a solution.

Work on problems involving constraints had been done at the University of Chicago years before. For example, Magnus Hestenes had discovered what had become known as the Pontryagin Maximum Principle. Will Karush had discovered what had become known as the Kuhn-Tucker condition.

We collected previous results of ours in a monograph.[1] This was translated into Russian and had a great influence there. Consequently, we have a book in Russian which does not exist in English. The material should have been put in book form. However, it needed a great deal more work and I had other things to do.

Thirdly, I wanted to work in time-lag processes. I had gotten interested in this area in Princeton. I decided that first I would find out what had been done. With John Danskin we did a survey of the field. This was the basis for the book by Ken Cooke and myself.[2]

When we had arrived in Los Angeles, Anna flew home. We rented a house, west of Fairfax and halfway between Santa Monica Blvd. and Sunset Blvd., and looked for a house to buy. We looked at many houses, and finally found one that we liked at 444 N. Bundy. The asking price was $35,000, quite a bargain for that area but all we could scrape up was $32,000. The real estate agent, Mrs. Durfee, called us many times asking us to increase the offer. Unfortunately, I could not

[1] R. Bellman, I. Glicksberg and O.A. Gross, *Some Aspects of the Mathematical Theory of Control Processes* (RAND Corp., Santa Monica, California, # R-313, Jan. 16, 1958).

[2] R. Bellman and Kenneth Cooke, *Differential-Difference Equations* (Academic Press, Inc., New York, 1963).

do that since we couldn't afford any more. To our surprise the $32,000 offer was accepted.

If we had known the conditions under which the house was sold we would not have bought it. The owner was a doctor who refused to sign the loyalty oath at Cedars of Lebanon Hospital and was fired from the staff.

After we had bought the house an FBI agent came around and asked how we had bought it. We told him that we had gotten it through an agent and found out the details.

Our neighbors on the left were the Skenes. He was an eight-goal polo player, an Australian who had been brought over to Los Angeles by several groups in Brentwood and Bel Air. He had just made "Stormy" for Walt Disney and had a number of anecdotes about the movie colony. He and his wife were very charming people, and we frequently dined at each other's house. They introduced us to liebfraumilch, and thereby hangs a tale.

The Beverly Hilton, at the intersection of the two parallel streets, Wilshire Blvd. and Santa Monica Blvd., had started the L'Escoffier Room. This was to be a gourmet's delight with price no object. As a matter of fact, the menu would have no prices on it.

Paul Brock, who always appreciated good food, wanted very much to go to the opening night. He could not manage this but could get a table for the second night. The room was full of celebrities. The L'Escoffier Room had been advertised for weeks before.

Paul picked the lowest item on the menu, hoping that it was the most inexpensive. As it was, the check came to $70. It turned out that he had ordered hamburger. The waiter asked him what wine he wanted with the hamburger, and how he wanted it cooked. He nodded approvingly when Paul said, "Liebfraumilch and rare." Paul had dined at our home the week before and knew the name liebfraumilch. After a few minutes, the waiter was joined by the maître de and the keeper of the wine cellar, with a big key around his neck. They were very apologetic. Every wine had come, but liebfraumilch.

Paul said it was a great moment. Every eye was on him. Obviously, he was a gourmet who had ordered a wine which L'Escoffier did not have.

The maître de said, "If we don't have liebfraumilch, what do you want?" Paul had to think fast because he didn't know the name of any other wine. He said, "If you don't have liebfraumilch, do the best you can."

Dynamic programming is useful for social situations occasionally.

The L'Escoffier Room did not succeed in that format. It was changed to a good, high priced restaurant, and Nina and I often took visitors who had an expense account there.

The Skenes had one son, a boy about six. This boy, unhappily, had severe dermatitis, and would scream all night from the itching. This screaming kept us up too. Unfortunately, the Skenes were Christian Scientists and did not believe in doctors.

Eric's asthma was acting up and we needed a respirator one night. We found we didn't have a dollar in the house. It would have been embarrassing to ask the Skenes for $10 to buy a respirator. Instead I borrowed $10 from them saying that we had no whiskey.

It was an interesting area. Right behind us, on Saltair lived General Omar Bradley. A little further north lived Libby of carbon 14 dating fame. At the time, Libby was writing a number of articles for the local newspaper on how cheaply one could build a shelter. Several years later, we had the big Bel Air fire. Libby and his wife took refuge in the shelter. The heat and smoke got intense. They only left the shelter when their clothes started to smoulder.

Szilard was told about the incident. He commented that it proved two things: God exists and God has a sense of humor.

It was important that the lawn be kept up. I didn't have any trouble with moles because the area was so built up. However, I had a lot of trouble with an Australian shrub which had been brought in to control the crabgrass. This shrub had very long roots with the result that if one tried to pull up one part, one found that one had to pull up twenty or thirty feet of shrub. This caused a great deal of trouble. Eventually, one just mowed over it.

One of the difficulties of living there was that everyone assumed that you were rich and jacked up their prices accordingly. One story will suffice. We had a tree in the back yard which had a limb which cracked. I was afraid that some of the neighborhood children would get hurt if the limb cracked all the way. I could have sawed off the limb myself, but it was easier to get a tree surgeon. I looked in the yellow pages and got someone nearby. The tree surgeon came out and tried to convince me to do all sorts of expensive things. I resisted and told him I merely wanted the limb sawed off. The price was $35.

At about three o'clock in the afternoon, Betty Jo called me up and said that four men were there playing cards with the limb half sawed off. I came home and found the situation as she had described. I told the men I would finish the job whereby they finished it in ten minutes.

I sent a check for $35 as agreed. The next thing was a telephone call from the secretary who said the bill was $75, and if I did not pay I would be taken to small claims court. I said, "Fine. I am retired and that would be a welcome diversion."

I heard no more from her. About one week later, I got a call from the tree surgeon. He said, "It's not a matter of money, it's a matter of principle." I interrupted him saying, "With me it's a matter of money, not principle."

That ended that conversation and the matter.

I spent a great deal of time and effort on the functional equations of dynamic programming. I was able to solve some equations and to determine the properties of the function and the policy for others. I developed some new theories, Markovian decision processes, and was able to reinterpret an old theory like the calculus of variations, of which I will speak more about below.

I decided to write a book on dynamic programming. I offered this book to McGraw-Hill because they had published the book on stability theory. To my great joy, they turned it down. I immediately gave it to Princeton. Herb was now director of the press, and I knew the book would do well. In the meantime, McGraw-Hill had changed its mind but it was too late! They were very aggrieved at this. The book was a scientific best-seller, at least 13,000 copies, and translated into Russian and Japanese, and made a good deal of money for Princeton. It was a way of my saying thank you for the Ph.D.

My grandfather died in 1953, and left about $6,000 which was divided equally between the three children, Sylvia, my mother and Arthur. I got my mother's share.

The $2,000 was, of course, very welcome. But, I would gladly have exchanged it for a dollar more a week in 1937. I decided, therefore, to do something extravagant which would have aggravated my grandfather. That was how I bought my first Packard, which I drove for about 130,000 miles. Then, I bought another Packard which I drove for another 130,000 miles. Then, I got a Lincoln Continental at cost, through Richard Beckwith, whom I had helped with his Ph.D. and I drove that for about 140,000 miles.

The extravagance of buying a Packard saved my life.

Every morning, I would take Eric and Kirstie and the little girl across the street to elementary school which was across Sunset on San Vicente. It was not a great distance, but it was a dangerous trip which the children could not make themselves. One of the reasons that it was so dangerous was that Marymount College juts out a little bit, enough to obscure the oncoming traffic on Sunset. Consequently, I would zig-zag, turning right on Sunset and then left on Kenter. That seemed a safe way to get across Sunset. While waiting to make a left turn on Kenter, I was hit from the rear by a car who saw me at the last minute. That gave me a component into oncoming traffic and I was hit in the front too. The collision from the rear knocked me out, but I was jolted into consciousness from the collision from the front. Fortunately, since I was driving a Packard, although, the rear was completely crushed and the front was completely crushed, the cab was pretty well intact. I had a banged knee and a stiff shoulder, but that was all.

Eric had been knocked out of the car by the collision and the traffic had to drive around him. Nobody stopped.

My first thought when I came to was that now the mortgage would be paid off. Unfortunately, the driver who hit me was not insured because he had a bad driving record. I sued him anyway to keep him from driving for a year.

Several months later, I picked up a woman who was waiting for a bus. She was going into Beverly Hills to see her lawyer about a traffic accident, and told me the details. After a few minutes, I realized she was describing my accident from a very biased point of view. Naturally, I didn't tell her so.

At that time, the car had about 60,000 miles on it. It required about

$1,300 worth of repairs, but when they were done the car was as good as new.

One could get a good bargain buying a Packard since Packard was on the skids. The only thing that saved Packard was that it made engines for the Air Force. A friend gave the coup de grace to Packard with a back of the envelope calculation which showed that the Air Force was buying about three times the number of engines that they needed.

The Packard was a prestige car. One night I decided to see the Academy Awards close up. It was then held at the RKO Pantages in Hollywood. I joined the line of Cadillacs without difficulty. When it was my turn to drive up in front of the theatre, I said "Not tonight," and drove off.

A number of mathematical models of dynamic programming type were analyzed using the calculus of variations. The treatment was not routine since we suffered either from the presence of constraints or from an excess of linearity. An interesting fact that emerged from this detailed scrutiny was that the way one utilized resources depended critically upon the level of these resources, and the time remaining in the process. Naturally, this was surprising only to someone unversed in economics, such as myself. But this was my condition, with the result that the observation of this phenomenon came as quite a shock. Again the intriguing thought: A solution is not merely a set of functions of time, or a set of numbers, but a rule telling the decisionmaker what to do; a policy.

The mathematical structure of these perplexing analytic problems was quite open. What was remarkable was the level of analytic intricacy of solution introduced by simple constraints. These constraints were an essential part of the background, introduced by immediate economic, engineering, and military considerations.

A problem of LaSalle's which caught my attention at the same time was the "bang-bang" control problem. This was a question of restoring a system to equilibrium as quickly as possible subject to constraints in the restoring force. This was a problem closely related to stability theory.

As a result of a detailed study of dozens of variational problems of the foregoing type, and filling hundreds of pages with equations and calculations, it became quite clear that there would never be any elegant, uniform way of solving problems of this genre in analytic terms. Each individual problem was an exercise in ingenuity, much like plane geometry. Change one small feature, and the structure of the solution was strongly altered. There was no stability!

Consequently, if one really wanted to obtain numerical solutions to variational problems in an effective fashion, we needed some other tools. I was reluctant to become over-involved, since all along I had no desire to work seriously in the calculus of variations. A course in the subject in college had given me simultaneously a rather low opinion of its intrinsic interest and a healthy respect for its intricacies. It appeared to be filled with complicated existence and uniqueness theorems with self-imposed restrictions, none pointing in any particular direction. This is pertinent to a comment made by Felix Klein, the great German mathematician, concerning a certain type of mathematician. When this individual discovers that he can jump across a stream, he returns to the other side, ties a chair to his leg, and sees if he can still jump across the stream. Some may enjoy this sport; others, like myself, may feel that it is more fun to see if you can jump across bigger streams, or at least different ones.

Despite my personal feelings, the challenge remained. How did one obtain the numerical solution of optimization problems? Were there reliable methods? As pointed out above, I did not wish to grapple with this thorny question, and I had certainly not contemplated the application of dynamic programming to control processes of deterministic types. Originally, I had developed the theory as a tool for stochastic decision processes. However, the thought was finally forced upon me that the desired solution in a control process was a policy: "Do thus-and-thus if you find yourself in this portion of state space with this amount of time left." Conversely, once it was realized that the concept of policy was fundamental in control theory, the mathematicization of the basic engineering concept of "feedback control", then the emphasis upon a state variable formulation became natural. We see then a very interesting interaction between dynamic programming and control theory. This reinforces the point that when working in the field of analysis it is exceedingly helpful to have some underlying physical processes clearly in mind.

What is worth noting about the foregoing development is that I should have seen the application of dynamic programming to control theory several years before. I should have, but I didn't. It is all very well to start a lecture by saying, "Clearly, a control process can be regarded as multistage decision process in which...," but it is a bit misleading. Scientific developments can always be made logical and rational with sufficient hindsight. It is amazing, however, how clouded the crystal ball looks beforehand. We all wear such intellectual blinders and make such inexplicable blunders that it is amazing that any progress is made at all.

All this contributes to the misleading nature of conventional history, whether it be analysis of a scientific discovery or of a political movement. We are always looking at the situation from the wrong side, when events have already been frozen in time. Since we know what happened, it is not too difficult to present convincing arguments to justify a particular course of events. None of these analyses must be taken too seriously, no more than Monday morning quarterbacking.

I strongly recommend the interesting study of these and related matters by Jacques Hadamard, the great French mathematician, in his book.[3]

As pointed out above, as of 1954 or so I had stumbled into some important types of problems and had been pushed, willy-nilly, into answering some significant kinds of questions. I could handle deterministic control processes to some extent and stochastic decision processes in economics and operations research as well. Where next? At this point, I began to think in a logical fashion, using a systematic methodological approach. The point about the suitable philosophy preparing one for the fortunate accident should be kept in mind.

There are several ways in which a mathematician can proceed to extend his research efforts, particularly one who is deeply interested in problems arising from the physical world. He can, on one hand, examine the equations he has been working with and modify them in a

[3] *The Psychology of Invention in the Mathematical Field* (Dover Publications, New York, 1945; Paperback).

variety of ways. Or he can ask questions that have not been asked before concerning the nature of the solution of the original equations. This is basically a very difficult way to carry out research. It is very easy to change the form of an equation in a large number of ways. The great majority of the new equations are not meaningful, and, in consequence, lead to both difficult and unimportant problems. Similarly, there are many questions that are difficult to answer, but hardly worth asking. The well-trained mathematician does not measure the value of a problem solely by its intractability. The challenge is there, but even very small boys do not accept all dares.

The trick that one learns over time, a basic part of mathematical methodology, is to sidestep the equation and focus instead on the structure of the underlying physical process. One learns to submit oneself to a catechism: "When I set up these equations originally, I made certain assumptions. How realistic were these assumptions? What state variables, and what effects did I ignore?..."

To obtain, in this fashion, a more interesting, and more useful, theory of control processes, we observe that the use of the calculus of variations in control theory presupposes, albeit tacitly, that we have cause and effect under control, that we know both the objective and the duration of the control process. As a matter of fact, also implicit is the assumption that one knows what to observe and that the state variables can be measured with arbitrary accuracy.

In the real world, none of these assumptions are uniformly valid. Often people want to know why mathematics and computers cannot be used to handle the meaningful problems of society, as opposed, let us say, to the moon boondoggle and high energy-high cost physics. The answer lies in the fact that we don't know how to describe the complex systems of society involving people, we don't understand cause and effect, which is to say the consequences of decisions, and we don't even know how to make our objectives reasonably precise. None of the requirements of classical science are met. Gradually, a new methodology for dealing with these "fuzzy" problems is being developed, but the path is not easy.

Upon first gazing upon the complexities of the real world, there is a certain temptation to return to number theory. Number theory, however, does not seem to be rewarding enough for continual effort. The problems are too difficult and the victories too few. Taking up the challenge of complexity, I felt that the appropriate thing to do was to start with deterministic control processes and to modify them stage by stage to obtain theories which could be used to deal with basic uncertainties in a more sophisticated fashion.

To this end, we can begin by introducing well-behaved uncertainty of the type extensively treated by the classical theory of probability. This leads to the modern theory of stochastic control processes where uncertainty is represented by random variables with known probability distributions, and where the objective is to maximize expected values. This gives rise to an elegant theory with a good deal of attractive analysis. It is a new part of pure mathematics.

The Riccati equation plays an essential role. I had observed this but had published little on it, saving it for Norman for a Ph.D. thesis. Unfortunately, he decided not to go ahead. In the meantime, others, like Rudy Kalman, had observed this, and published various results.

In order to make any progress, it is necessary to think of approximate techniques, and above all, of numerical algorithms. Finally, having devoted a great deal of time and effort, mostly fruitless, to the analysis of many varieties of simple models, I was prepared to face up to the challenge of using dynamic programming as an effective tool for obtaining numerical answers to numerical questions. A considerable part of the motivation in this direction at that time was the continuing development of the digital computer. Before it was freely available, it was not very interesting to conjure up hypothetical algorithms. Once there, it was challenging to utilize this Sorcerer's Apprentice.

Once again, what became a major endeavor of mine, the computational solution of complex functional equations, was entered into quite diffidently. I had never been interested in numerical analysis up to that point. Like most mathematicians of my generation, I had been brought up to scorn this utilitarian activity. Numerical solution was considered the last resort of an incompetent mathematician. The opposite, of course, is true. Once working in the area, it is very quickly realized that far more ability and sophistication is required to obtain a numerical solution than to establish the usual existence and uniqueness theorems. It is far more difficult to obtain an effective algorithm than one that stops with a demonstration of validity. A final goal of any scientific theory must be the derivation of numbers. Theories stand or fall, ultimately, upon numbers. Thus I became interested in computers, not as electronic toys but rather because of what they signified mathematically and scientifically. This interest led in many unexpected directions, as I will indicate subsequently. This is a significant part of the story of scientific methodology. It is usually, if not always, impossible to predict where a theoretical investigation will end once started. But what one can be certain of is that the investigation of a meaningful scientific area will lead to meaningful mathematics. Inevitably, as soon as one pursues the basic theme of obtaining numerical answers to numerical questions, one will be led to all kinds of interesting and significant problems in pure mathematics.

I got a programmer, Stuart Dreyfus. Stuart was a highly intelligent person who knew little mathematics. He had spent his time at Harvard playing chess. Chess and bridge are the traditional time wasters of intellectuals.

At the time, programming was done in machine language and was quite difficult. This was before Fortran and other simple languages.

I had a programmer, but no time. Time on the computer was preempted by the physics and engineering divisions. Consequently, Stuart slept during the day so that we could use the computer at night. At the time we used the Johnniac. This computer used vacuum tubes which created so much heat that the computer had to be on two floors to dissipate this heat. Subsequently, when computers were transistorized, this problem did not exist.

Stuart and I investigated many processes and the algorithm worked uniformly well. Stuart and I became colleagues rather than Stuart remaining a programmer. The same simple argument that I had used for existence and uniqueness showed that approximate methods could be used. Naturally, first I did the computations then I showed why the method worked. We decided to collect our results and some theoretical results suggested by these in book form.[4]

[4] R. Bellman and S. Dreyfus, *Applied Dynamic Programming* (Princeton University Press, Princeton, New Jersey, 1962).

There is an amusing story connected with the book. The book was dedicated to von Neumann. Stuart had wanted to dedicate the book to his mother. When the book was translated into Japanese, I wrote to the publishers and asked that the dedication read to John von Neumann and Stuart's mother. I figured that this would be a good joke on Stuart. He certainly would not believe me, and would ask others who knew Japanese to translate the dedication. However, when they translated, he would think I had gotten there ahead of him, and finally he would have to learn some Japanese himself.

Unfortunately, the publishers would not do that. I got back a letter saying it wasn't customary in Japan to dedicate a book to a woman.

Stuart was so bright that I wanted him to get a Ph.D. I used my influence at Princeton to have him admitted to the graduate school. After one year at Princeton, he transferred to Harvard and got his Ph.D. in a program of applied mathematics there, under Bryson. It reminds one of the old joke about the student who flunked out of Princeton and went to Harvard, thereby improving the academic level of both institutions.

He is now a professor of industrial engineering at Berkeley, and an expert on dynamic programming.

This interest in the abilities of computers led to several things. The first was controversy.

About twenty years ago, some people decided they were going to stake out the field of artificial intelligence. They proudly planted their flag and they loudly claimed that they had computer programs which would think, create, compose music, play chess, invest in the stock market, translate languages, prove mathematical theorems, and so on and so on. At the time, you may remember, there was a great deal of Sunday supplement thinking around; magazines and newspapers were filled with speculation about "giant brains". There was a great deal of anthropomorphism. Stuart Dreyfus and I, who had been trying to use computers to solve simple deterministic control processes, as mentioned above, were rather miffed by these extravagant claims. There were only two possibilities we could think of: Either these individuals were making wild statements, or they were very much smarter than we were. We couldn't even use computers as effectively as we desired to solve these relatively simple decision processes arising in control theory. Dimensionality was, and is, a formidable barrier.

Obviously the alternative of intellectual superiority was unthinkable, so we had to examine the first hypothesis carefully.

This has been one of the very interesting aspects of using a computer, interesting both methodologically and philosophically. If one were to look at where the great advances in thought have occurred, the answer would be that probably the greatest single advance in thought occurred as the result of an electro-mechanical device, namely the digital computer. With the aid of a digital computer, for the first time you can tell people, "Put up or shut up. Don't tell me that you have a method for understanding how people recognize pictures, don't tell me that you know how people make decisions, don't just tell me about it; show me. If you really are assured that you have a method for determining how people recognize pictures, or how people make decisions, or how people play chess, write a computer program." We now have digital computers that are fast enough and big enough to carry out precise instructions in a reasonable space of time. Up until very recently, it was easy to say, "Here is my formula for doing it. I'm awfully sorry, but clearly this might take thirty years to implement by hand or computer calculation. You can't expect me to implement this theory. You'll just have to take my word." Today we have computers that can perform these giant operations in a half hour or a couple of hours.

In general, we now possess simple, direct ways to test hypotheses. What is quite interesting is that all of this is a very natural extension of the work in control theory. One gets quickly into the general area of philosophy because when you have to use a computer, you can't wave your hands. You can't say, "Behave in a reasonable fashion. You know what I mean." You have to be precise: "What's the input? What are the data, what are the state variables, what processing does one do with the state variables, how does one evaluate, and so forth?" Consequently, I feel as far as scientific methodology is concerned, the biggest single advance has been due to the development of the digital computer. For the first time, we have a good chance of getting rid of a great deal of hot air. This doesn't mean that other evils won't spring up in their places – but at least they will be different ones. We can put up with different ones because we can stand almost anything rather than be bored. There will be different difficulties and there will be more sophisticated difficulties. It's going to be a great deal harder to know what to do with the charlatan of five or ten years from now. He's going to be a quite different charlatan from the Morgan character in The Wizard of Oz. He is going to be a person who has his Ph.D., all of the appropriate academic titles, knows how to use a computer, and has just a little kink some place. But it's not going to be so easy to find out where that kink is. It's going to be a much more difficult task, and the general public doesn't even realize the existence of the high-level charlatan yet.

The digital computer is important scientifically because it can do arithmetic. Why can't it recognize patterns, prove theorems, or play chess? The answer is that we don't understand what structure is. In some processes it is easy to define what we mean by "structure". But, in general, we cannot state what we mean by structure, and what we don't understand a computer cannot do.

The controversy got me very interested in artificial intelligence. Over the years, I did a lot of thinking about it, and a little work. This will be described in Chapter 16.

About that time, the application of computers to operations research began to be realized. The day was long past when IBM thought that eight computers could handle all the needs of the country. I went to several dinners where this was discussed. At these dinners there were so many vice-presidents that I introduced myself as the vice-president of operations research at RAND. At one dinner, I was seated between a vice-president of an aircraft company and a vice-president of a motion picture company. They spoke about the traffic in Beverly Hills, which was bad then and worse now. Eventually, I got bored with the subject and introduced a favorite theory. I stated that the movies didn't imitate life, but that life imitated the movies.

Surprisingly, the vice-president of the motion picture studio agreed. He said that at the beginning of World War II, all the major studios received a letter from the War Department. Henceforth, would they please portray a sergeant as a scoutmaster, rather than the sergeant

Flagg character immortalized in "What Price Glory".

This work with computers got me very interested in the effect of computers upon society. Thus, I became the RAND expert on automation. At first, I used to preface my remarks by pointing out that I was not a sociologist. After a while I left this out. In this way, I met many reporters who were interested in this topic, and I became friends with them. There was, for example, Irv Bengelsdorf who wrote for the Los Angeles Times, Marino de Medici, who was based in Washington and wrote for newspapers in Italy, Rex Malik who wrote columns for several computer magazines in England, and Sy Bourgin, who at the time was with Newsweek. Later he took a position at RAND.

Sometimes, it comes in handy to know how computer systems work. I received a bill from Shell Oil in connection with my credit card, which was incorrect. The error was easy to find. I wrote to Shell Oil, pointing out the error. After several weeks, I received a form dunning letter, signed by Mr. Compton. I wrote again, again pointing out the error. After several weeks, I received another form letter, more threatening, signed by Mr. Upperman.

I called up Shell headquarters in Ponca City, Oklahoma, collect, and got a very nice woman to whom I explained the situation. She promised to remedy it. After several weeks, I received another form letter signed either by Mr. Compton or Mr. Upperman, I forget which, even more threatening.

There were now several things I could do, all legal. As recreation, I had devised several methods for getting the computer into a loop. Alternatively, I had devised methods for making the computer branch indefinitely.

However, I decided to play the following game. The next time I got an incorrect bill, I wrote back and said there was obviously something wrong with their computing system. I was a computer expert and would be glad to fix it at a charge of $200 an hour. I even prepared some form letters in the style of Mr. Compton and Mr. Upperman and I was ready for the fray.

Unfortunately, they folded immediately. I received no more bills and no more threatening letters. In return, I never used the Shell Oil card again. It was a Mexican standoff.

The temptation was to become a sage. I had to constantly remind myself that I was a mathematician.

Life magazine decided to do a picture story on RAND and sent out one of their best photographers, Leonard Maccombe. We became good friends. Leonard told a number of stories about his experiences.

One day, we were standing at the entrance to RAND when someone at RAND drove by in their sports car. I waved hello to him. Leonard said, "You don't like him do you?" "No," I said, "But how do you know?" He replied that he could look at my face and tell.

At that time, there was the $64,000 question scandal. Charles Van Dorn had confessed that he knew the answers ahead of time. Leonard said he could tell by looking at Van Dorn's face that he was not listening to the question for the first time.

It was just as well that Leonard and I were good friends. One day, I had gotten dressed absentmindedly, and put on sox from different pairs. Not only were they from different pairs, but they were different colors. Leonard took a picture of this, but never published it. That was just as well since I already had a reputation for eccentricity because I would take off my shoes at every opportunity.

I was invited by the AAUW, American Association of University Women, to give a talk on computers and automation. The title of my talk was, "Sex and Automation". Actually, it was a quite serious talk in which I sketched the effects of computers upon positions for women. What was amusing was that the Los Angeles Times refused to announce a talk with the title. The talk itself was quite successful and I gave it before several other organizations.

I was always interested in simulation. In 1948, when I found that a mathematical analysis of bargaining led to non zero sum games for which no mathematical theory existed, I suggested that one look at actual bargaining done by insurance companies. When I found that people were interested in conflict situations, I suggested that two species of insects be used rather than differential equations.

At UCLA, I heard some good lectures on stochastic processes. The thought occurred to me, keeping in mind the famous dictum of Jacobi, "Man muss immer umkehren", why not solve the equation by using the original process. It was a good idea but had already occurred to von

Neumann and Ulam at Los Alamos. It was the basic idea of the Monte Carlo method.

Actually, I got involved in simulation through kriegspiel. Kriegspiel was played in the mathematics conference room. Although, RAND didn't have a cafeteria, it had a snack bar at which various things could be purchased. Consequently, many people played kriegspiel and ate their lunch at the same time. There were two drawbacks to this. Gradually, the length of time during which people played kriegspiel grew longer and longer. It was not unusual for games to last until one-thirty. Secondly, people did not clean up after lunch, and the room was frequently a mess. Memo after memo was sent by John Williams and people in administration. After each memo, things would be better for a while and then revert.

I found it useful to get to the mathematics conference room a little before twelve in order to make sure that I would play. From ten to twelve, the room was used for war games. In that way, I was able to see what was done in this area. I disapproved strongly of what I saw. However, I kept silent since I didn't want to get involved in this area.

Bill Pocock, a senior partner of Booz, Allen, and Hamilton, came to town. He was quite an interesting fellow. He flew his own plane and had once played baseball for the St. Louis Cardinals at the same time as Leo Durocher. We had dinner together at the Cock and Bull. He asked me if I would construct a business game for the American Management Association. It was a case of put up or shut up. On one hand I wanted to see if my ideas were correct. On the other hand, it would give me a chance to look into the business world; an area in which I knew nothing.

I had a very good team, Don Malcolm and Charlie Clark from BAH, Frank Ricciardi and Chris Craft from AMA. Charlie acted as a devil's advocate and did an excellent job.

We met in Chicago and Albuquerque, had a dry run in Los Angeles and unveiled the simulation in New York.

In Albuquerque, I asked the others whether they wanted a good dinner. They said, yes. I said we would go then to the La Fonda in Santa Fe. They were horrified at the idea of going to a different city, sixty miles away for dinner. I pointed out that out west we measured things by time, not distance. It would take as long to get to the La Fonda as if we were in Manhattan and wanted to go to Sheepshead Bay.

They greatly enjoyed the ride across the desert and the dinner at La Fonda.

The night before the simulation was shown to the public in New York, there was a reception because Courant's youngest daughter was getting married to Jerry Berkowitz. The entire Courant clan was there. Courant made several sarcastic remarks about my involvement with the business world. Finally, I told him the following story. Several months before a friend of Stuart's had come in to see me at RAND. He had been a pupil of Zariski in algebraic geometry for four years and had decided that that was enough. Now, he wanted to do something different. He wanted to get a job at an aircraft company. I asked him what else he knew. He replied that he also knew algebraic topology. I pointed out that directors of research at aircraft companies would not perform entrechats when they heard a candidate knew algebraic geometry and algebraic topology. I asked him whether he knew anything about differential equations, ordinary or partial. He drew himself up proudly and said, "I have never done any applied mathematics."

Courant got the point, and there were no more sarcastic remarks. As a matter of fact, he went to Washington the next day to get money for simulation.

It reminds me of the story that Chuck Dolph likes to tell. Chuck is a member of the Department of Mathematics at the University of Michigan and is regarded by many people as an applied mathematician. He has suffered in pay and promotion accordingly. One evening, a member of the music department was asked what instrument he played. He said, "I am not an applied musician."

There was a certain amount of propaganda in the game. It was impossible to do well without spending money on R and D.

I was gratified that successful businessmen did well in the game, whereas, I who had designed the game and knew the inner workings of the computer never could.

There were many other amusing incidents. Let me mention two.

In Los Angeles, we made the mistake of putting two controllers on the same team. These gentlemen, true to their training refused to spend any money. Consequently, their share of the market dwindled to zero. We were forced to slip them money illegally to keep them in the game. We learned two lessons from this. First of all we never put two controllers on the same team again. Secondly, we modified the program so that a team got a share of the market regardless of what it did.

In Los Angeles, I noticed a very pretty girl wearing the badge of some company. I asked her what she did. She said she was a friend of one of the players. A great light dawned.

This player had to travel frequently. When he did so, he picked up quite a few stewardesses. When things got serious he took refuge in Catholicism. He would tell the girl that he loved her dearly but that his wife would not give him a divorce.

As a result of the business game I spoke before many business groups. I would always ask them why they were in business. They would say, naturally, to make a profit. I would say, if they wanted to make a profit why didn't they sell their business? Then they would make a great profit overnight.

They would respond that they wanted to stay in business. Then I would ask them over what period did they want to make a profit, one year, five years or ten years? I wanted to get across the point that one of the principal difficulties in applying mathematics to economics was determining the time period over which one did planning.

I also wanted these groups, who prided themselves on being practical, to realize how much they were guided by theory. I often quoted the statement of Boltzmann, "There is nothing as practical as a good theory."

I enjoyed kriegspiel very much but thought it unhealthy to concentrate on kriegspiel during the lunch hour after concentrating on mathematics during the morning. Consequently, I decided to go out for lunch. There were many good restaurants in and around Santa Monica. Not only did one have a choice of good American food, as well as a delicatessen, but there were good French, Italian, Chinese, Japanese, Yugoslav, restaurants and even an Indonesian restaurant.

There were also many people to go out to lunch with, Charlie Goldstein, Ted Harris, Stuart Dreyfus, Bob Kalaba and many visitors.

Going out to lunch considerably extended my working day. We had many visitors at RAND which ordinarily interfered with my work. This way, I could have many discussions over the luncheon table.

If the person was very interesting, or unable to come to lunch, I would take him to dinner. I had a tour all arranged. We would have dinner at the Cock and Bull or one of the restaurants on restaurant row on La Cienega. After dinner, we would visit the Roaring 20's and the Gay 90's. After that, we would visit the Japanese Gardens, from which one could obtain a fine view of Los Angeles. Finally, we would end up at the Luau.

This worked well except once. The person involved did very dangerous experiments on the eye which he would not allow graduate students to do, but do them himself. In addition, he had been in the Dutch underground for five years making false papers. He discovered he had a talent for forgery.

When I took him out, after his talk, I discovered he never watched TV or listened to the radio. When I took him to the Roaring 20's he said it reminded him of the red-light district in Amsterdam. Finally, at nine-thirty I said that it was my bedtime and took him home.

A few weeks later I took out Uhlenbeck, who was then president of the Physical Society. He said there were two types of Dutch, the drinking Dutch and the nondrinking Dutch. I had met a typical nondrinking Dutchman.

Uhlenbeck told us the following story. We had asked him why he and Goudsmit had not received a Nobel prize for the spin of the electron. He said the reason was probably that everybody thought they had one.

When he and Goudsmit got the idea, their professor had them write up a short paper for the British journal, *Nature*. However, to be safe he thought it would be a good idea for them to see Lorenz. Lorenz tore the idea to pieces. They returned very dejected. But their professor had already sent in the paper that made them world famous.

RAND had a very liberal expense account, and I charged all of the above to this. One day, Will Eisner came into my office, "Do you realize," he said "You are spending more than Collbohm?"

"I have more friends," I replied. That was the end of the discussion.

The RAND hours were officially eight to twelve with an hour for lunch and then one to five. I paid no attention to these. I usually came in the morning at ten and then, as described above, went out for a two-hour lunch. Then, I would return and stay until about five. I did a lot of work in the evening and on weekends. That is one of the advantages of being a mathematician. One needs no equipment and one can do mathematical research anywhere. My usual week would involve about sixty or seventy hours of mathematical work.

Now that I was seriously working in simulation, I went to various conferences to give lectures. One such conference was at Northwestern. I was first on the program and gave a talk entitled, "Simulation and Stimulation". The speaker following me was quite chagrined. His talk had the same title. After the talks, there was a press conference, concerned with the social effects of computers. During the press conference, I said that the labor force engaged in agriculture and manufacturing would be severely decreased by automation. Someone asked, how many people would be involved in this endeavor. I replied, "Two percent." It was not a bold prediction. At that time, about seven percent were involved. What I wanted to emphasize was the decrease. I picked the figure two percent because it is often used for a very small amount.

I imagine that today the figure is about four percent. It would be much smaller were it not for executive and union featherbedding. This worry about the effects of automation is not new, dating at least back to the industrial revolution. However, computers make automation feasible and greatly speed up the process. We are in transition, from a society based upon large industries to a society based on services. This can be seen in many areas.

I decided to do some book writing in addition to the research mentioned above. First of all, I decided to do a book on matrix analysis. I had looked around and found that the books that were available were for algebraists. There was no book for analysts, mathematical physicists, or engineers. My work at Princeton and RAND had shown me how important matrix theory was. I felt strongly that matrix theory was the arithmetic of advanced mathematics.

Ed Beckenbach stopped by my office one day. I had grown quite friendly with him due to our interaction at RAND and UCLA. He said that Springer wanted him to write a book. I suggested that we join endeavors and write a book on inequalities, a subject in which both of us had done a great deal of work. He agreed.

We wrote an advanced book, and an elementary book for Random House. Anneli Lax was editor of the series for Random House and made many good suggestions for our book.

Alice Tucker had divorced Al and was now married to Ed.

Holt, Rinehart, and Winston were starting a new series, the Athena series, and I wrote two books for the series. The first one was on perturbation methods. The second one was more self indulgent.[5] This was a labor of love. I really enjoyed writing it. It contained many results from my Stanford days. It sells about eighty copies a year, not a financial success, but a good book. By no stretch of the imagination could it be called contemporary mathematics. Let me quote from the foreword:

> *The theory of elliptic functions is the fairyland of mathematics. The mathematician who once gazes upon this enchanting and wondrous domain crowded with the most beautiful relations and concepts is forever captivated.*

I wanted to write a book on adaptive control processes, containing some ideas that I had. That posed some difficulties. At the time RAND took various bids for books and the author had little to say where his book would go. I wanted the book to go to Princeton, not McGraw-Hill or Wiley, who could easily outbid Princeton.

I wanted this for two reasons. In the first place I wanted to do various things which I felt a commercial press would not allow. In the second place, I knew the book would sell well and again I wanted PUP to make money. How to do it?

What I did was pretend that the book would be done privately, which allowed me to sign a contract with Princeton. Then after the

[5] R. Bellman, *A Brief Introduction to Theta Functions* (Holt, Rinehart, & Winston, New York, 1961).

contract was signed I changed my mind, it would be a RAND book. But, the contract was still valid. Naturally, McGraw-Hill and Wiley screamed to high heaven but there was nothing they could do.

Herb Bailey and I had a great deal of fun with the book. For example, there was the dust jacket. Wiener had used the word "cybernetics" which means oarsman. I thought it would be amusing to go Wiener one better and use the Egyptian hieroglyphic for oarsman. I referred to my hieroglyphic dictionary, Gardner's, and was delighted to find there were two hieroglyphs for oarsman. I used the shorter.

At the beginning of each chapter, I had apt quotations. One quotation came from Satchel Paige, who would have been astonished to find his words in such a place. One such quotation came from Buddha. According to Letov, this quote held up the Russian translation for one year. The quote from Buddha was, "Believe nothing even if I said it myself."

Also, there were snatches of poetry throughout. The longest piece of poetry was a parody on Hiawatha, by Kendall. Since the book was translated both into Russian and Japanese, it was quite amusing to see the translation of this.

Also, Herb and I cooperated to complete a very famous couplet by Pope. As I say, we had a great deal of fun, none of which would have been possible with a commercial press. Again, however, the book was a scientific best-seller, probably, at least 13,000 copies in English.

I also wanted to write a book for the high schools. This was to be an application of dynamic programming to classical puzzles such as wine pouring and cannibals and missionaries. The more that Ken Cooke and I wrote the higher the level became. Finally, we gave up and made it a research monograph.[6]

Many of my books have private jokes. For example, the name index for dynamic programming has Oveta Culp Hobby. If one looks on the appropriate page there is no mention of Oveta Culp Hobby. There is an exercise dealing with the preparation of vaccine. The story is the following.

[6] R. Bellman, K. Cooke and J. Lockett, *Algorithms, Graphs, and Computers* (Academic Press, Inc., New York, 1970).

At that time, the Salk vaccine for poliomyelitis was perfected. Canada had enough vaccine for everybody. United States, which is far richer did not have enough. When Oveta Culp Hobby, then Secretary of Health, Education, and Welfare, was asked about this, she responded with the classic remark, "I didn't know that poor people cared that much about their children."

She resigned with appropriate honors.

When one writes a book, one receives a form from the publisher which will be used for promotion purposes. It always contains some space of noteworthy facts. With tongue in cheek, I always put down the following two pieces of information: 1. I had won the table tennis tournament of Brooklyn College in 1941. 2. I was president of the first Jane Russell fan club of Belleville, Swansea, and East St. Louis in 1942.

As far as I knew, this important information was never used.

I also decided to collect some great papers in analysis.[7] I remembered the famous saying of Abel, "Read the Masters, not the pupils."

Naturally, I included the famous paper on fixed point theory by Birkhoff and Kellogg.

When Lefschetz saw the book, he thought it was quite nervy to put out such a collection. However, I felt it was more important for students to read some great papers than to worry which ones were greatest.

Eisenhower didn't do a very good job in choosing his cabinet. I have spoken about Charlie Wilson and his hatred of research. In 1957, he tried to destroy all the research organizations. The RAND budget was cut fifteen percent.

To give some money to John Williams so that he could save the jobs of many others, I took a visiting professorship at UCLA in engineering. That was not difficult to do since I had been friendly with Dean Boelter for many years.

At that time, their department of engineering was very interested in containerization. There were very good reasons for this step. It made it easy to load and unload and ships could be designed for these containers which were about 12 × 12 × 12. Naturally, the unions

[7] Bellman, R., *Modern Mathematical Classics — I: Analysis* (Dover Publications, New York, 1961).

were very much opposed since this speeded up loading and unloading. But, the principal reason for containers was that it prevented theft. This theft was most serious at American ports.

One of the scions of the Mafia had decided to get his Ph.D. in engineering. He made the mistake of going to the mathematics department which said that he would have to solve the packing problem first. He came to me in desperation. I told him that since the loading and unloading were to be done by longshoremen there was no need for a very sophisticated technique. He devised several simple methods which could easily be implemented and got his Ph.D.

I have a favor owed me by the Mafia which I can collect any time.

I also learned how to play doubles chess. This is a very interesting game in which one plays chess with a partner with no communication. Abe Kaplan liked to play this every noon. I joined forces with a young chess master, Bob Cross, which made things fairly equal. At the time, Abe was a much stronger player.

One day, I was playing with Bob Cross, and made what appeared to me to be a serious blunder. Bob Cross looked at my move and frowned. Then his face brightened and he made the second move of what turned out to be a brilliant combination. He complimented me on seeing this combination, and I took the compliment modestly.

I have always felt guilty about this. I should have spoken up and said it was a blunder but, I didn't. Guilt is a peculiar thing. One does all sorts of things for which one should be guilty but one isn't. But, something like the above haunts one forever.

My office at UCLA was across the hall from the engineering library which I often visited. The engineering library had two librarians. The older one was a prototype of a librarian. The younger one, Barbara Westerveldt was a very lively and intelligent girl with whom I soon became good friends. Her husband John Westerveldt was an artist. Betty Jo and I dined several times at their house.

Some years later, we were visiting a gallery on La Cienega with Elaine Haight, when we saw a girl dressed entirely in black, with pan-cake makeup. It was Barbara Westerveldt. I exclaimed at the getup. She said her name was now "Bobo" and that she had become an artist with the ability to paint in all styles.

Through Elaine I met many artists, some good, some bad. I even bought a painting more to help the artist than because of the painting. The painting was full of sexual symbolism and it was a good party game to try and spot them. Eventually, I got tired of this and gave the painting to Elaine. It now hangs in her living room.

Subsequently, Bobo married Tom Runyon. Tom was a very good cook and finally opened a restaurant, The Old Place, at Cornell Corners. Nina and I often eat there.

What was particularly amusing was that Bobo was always a free spirit and a devout Republican.

Then there was the matter of the battery additive. A manufacturer claimed that a powder sprinkled on a battery could prolong the life of the battery. This was tested by the Bureau of Standards and found to be completely worthless. The manufacturer complained to his friend the Secretary of Commerce, who obligingly fired Astin the Director of the Bureau of Standards. The outcry from the scientific and business world was such that he had to rehire him.

However, he retaliated by cutting down on the appropriation for the Bureau. An immediate casualty was the Institute for Numerical Analysis at UCLA. This institute had built up a very good group of mathematicians, such as Astrowski and the Todds.

There were many other scandals with the Eisenhower cabinet. A man who was impeccably honest was Dulles, the Secretary of State. Eisenhower gave him a free hand except for war. Dulles could not invade Cuba or get us into Vietnam. That remained for Kennedy to do.

Now that mathematical research was going well, I decided to spend some time building up our social life. I felt that it was very important that I be well-rounded. I wanted to resist the temptation to do mathematics constantly.

We had a good foundation. There was Ted and Connie Harris. Charlie, who was my dentist, and Shirley Goldstein, and Paul and Anne Brock.

Paul and Anne had gone to high school with me, about two years behind. Paul was on the mathematics team. Then they went to Brooklyn College where both were math majors.

Also, Eddie Kanner and his wife had moved to Los Angeles.

Through Penny Kanner, I met Beverly Sills. She and Penny had started out taking singing lessons at the same time. Penny had decided to pursue an academic career instead. Beverly Sills didn't think much of Mozart because she felt he had not written good parts for women. I listened politely. I didn't feel like telling her that wasn't the way I judged Mozart.

Connie's younger sister, Marlene, had also married a Princeton graduate and Randite, Mel Peisakoff. Obviously, it was felt this was a good breed.

At the time, the Goldsteins lived in Westchester. Charlie was even then a good cook. Often, we would go to their house on a Sunday for a barbeque.

Paul and Anne Brock lived in Pasadena, where Paul had a position with Electro Data. One of the girls that worked for him was Gloria Bullocks, a black girl. She used to amuse herself by going into Bullocks in Pasadena and downtown Los Angeles and saying her uncle owned the store. This never failed to get a reaction from the sales girl.

Paul worked first at Electro Data, then moved to Hughes. He did some interesting things there, including having blueprints drawn by computer. When Paul moved up to Monterey to work on simulation, Alan Rowe took his position at Hughes. That is how I met Helen and Alan Rowe.

I proceeded very slowly and carefully. I have never felt that a person being in the same field or being a relative was sufficient reason for social intercourse.

I had learned from several experiences I could not work on mathematical problems too late. It was impossible to turn my mind off, and I might as well stay up all night. Consequently, I decided on the cut off time of eleven p.m. From eleven to twelve, I would decompress intellectually by reading murder mysteries. My favorites were Dorothy Sayers, Lord Peter Wimsey, Margery Allingham, and Albert Campion. There were many good novels. Indeed, many people felt that some of the best writing of the time was done in this format.

I never thought much of Agatha Christie's detective, Hercules Poirot. On the other hand, her "Miss Marple" series made charming movies. Nina and I saw them all. Margaret Rutherford was typecast as the heroine.

Unfortunately, Dorothy Sayers turned to theology and discontinued the Lord Peter series. Margery Allingham continued writing and had her detective get older with time. When Nina and I travelled, we frequently read her stories. By then, however, my taste had turned to espionage. At that time CIA men were still heroes.

At RAND, I had gotten quite friendly with the PR man, Brownlee Haydon. Often I would drop by his office for a chat.

One day, while chatting with him, the New York PR man, Manny Berlinrut, dropped in. I was struck by the name and asked him if he knew Lou. Indeed he did. His grandfather and Lou's grandfather had come from the same small village in Russia.

Occasionally, I would comment on some bit of nonsense that was put out in a RAND report. He asked why I didn't write a report telling this. I replied that if I spent my time on all the nonsense that came out of RAND, I would never do anything positive.

Also, at RAND, I had started to work with Bob Kalaba, and we often saw him and his wife Wilma.

Frank Haight was spending a year in Los Angeles. He had gone to New Zealand to get away from the United States. He got a job as a consultant at RAND by the simple expedient of asking for it. We got very friendly with him and his wife, Elaine, who gave very interesting parties.

After the year, the Haights went back to New Zealand, where they stayed a few years. Then they came to UCLA where Frank worked on transportation problems.

Bella Shiffman had separated from Max, and come down to Los Angeles to support herself and two children. Although she had a Ph.D. in mathematics from the Courant Institute, she took a job as a supervisor of programmers at Ramo Wooldridge. She got married to a very nice man, Manny Kotkin, and through Bella we met Bob and Shirley Rod and John Richardson.

Bob was a member of YPO, Young Presidents' Organization. He was the president of *Acoustica* and had been written up in *Fortune*.

John tried to hire me at Hughes, thereby raising my salary at RAND.

I didn't think RAND would meet the Hughes offer and on that basis bought a color TV, which was awful at that time. We referred to it as Richardson's folly.

Finally, we decided it would be best if I became a consultant for Hughes, a position I had for about ten years.

In 1957, the Friedlands came to town, Steve and Anne. Betty Jo had known Steve from Borough Park. I knew Steve from Brooklyn College, where he was a physics major.

Steve had a position at Hughes where his first job was to find the effect of radiation on electronic equipment.

I met Will Karush at UCLA once or twice. However, we became friendly when we intersected at Chuck Dolph's house. Chuck Dolph was spending the summer in Los Angeles.

In 1955, Chandrasekhar published his book on radiative transfer. I was curious to see what it contained. From my work at Los Alamos, I knew the equations of radiative transfer were the same as the equations of neutron diffusion. Progress in one area meant progress in the other. My attention was immediately caught by the chapters on the principles of invariants. I grasped the idea of Ambarzumian immediately, with the extensions of Chandrasekhar. My first thought was "that is dynamic programming without optimization."

The first task was to put this on the computer. Ambarzumian and Chandrasekhar didn't have a computer available at the time. It worked beautifully.

I knew that dynamic programming could take problems in the calculus of variations and by introducing suitable variables make them initial value problems. It was clear that Ambarzumian's method could do the same for many parts of mathematical analysis and mathematical physics.

My attention had been attracted to problems of this nature in the course of conversations with Max Shiffman at Stanford. He had told me about Hodge's theory of harmonic integrals and how Lefschetz had advised him to use Fredholm integral equations. Rosenbloom, "Rosie", had shown how the same results could be obtained by initial value methods. Fredholm integral equations have well-known difficulties.

Incidentally, one of the most valuable things that a senior mathematician can do is to guide younger mathematicians into meaningful theory and problems. For example, Weyl suggested to von Neumann that he could handle the ergodic theorem by means of his methods.

The second task was to try the time dependent case. The equation was very complicated, so complicated that even digital computers couldn't handle it well. However, if one took the Laplace transform, the equation simplified considerably, and there was no difficulty in obtaining the computational solution of the transformed equation. It remained to obtain the inverse transform, and that was a well-known difficult matter. However, it was a case of sink or swim. Either we could derive a method for obtaining the inverse transform, or we would have to admit that we could not handle the time dependent case. Fortunately, we found a method which worked. Once we had this method, we applied it to many other problems.

A principal step was to find a name for what we were doing. This was the origin of invariant imbedding. Then we collected our results and published the three books.[8,9,10]

Then, as I said above, it occurred to me that this method could be used for many other processes of mathematical physics and analysis. Ken Cooke, Bob Kalaba, Sherman Lehman, Milt Wing, Sueo Ueno, R. Vasudevan and I systematically did this.

I had noticed that Sueo Ueno had published many papers on radiative transfer using invariant imbedding. Consequently, I invited him to spend some time at RAND working with us.

I met Vasudevan through Alladi Ramakrishnan on one of his trips to the United States. Alladi came to RAND to meet Ted Harris and myself. He was so impressed with RAND that he had Subramaniam, then a powerful minister in India, come to RAND also. Subramaniam was equally impressed with RAND. When he returned to India, he allocated funds to start the Madras Mathematical Institute. Alladi

[8] Bellman, R., R. Kalaba and M. Prestrud, *Invariant Imbedding and Radiative Transfer in Slabs of Finite Thickness* (American Elsevier Publishing Company, Inc., New York, 1963).

[9] Bellman, R., H. Kagiwada, R. Kalaba and M. Prestrud, *Invariant Imbedding and Time-Dependent Processes* (American Elsevier Publishing Company, Inc., New York, 1964).

[10] Bellman, R., R. Kalaba and J. Lockett, *Numerical Inversion of the Laplace Transform* (American Elsevier Publishing Company, Inc., New York, 1966).

became the first director, and some years later, Vasudevan became a professor there.

At the time, Vasudevan was studying theoretical physics in San Diego. He came up to Los Angeles to visit me and we became fast friends.

Some years later, Milt Wing and I collected these results in book form.[11]

It was obvious that this method could be used for particle processes. It was not so obvious that the same method could be used for waves. Hence, I was excited by the paper of Bremmer which Bob Kalaba, Milt Wing, R. Vasudevan, and I generalized in many ways.

One point nagged at me however. The Riccati equation played a basic role. In dynamic programming, it is easy to show that the solution of the Riccati equation which occurs, exists for all time or space. It was not so easy in invariant imbedding. How to establish this intuitive result rigorously?

When I was about thirteen, I had gone to many bar mitzvahs of my friends. I went not for religious edification but for the sandwiches. It was the custom after the ceremony to have a party. At the party I could eat several sandwiches and stuff about six in my pockets. This was easy to do because the sandwiches were neatly wrapped. Around that time, in 1955 or so, I went to three more bar mitzvahs. The first was the Harris bar mitzvah. I was rather amused by the comment that young Harris obeyed the religious laws because it pleased God. It seemed to me that God had many more important things to do.

Then, I went to the Goldstein bar mitzvah, which was held at the synagogue at Sunset and Saltair. Charlie had had great difficulties with his firstborn and his friends came to the bar mitzvah to show their solidarity. About half of the audience was non-Jewish. The rabbi, either because of this, or stupidity, had chosen a text in which the Israelites slaughtered their enemies. The audience got more and more apprehensive expecting armed men to come out of the wings with swords. Finally, I went to the Friedland bar mitzvah. The question of the Riccati equation was bothering me and I settled down for some

[11] Bellman, R. and G.M. Wing, *An Introduction to Invariant Imbedding* (John Wiley & Sons, Inc., New York, 1975).

serious thought. This was a trick that I had learned on the New York subways. They were very noisy, but ideal for reading once one learned to ignore the noise.

Halfway through the bar mitzvah I got the solution: conservation. Not only does this method work in the case of the Riccati equation, but it can be used for many other processes as well.

In dynamic programming, we have a type of approximation, approximation in policy space, which does not exist in classical analysis. Every sequence of decisions corresponds to a function, but not every function corresponds to a sequence of decisions. What makes the method so powerful is that many equations can be considered to arise from a decision process. In invariant imbedding, we have approximation in process space, again a method which does not exist in classical analysis. Every process gives rise to a function but not every function corresponds to a process.

Incidentally, Ray Redheffer discovered the method of invariant imbedding independently. He and his pupil, Wang, did many interesting things.

About that time, I became very interested in the theory of scheduling. The trigger was a postcard from Joel Franklin. He had been on a plane which had encountered some turbulence. To avoid the turbulence, which was uncomfortable for the passengers and dangerous for the plane, the pilot had changed course. Being a mathematician, Joel immediately thought of the problem of tracing a path of shortest length through a finite network. This was the problem he posed to me.

I was not anxious to work on a problem of such obvious combinatorial nature. I couldn't even solve problems involving the drawing of the balls of different colors from an urn. Norman would always get the correct answer but I never could.

However, politeness dictated that I look at the problem. I was delighted to find that a simple dynamic programming argument converted this combinatorial problem into solving a nonlinear equation. Furthermore, simple approximations gave upper and lower bounds, and these approximations had simple interpretations as approximate policies.

At that time, I thought of this as an interesting problem. Soon, I began to realize that this was one of the fundamental problems of mathematics. Indeed, the theory of artificial intelligence can be based on this problem.

I also posed the problem of processing *m* items on *n* machines. There are many applications of this problem to manufacturing, to scheduling of patients through hospitals and to running a computer installation. However, at the moment I wasn't interested in the applications. It seemed like a very attractive problem and I was curious as to what the answer was.

Selmer Johnson found a very elegant solution for the case of two machines. This solution can also be obtained by means of dynamic programming. However, the case of three or more machines seems quite difficult and no solution is known at present. It is quite possible that no solution comparable to that for two machines exist.

Since these are problems involving a finite number of cases, it might be thought that we could use a digital computer to solve these problems by enumeration. This is not the case. Mathematical analysis is definitely required.

To see this, suppose that one case can be examined in a second. A convenient number is 10! equal to 3, 628,800. 20! is at least 10^{10} times as large. In combinatorial problems of this type, it is not at all unusual to meet numbers like 100! or 1000!.

Another convenient number to remember is that a year contains about 3×10^7 seconds. Thus, even if we assume that a case can be looked at in a microsecond, we see that enumeration is not a feasible procedure.

I also got interested in the theory of search. In dynamic programming, one is always obtaining the maximum or minimum of a function. Various elegant results by Selmer Johnson and Oliver Gross may be found in book form.[12]

There is another book devoted to this topic.[13]

[12] Bellman, R. and S. Dreyfus, *Applied Dynamics Programming* (Princeton University Press, Princeton, N.J., 1962).

[13] Stone, L.D., *Theory of Optimal Search* (Academic Press, Inc., New York, 1975).

It is always a thrill to see new domains of pure mathematics emerging. There are tremendous opportunities here, particularly for students trained in topology. When one sees what they do at present, one is reminded of the famous statement by Auntie Mame, "Life is a banquet, and most poor bastards are scrambling for crumbs."

Problems of this type had been worked on before by many mathematicians, Euler, Hamilton, and Steiner, but the systematic study of problems of this type was done at RAND starting in 1948 under the inspiration of von Neumann.

Up at Stanford, I didn't have to worry about muscles. I had a lot to do on the house and on the lawn. In Los Angeles, it was different.

To begin with, I tried volleyball. Once a week, I played with Harvey and another remote cousin. Volleyball is an excellent game, especially when there are only three men on a team. However, it bored me.

Next, I tried bowling. That seemed to be a good game, and I bowled 150 or 160 regularly. My style was a little unorthodox. My footwork was not good and I held the ball with three fingers, one of which was the thumb. That was a little hard on my thumb, but I figured it would get calloused soon.

I joined the RAND bowling league, and soon attracted the attention of Roger Snow, a very good bowler. He corrected my footwork and my grip with the result that could not break 100. I soon gave up the game.

Next, I turned to fencing. I found a fencing studio on Santa Monica Boulevard run by a Hungarian ex-champion with a number of trophies to prove it. He gladdened my heart by asking me whether I wanted to learn real fencing or movie fencing. When he found I was left-handed he said he would make me a champion.

I bought a foil and learned a few positions. However, it took a great deal of time. I complained about this to Pete Stevenson, who had been a sabre champion at Princeton. He said the thing to do was to take a book and read while waiting. However, the time was too much. I kept the foil and practiced the positions, but gave up the lessons.

I decided to concentrate on tennis. On Wilshire Blvd., between 24th and 25th, there is a small park, Douglas Park one-block square. On the California Avenue side are two tennis courts, probably the best tennis courts in the city. I played on them. In the beginning, I played with

RAND consultants such as Dave Widder and Merrill Flood, and singles with John Walsh, another left-hander. On weekends, I played various pickup games. Gradually, I got into a very good group and learned how to play doubles. In the past, I could play singles because my forehand was very strong, but I had no net game. With this group, I learned how to play net.

RAND joined the industrial league, and I played number one singles, and doubles with Ray Fulkerson. At that time Ray was not a strong player. However, he was very enthusiastic about the game and soon became a very strong player indeed.

Every Saturday and Sunday morning I played tennis.

Ray and I would enter the doubles competition in the industrial league every year. We won most of the time, and I have various trophies and ash-trays in my office and around the house.

I avoided controversy. On one hand, I had many things to do; on the other hand there were other people to say the same things, and usually better.

Thus, for example, when Teller came out with "the big hole theory" to show that inspection was useless and above surface testing should continue, I stopped in at Brownlee Haydon's office to tell him about the various errors in Teller's reasoning.

The "big hole" theory was dreamt up by the Latter brothers, and they convinced Teller of its validity.

Brownlee as usual, suggested that I write a report on this. I replied that it wasn't necessary since Hans Bethe would take care of it and in a much better fashion.

Hans Bethe deserves a statue in every public square in every city. He gave up his scientific career to systematically show the mistakes and omissions in Teller's argument. He effectively neutralized Teller.

At this time, above surface testing of atomic weapons are still done. Pauling went around the country talking against this, pointing out that the fallout caused cancer and that about 5,000 deaths occurred each year as a result.

When Pauling spoke in Los Angeles under the auspices of the FAS, Federation of Atomic Scientists, I went to the talk. After the talk, I went up to Pauling and pointed out that a nation that could endure

50,000 deaths a year and about 500,000 injuries from the automobile could easily take another 5,000 for national defense. I didn't think his argument was very convincing.

I pointed out that far more convincing was the economic one based on overkill. Why build more and bigger bombs when we already had enough to destroy the Russians three times over? There were not enough targets to justify any additional stockpiling. Pauling listened intently and when he went to Seattle the next week, gave the overkill argument.

But, I had to speak out when Herman Kahn published his book on thermonuclear war. Like Sir Thomas Moore, I believed that silence denotes assent. Kahn's thesis was that we could absorb a nuclear attack, recover from it in ten years and be stronger than ever. I felt that this was pernicious nonsense. I had seen minor disasters like fires, floods, snow storms, and explosions, and I knew that a major disaster like an atomic war which would kill an estimated fifty million people would destroy our civilization. Furthermore, I did not want to see RAND identified with Kahn's viewpoint. I felt that many things were done at RAND and it was no more reasonable to identify RAND with Kahn's point of view than to do the same for Harvard or Berkeley based on one professor's work.

Brownlee Haydon and Ted Harris wanted me to debate Herman Kahn in RAND. I pointed out since Kahn had published a public book the debate should be held in public. I was willing to challenge any number in the book except the page numbers.

I pointed out that if I were at a university, I would have no compunction about attacking the ideas of a fellow professor.

John Williams said I didn't have a ticket to this ball game. I pointed out since I had been at Los Alamos and worked on the H-bomb I had a lifetime pass.

Gradually, it was realized what a poor job of operations research Herman Kahn's book was and it soon became a curiosity.

The book was a commercial success, selling about 30,000 copies. I saw Herb Bailey some time after, and asked him in view of this why PUP did not publish Kahn's second book, "Thinking about the Unthinkable". He replied that the second book was a rehash of the first and he didn't see any need to publish it. He felt, however, that the matter was an important one that should be discussed and that the first book should have been published.

I fully expected to be fired because of my stand. To my relief, nothing happened.

What made the affair particularly painful was that Herman and I were close friends. I had great respect for his intelligence, particularly for his mathematical ability.

At that time, Betty Jo was very active in the Democratic party in Santa Monica. They were busily choosing a candidate for Congress. I felt that this was a waste of time since Santa Monica was solidly Republican.

At the time, our Congressman was Donald M. Jackson. He did not have a good reputation. Some referred to him as the worst Congressman in the house; some referred to him as the McCarthy of the house. The fact that he was a lobbyist for Trujillo did not help his reputation. The only bill he introduced was to make Prince Michael Romanoff an American citizen. This was quite amusing. "Prince Mike" was a well-known imposter. He claimed to be from the Romanoff family and had taken in a large number of people. An alert reporter from the St. Louis Post Dispatch found that he was actually born outside of St. Louis. I knew the reporter since he and his wife had retired to Santa Monica.

Romanoff like many Hollywood characters opened a restaurant in Beverly Hills, Romanoff's, which did very well for many years.

The prospective candidate that week was Najeeb Halavy, a very attractive personality. Betty Jo persuaded me to come to his talk.

He spoke about many things and then invited questions from the audience. I asked him how he stood on the stockpiling of atomic bombs. Instead of answering the question, he turned to me and said, "Have you ever seen an atomic bomb?"

I decided to teach him a lesson. I said, "Seen them! Hell, I've built them."

That crushed Halavy completely and ended his political aspirations. He left shortly after. As he left, he said bitterly, "Why didn't someone tell me who was in the audience?"

A listener said, "After all, we are only two blocks from RAND."

I had wanted to apply mathematics to cancer since 1948. However, I had no sympathy with simplification of the process to obtain analytic results. As computers became more powerful, I felt that the time was ripe for an attack on biological and medical problems.

The first step was to join forces with someone who understood about these matters. I knew how complicated they were. On one of my trips to New York, I stopped in at Sloan Kettering, SKI, to meet various doctors. The first few I spoke to were not encouraging. They felt that I ought to spend two or three years at SKI to find out what the problems were. Then I met John Jacques. We took to each other immediately. John was a most unusual person, a medical doctor, a researcher in chemotherapy in cancer, and with a good knowledge of mathematics.

The first question was what problem should we investigate. The problem of the action of a chemical on a cell was much too complicated. We decided that we would investigate the time and spatial distribution of a drug. That was difficult enough.

I wanted to investigate this problem for several reasons. To begin with I wanted to see what physiological assumptions were needed. Then, I wanted to see what kind of analysis was required. Then, I wanted to see if the equations we derived could be treated by a digital computer. We tried to make the model very realistic.

I was astonished to find that differential-difference equations had not been treated numerically. The circulation of the blood introduced these equations automatically. In trying to find a way of treating these equations in an efficient manner, I found a good way of handling successive approximations without storage. The basic idea is that one determines the successive approximations simultaneously.

There were practical reasons too. We wanted to study side effects, a major medical problem.

Ideally, one would like to determine all these results experimentally. There are several difficulties. First of all, some experiments cannot be done in the laboratory. Then there is the bugaboo about reproducibility. One is never sure that one is doing the same experiment twice.

It is not ethical to experiment on human beings. If one gets permission from a dying patient, it is very difficult to disentangle the effects of the disease and of the experiment. If one experiments on animals, the results can be 180 degrees out of phase. Animal systems are not human systems.

Finally, we wanted to study the result of using two drugs simultaneously.

For these reasons, a realistic mathematical model is essential.

The next problem was to get support. This was done accidentally. I overheard a conversation about RAND sponsored research, RSR. This was money that RAND had accumulated for support of research which by no stretch of the imagination could be charged to the Air Force and there was considerable stretching of the imagination at RAND. Naturally, no one would touch the money.

This fund was administered by Will Eisner, who was delighted that I wanted some money for this endeavor. He asked how much I wanted. I pulled a figure out of the air, $50,000 a year

John and I had dinner with Will and his wife Betty. Betty was a psychologist doing work with LSD at the VA at Sawtelle. After dinner she described some of her work. She believed in ESP, and felt that she could communicate with her patients by entering their minds. I kept hoping that John would say nothing. Finally, the evening was over.

John and I compared notes. It turned out that he kept hoping that I would say nothing.

We got the money and started our research.

We constructed various models of the distribution of a drug and then wanted to see how the numbers would compare to actual experiments. The computer program was quite complicated. Fortunately, the computer program was written by Bella Shiffman who was very interested in this area. Now that we had money, we could afford to hire her at RAND.

The first run was a fiasco. We were in a quandary. We didn't know whether the model was reasonable, whether the mathematical methods we used to produce numbers were sound, or whether the program was correct. Fortunately, the second run was reasonable. We were on our way.

We did this for two years to convince ourselves that the procedures were sound, and then we got support from the MIH. At that time, it was easy to get money. We got five years support at $100,000 per year.

Now that we had chemotherapy going we wanted to investigate some other fields. Steve Friedland was an expert in nuclear medicine. Through him, we made a number of valuable contacts with the group at Stanford under the direction of Cohn. The effect of radiation on the cell seemed a very promising direction. The more we looked into it, the more complex it became. Work had been done some years before by Arley and Borchsenius, target theory. Here, one didn't know the nature of the targets.

I was not interested in a theory of this type. I wanted to know the physiological mechanism. Reluctantly, I decided not enough was known to justify any further mathematical work.

The work in chemotherapy was quite analytic. Now I wanted to tackle something which was on the opposite end of the scale, psychiatric interviewing. It was clear to me that interviewing could be regarded as a multistage decision process, and I wanted to know what were the state variables and the objectives.

I gave a lecture at a seminar run by Yamamoto at the Country Hospital and met Leonard Kurland that way. Merrill Friend, "Buddy" Friend, was a friend of the Friedlands. He had an ideal name for a psychiatrist and actually got several patients that way. I met with Friend and Kurland once a week to ask them what questions they asked and why.

I had decided that I would concentrate on training. Obviously, I had no desire to alter the habits of an established psychiatrist. Simulation seemed an ideal tool.

In the construction of a simulation, we encountered a very difficult problem, branching. Take the simplest case where there are two possible questions and two possible answers. That yields four possibilities. If we allow ten interchanges there are now more than a million possibilities. A very convenient number to remember is that 2^{10} is equal to 1024. An average 50-minute interview has about 150 interchanges between therapist and patient.

The construction of a simulation is not easy. The questions and answers were patiently typed on cards by Ricky Karush. I tried various procedures and finally found the best one was to spread the cards on the floor and crawl around. My memory came in very handy. Actually,

I have devised a computer program for constructing a simulation like this, which was never used.

This work made it very clear why progress in artificial intelligence was so difficult.

I had a second motivation. I wanted to learn more about psychiatry and psychiatrists. I had always been interested in psychology and I knew a little about psychoanalysis. I had read the works by Freud on humor and slips of the tongue.

Freud also subscribed to the theory put forth by several historians, that the Hebrews had gotten monotheism from Ikhnaton, and that Moses had been a priest of the Ikhnaton persuasion. There is much to substantiate this theory, including the fact that Moses is an Egyptian and not a Hebrew name.

Freud had written a book on this subject, "Moses and Monotheism". The first half of the book is quite interesting. The second half where Freud uses psychoanalysis on Moses is quite unsound I felt. It is a good party game to try and understand Moses or Da Vinci, but few of us know enough about the surrounding culture to do a sound job. It is hard enough to understand the actions and motives of contemporary Americans from a different part of the country.

I had been interested in neurophysiology since the work of Lou on piknolepsy. Now that computers were available it was possible to test large networks. I had many conversations with Don Perkel about this. With the aid of the RSR money he was able to come to RAND and do that work full time. Subsequently, he went to Stanford, where he is now.

Some time after this work had begun, I was approached by doctors Selvester and Collier in connection with the use of leads for heart analysis. That aroused my interest in identification. Not only was there the medical problem but the general question as well: How did one determine the various parameters that one used?

At first, to answer this question, we used a variant of the Newton-Raphson method. This procedure could be made rigorous if the initial guess was good enough. However, I was not satisfied with this. It seemed quite circular to me. Often the objective of an investigation was to obtain an approximate value for a parameter. If we could start sufficiently close, there was no need for any further investigation.

Fortunately, after worrying about this question for several years, I devised a better procedure.

One of my objectives was to find out what else was done in this field. I would peruse the journals and if there was anything interesting done, I would call up the person and invite them out. In this way I met Fred Grodins and Homer Warner. Fred had done some very good work applying control theory to the study of the respiratory system. Homer was interested in the use of the computer for medical data.

I had discovered a very simple way of doing research. All that was necessary to do was to take a significant process and ask obvious questions. For example, I wanted to know what to formulate and how to formulate it, once I had the equations it was necessary to analyze the equations, then I wanted to know how to get numbers from the equations, how did I use experiments, what experiments did I plan, how did I generalize? There are many other questions, but it will be clear that there is an endless amount to be done.

My interest in neurophysiology led me to meet Warren McCulloch who was giving a lecture at UCLA. Warren was an unusual man, a psychiatrist, a neurophysiologist and an expert on computers. One had to listen very carefully to Warren because he was often fanciful and often with tongue-in-cheek. However, he was well worth listening to because occasionally he had a very profound idea.

For Warren, who could trace his ancestry back to Plymouth Rock on both sides, American history was a very personal matter. Whereas, I would say, "I read," Warren would say, "My great grandmother was talking to Daniel Webster one day," or "I was reading the diary of my granduncle at Valley Forge." One of Warren's granduncles had been the chief lawyer for the Lincoln conspirators. They were the only people in American history who were tried with hoods over their heads at Stanton's Waters.

Whenever an assassin is shot by the police or soldiers one looks for someone high in the government who is behind it all. It is generally agreed by historians that Stanton was the brains behind the Lincoln shooting.

On the other hand, the shooting of Oswald by Jack Ruby,

particularly since Jack Ruby died of cancer in jail, had the Mafia earmarks. The details of the bizarre union between the Mafia, the CIA and Hughes in attempts to assassinate Castro were described in columns by Jack Anderson several years ago.

Warren had a reason for the assassination of Lincoln by Booth which I have seen no other place. According to Warren, Lincoln and Booth were interested in the same actress. Furthermore, Warren claims to have seen a letter from Lincoln to Booth talking about this, and claims that the letter was now in the British Museum for safekeeping. Since Lincoln was a well-known womanizer the story is possible.

I enjoyed my life at RAND because it gave me a chance to investigate many areas. RAND did not suffer from the parochialism which afflicts universities. To quote from a pamphlet, "Careers in Mathematics", which was put out in 1961 by the National Council of Teachers of Mathematics, 1201 Sixteenth St., N.W., Washington, D.C., and the National Academy of Sciences, National Research Council, Washington, D.C.

> "I spent Monday conferring with a RAND colleague and a scientist from the Sloan-Kettering Institute for Cancer Research, New York. We think we can apply mathematics to cancer research. We have found similarities between the biological functions of the human body and the business dealings among groups of industrial companies. By pursuing this analogy mathematically, we hope to learn more about the effects of certain anti-cancer drugs, and to carry out biological experimentation by means of digital computers.
>
> On Tuesday a friend and fellow mathematician from the Los Alamos National Laboratory paid me a visit. We discussed mathematical problems that arise in neutron theory. They will ultimately have a bearing on the design of atomic piles as well as on the construction of nuclear-powered airplanes.
>
> Wednesday I worked with a colleague on some mathematical aspects of launching earth satellites. We know how to get a satellite into orbit, but we don't fully understand the mathematics behind it. These are problems in feedback control.

Thursday I delved into the mathematical theory of how radio and sound waves travel through different media. This work has a direct bearing on radio communication with such remote places as the South Pole and also on getting information from earth satellites and space stations concerning the composition of the atmospheres of Mars and Venus.

Finally, on Friday a group of us spent a few hours discussing the philosophy of problem solving. We are interested in a number of questions. How do you define a mathematical problem? How do you recognize one? How do you formulate it? How do you go about solving it? This is not merely idle speculation. Questions of this sort have a direct bearing upon economic and industrial programs, weapons systems, and even the national budget."

Bob Kalaba and I used to give an extension course at UCLA for two weeks on the application of mathematics to medicine. Theoretically, we were supposed to lecture from eight to five. That seemed much too long to me. I used to start the course at nine-thirty with the coffee break and go until three-thirty. The course was well attended. One of the attendees was Bob Roth who was very interested in neurophysiology since he had had cerebral palsy as an infant.

We had the usual vicissitudes raising Eric and Kirstie and expected them. I got to know the emergency ward at Santa Monica hospital quite well.

I have described above the worst experience we had with Eric when he got bulbar polio. The worst experience with Kirstie was when she wandered away from nursery school. She was then about four and a half. The nursery school was located on the south side of Wilshire around 25th Street. Someone had carelessly left the gate unlatched, and away she went. The women in charge of the nursery school looked for her for an hour without success. Then they called us and the police.

I looked in the vacant lots around, dreading what I might find. Finally, a motorcycle policeman found her on the north side of Wilshire, around 13th Street. Miraculously, she had not been hit by a car or molested. It was a very unpleasant three hours.

I got a case of Scotch and gave it to the sergeant at the Santa Monica police station. I am sure he knew what to do with it.

However, we were not prepared for the asininity of the educational establishment which gave up the alphabet in favor of hieroglyphics. I bought a blackboard, some chalk and an eraser and remedied the situation somewhat. But Eric and Kirstie never learned to spell the words they should have.

After several years, when it became imminent that this technique didn't work it was given up. In the meantime, hundreds of thousands of students had been ruined.

We also had fun. Eric and I had a joint stamp collection and every Saturday we would go to a stamp shop in Hollywood where they had an auction. We would bid on stamps and sometimes we would get what we wanted. Also, we kept a tank of tropical fish. About once a week, we would drive to one of the tropical fish stores on Melrose and buy some exotic fish.

I have always been fond of dogs. We had two boxers and a chihuahua. Most chihuahuas have nasty temperaments. This one, which we called Tom Thumb for obvious reasons, had a very sweet temperament. He made an ideal pet for the children. I soon learned that it was impossible to take two full grown boxers for a walk both at a time.

We built a pool in the back yard and I had a great deal of enjoyment teaching Kirstie and Eric to swim. It was a good case of the blind leading the blind since I never was a good swimmer. In addition, we gave many pool parties.

We also built on a bedroom so that I could use the former bedroom as a study. For some reason or other, we had to get permission from the previous owner to do this. He gave it readily and then went off to Europe. Unfortunately, he had not signed on the dotted line. Some official at Glendale Federal didn't think that this was right. Consequently, we had to track him down in Europe to have him sign to her satisfaction. The small contractor that was building the bedroom could not take this delay. Consequently, he had to take another job meanwhile. The result was that one of the walls of our bedroom was gone for about three months.

I was pretty angry about this and refused to have anything to do with Glendale Federal for years.

I have had both good and bad dealings with banks. The result is that I view them with suspicion.

Kirstie displayed a great deal of artistic talent. She painted well, wrote good poetry and played the violin well. I urged her to submit some of her poetry to magazines, but she was too shy. Her violin teacher wanted her to become a professional violin player, but I thought that was too hard a life, particularly for a woman.

I wanted Eric and Kirstie to know something about religious history, but I didn't want to expose them to organized religion. There was in Santa Monica a very good Unitarian Church, headed by Ernie Pipes, a very nice and very intelligent person. I enrolled them in this. Every Sunday, I took them to Sunday school there. I even gave a guest sermon.

This was also pragmatic. The average person thinks Unitarianism is a branch of Protestantism. That is not the case. Incidentally, the mathematical joke about Unitarians is that they believe there is at most one God.

I wanted Eric and Kirstie to be professionals, since I felt that would guarantee that they would have a productive and lucrative life. The only condition I imposed is that I didn't want either of them to be mathematicians. I felt that comparisons would be invidious.

Kirstie and Eric had good heredity. I have described in Chapter 1 my background. Betty Jo also had a good background. Helen was quite intelligent and her husband had been likewise. Helen's father had been a "trader horn" and had spent a lot of time in Africa. Helen was also quite proud of the fact that two aunts of hers, sisters, had been medical doctors in Poland.

Things worked out very well. Kirstie got interested in neuropsychology and is geting her Ph.D. in San Diego at UCSD; Eric is interested in writing and TV, and is a TV producer in Eugene, Oregon.

When major league baseball came to Los Angeles, Eric and I went to many games. We tried various seats, and finally decided that we had the best view of the field from the bleachers.

One day, I took a visiting Australian to a baseball game. Eric and I had seen many exciting games but as luck would have it, this was the worst game we ever saw. I think there were three infield singles by one side, and two by the other. We endured this dreary game until the final out. Then the Australian arose and said, "This is what killed cricket."

I was always interested in the problems of communication, writing, lecturing and publishing. When I was about thirteen, I was editor of the Boy Scout newspaper. I wrote an article for the high school magazine, and edited the Brooklyn College Math Mirror for two years. I enjoyed writing. This does not mean that writing was an easy task. I read somewhere, if one cannot stand the sight of one's own blood on a page, one should not write. It is always astonishing to me how difficult it is to translate a clear thought into a clear statement.

I was an inveterate letter writer. I wrote to the New York Sun and to PM; when I was in college I wrote several letters to the school newspaper.

I also wrote to various people, and they invariably answered. I tried to do the same.

In college, I forced myself to give lectures. This was quite painful, since I was very shy. I'll never forget my first teaching at Johns Hopkins. When I give a lecture these days, I always think to myself, "You didn't have to accept this invitation, you could have been home comfortably." What comforts me is the knowledge that once I get started things will go well. I have read that many famous actors and actresses have stage fright and have to be pushed on stage.

When I went to New York, I would drop in at McGraw-Hill to see Carl Nagel, and Ken Haddock at Wiley's. When I saw Carl, I usually had lunch with him at the executive dining room on the thirty-third floor at 330 W. 42nd Street. Up that high, the people on the street looked like ants. One day, I asked him why he stayed in New York. He said he had asked the same question of McGraw who had grown up in Arizona. McGraw said, "Arizona is full of nice people who aren't interesting; New York is full of interesting people who aren't very nice. Between the two I would rather take New York."

Ken took me to lunch at the publisher's club. In those days, I drank grasshoppers. Today, a grasshopper would seem much too sweet.

I also went to see Hayward Cirker, the publisher of Dover

Publications. I told him what a wonderful job he was doing in making this material available inexpensively. My book on stability theory was translated into Russian, with several editions. I suggested to McGraw Hill that they could publish a second edition of "Stability Theory" by translated into Russian, with several editions. I suggested to McGraw-out a second edition, and I sold the rights to Dover.

I also went to visit Dennis Flanagan, the publisher of *Scientific American,* and again told him what a good job he was doing in making this material available.

In those days, a propeller plane would take about twelve hours to go east, and about thirteen hours to go west. The planes were about half full, which meant that the stewardesses had lots of time to serve meals. Drinks were free, and a bowl of fruit was available at all times. The airlines made every effort to make flying attractive.

Someone even got the bright idea to write a letter to the wives afterwards. They stopped this in a hurry when they got back letters which said that the wife had never flown.

I had a seat on the first jet plane from Los Angeles. However, a friend who worked in an aircraft factory said it was a good idea never to take a new plane until there were three crashes to eliminate all the bugs. Consequently, for about a year I went east by train. This took two and half days to Chicago, and then one day more to New York. It was very leisurely, I got a roomette, and wrote a book. I would emerge from the roomette only for meals. It was wonderful not to have the interruption of a telephone.

When I went to New York, I would stay with Helen who would act as my secretary during that period. In return, I would take her out to a show in the evening. This caused a bit of a scandal when somebody spotted me with a very attractive woman at my side. Fortunately, Betty Jo knew about this.

I went to New York as often as possible since I wanted to see Sylvia. She was in a hospital at the time, and I knew she didn't have long to live.

In the beginning RAND books were published by McGraw-Hill which had an exclusive contract. Fortunately, these books did not sell well, and McGraw-Hill decided it didn't want an exclusive contract. As soon as I heard about this from John Hogan, I told Herb Bailey. The result was that PUP published many books which came out from RAND.

On one of my trips to New York, I visited Columbia at the invitation of Merrill Flood. I met Lotfi Zadeh and Rudy Kalman. Rudy was working in differential equations. I convinced him that control theory was the natural extension of differential equations and he started to work in control theory.

I now had a very busy time in New York. I saw several publishers. Peter Lax at the Courant Institute, John Jacques at SKI, Lotfi Zadeh at Columbia and Norman and Fay in the evening.

Some years later, Lotfi moved to Berkeley and started his work on fuzzy systems. We had many discussions and I saw the importance of his work immediately. With the aid of fuzzy systems, it was now possible to apply mathematics to social systems and to handle types of uncertainty which escaped classical probability completely.

On my trips to New York City I always made sure that I had some clams. Either I would have them at a seafood bar at McGinnis' or at Grant's. One of the disadvantages of living in Los Angeles is that it is very difficult to get clams. They are flown in from the east but they are not fresh and are very expensive.

I did a lot of travelling at that time, giving talks on dynamic programming, control theory, and computers. It didn't add to my popularity to point out that with the aid of a computer a graduate student could do overnight what a senior professor had tried to do for twenty years. I reflected, however, that I had not started out to win any popularity contest.

Because of Norman and Fay, I picked up the only girl I ever picked up. The story is the following. I was waiting for Norman and Fay in front of the 42nd St. library at five p.m. Suddenly, as is very common in New York in the summer time, there was a torrential downpour. I took refuge with others in the entrance to the 42nd St. library. I started talking to a girl, Ala Botwin, the name is easy to remember since she is related to the former Russian chess champion, Botwinnik. It turned out that her former husband had been a physics major, a pupil of Bethe. She, herself, was a psychiatrist. After waiting half an hour, Fay had a bad habit of always being late, I asked Ala if she wanted to have dinner in some restaurant in Greenwich Village. She agreed, provided there was no hanky-panky. Ala was a very attractive girl, but she did not appeal to me sexually, so I assented readily.

We had dinner together, and spoke about intimate things, the way people do who never expect to see each other again. I had come to realize that I had never loved my mother and she had never loved me. I was curious to hear what theory Ala had for that.

Ala got married again, and moved to San Francisco. I used to call her up from time to time to say hello. However, she had the usual habit of psychiatrists and asked, "Why did you call me?" I got tired of saying that I just wanted to say hello, and I stopped the habit.

One day in 1960, I saw a publisher's representative whom I had never seen before, Richard Jones. He was representing Academic Press, which was trying to build up again. Academic Press had been Academische Verlag. Hitler had confiscated the press and had driven out the owners. Richard Jones and I hit it off immediately and became good friends. I gave him many leads and we often had lunch together.

We went to several parties at his house in Monterey Park and met Welsh separatists there. I said I would join the Welsh separation movement if they would join the movement for the separation of southern California from northern California.

Through Richard Jones, we met the Anangs, George and Polly. George was a librarian at the local library and Polly was a librarian at Cal State. Polly's name was actually Charlene. But, she didn't like that name particularly, and used her maiden name Paulene. This was distorted into "Polly". She was a very good cook of Indonesian food, and we often had some at her house.

Richard Jones wanted me to start a series and a journal.Both were attractive ideas. With the model of Borel, a series of books seemed like an excellent idea. I knew how important it was to make new results available.

The series has been very successful. At the moment of writing, 138 volumes have appeared and 11 more are in production.

As for the journal, I had very definite ideas. I had a number of fights about papers at RAND. There were three difficulties. First of all, I was working in a new field. Secondly, there were the usual difficulties with referees. Thirdly, the RAND imprimatur automatically caused trouble. I am sorry that I didn't keep all the referees' comments. Some of them were helpful, but in general they would make a fine study of psychopathology.

I was determined that if I ran a journal there would be no anonymous referees. If anything was worth saying it should have a name attached to it. In return, the associate editors would have the privilege of sending in a paper directly for publication. However, their name would appear underneath the author's name, reading "submitted by..." I had many dicussions with Alan Liss and Mr. Jacoby about this. They, naturally, were dubious about a departure from the ordinary format. However, I made it clear that this was my condition for becoming editor.

It remained to find a name for the new journal. I chose, "Journal of Mathematical Analysis and Applications", JMAA. It, too, has been very successful. At the moment of writing, it has reached 61 volumes with a high level.

Mr. Jacoby was a charming gentleman of the old school and I greatly enjoyed our discussions. In particular, he showed me some pornographic poetry in Latin that Leibniz had written.

Elsevier, a Dutch company was starting an American branch, American Elsevier, under the direction of Ben Russak. I started another series for American Elsevier since Bob Kalaba and I had several books which we wanted to publish. That made another set of publishers to visit when I went to New York.

RAND had a very liberal travel allowance which I used frequently. I wanted to spread the gospel about dynamic programming and control theory. I felt like St. Paul. I reflected to myself that I had to be both Darwin and Huxley.

On one of my trips, I went to a conference at Purdue. Wiener and I were the principal speakers. Wiener was quite discouraged and wanted to know whether he had really done anything significant. I have always been a great admirer of Wiener and knew his work well. I convinced him that his work was fundamental and that he would be an immortal. During their lifetime, von Neumann had a greater influence.

However, I think that Wiener's work is more important. In 100 years, Wiener's work will be remembered and I don't think von Neumann's will be.

The weather in Lafayette was bad as usual and I wanted to escape. However, I had forgotten to reconfirm my ticket on the feeder airline. It had the name, "Experimental Airline", which was not reassuring. For some reason, no Greyhound bus was available. I decided to rent a car. It cost $60.00, but I was determined to escape from Lafayette.

The driver of the car thought that since I was paying all that money to go to Chicago, he had to drive fast. Since it was only a two-lane road, and wet, fast driving was dangerous, I told him repeatedly that there was no hurry, but he wouldn't believe me. Finally, I just sat in the back seat and hoped.

We got to O'Hare without incident, about two hours early. The plane, however, developed engine trouble and had to stop at Salt Lake City. From Salt Lake City, I took a prop plane at Los Angeles, arriving at four o'clock in the morning.

The mathematical work at RAND made it world famous, and had a tremendous influence on research in this country and abroad. Ironically, there is no longer a mathematics division at RAND.

CHAPTER 14

DIVORCE AND REMARRIAGE

In 1957, Betty Jo got a ruptured disk from a seat-belt. We visited a number of Los Angeles doctors without success. Finally, we decided to go to the Mayo clinic. Before we went, we were persuaded to see Emil Seletz, a neurosurgeon, who had done some remarkable things. I was quite belligerent when I saw him. I told him that we were on our way to the Mayo clinic and that he had fifteen minutes to convince me that this visit was not a waste of time. Emil was delighted. A great deal of his surgery was correcting the mistakes of other surgeons. He, also, did not have a high opinion of Los Angeles doctors. A few minutes conversation with him showed me that he was an extraordinary person and a quite gifted doctor.

He shared an office with his sister, Rachel, a proctologist. As a result, they had various names, "Odds and Ends", "Nuts and Butts", "Rears and Queers". She, also, was a gifted surgeon and a fine doctor.

Emil was very reluctant to operate. He kept Betty Jo in the hospital for some time. Hospital again! My ability as a short order cook came in handy. Every evening, I would make dinner for Eric and Kirstie and then visit Betty Jo at Cedars of Lebanon Hospital. Occasionally, Anne Friedland and Ricky Karush would make a dish for dinner so that I didn't have to cook. When I felt lazy, we would have TV dinners.

In the morning, Ella Mae would make breakfast and send the children off to school.

Finally, after several months, Emil operated. The operation was a success. Unfortunately, several months later, Betty Jo was on a bus which hit a curb to avoid another car. This gave her another ruptured disk. Again, Emil put her in the hospital. This time, he clipped a nerve so that she would not feel any pain. Again, the operation was a success.

Emil was also a brilliant sculptor. He had been born on Lincoln's birthday and made many busts of Lincoln.

As I have said above, I was fortunate enough to get in to a good tennis group. As a result, my game got very much better. Finally, I decided to try the California big games. This involved a hard serve, which usually was an ace. If the serve was lobbed back, an overhead smash put the ball away. It was not difficult for me to do this, since I am about 6 feet 1 inch and have long arms. When one adds to this, the length of the racket, a simple geometrical calculation shows that a hard serve is quite simple. For several weeks I had a great deal of fun. Then I pulled a back muscle.

I patiently waited for the pain to subside. Instead, it got worse and worse. At length, I could not sit up straight and had to drive sitting on one side.

Finally, when I was convinced I was dying of back cancer, I went to see Emil. He put my arm behind my back and had me feel the muscle spasm. All he said was, "You are not eighteen any more."

From that point on I used a moderate serve well placed.

I needed money because of Betty Jo's illness. Charlie Goldstein introduced me to a group of professional people who played poker. Charlie was an enthusiastic player.

I had been a minor professional gambler. I don't indulge in card games anymore, but from the time I was about sixteen on, any time I needed money, either for social or more serious purposes such as paying medical bills, I used to look around for a congenial group of people who could afford to lose and play poker with them. The easiest way to win money in Los Angeles is to play poker with doctors. Without any difficulty, one can average about $500 or $1,000 a week. The underlying reason is quite simple. It is not that these people are stupid, quite the contrary. It is just that they have very responsible jobs during the day, requiring the utmost care and concentration. Consequently, when they play cards at night, they relax and gamble in rather a reckless fashion. I, on the other hand, as a mathematician, had no particular responsibilities during the day. When I "gambled", I played to win. To win in a group of the type I described, it is sufficient to play the odds; simple, consistent poker. I could never convince the other players of this. They were firmly convinced that I used formulas from the mathematical theory of games to beat them.

When Helen heard about Betty Jo's injury, she decided to move to Los Angeles so that she could help us with the house and children. It was a great help to have her.

One of the fringe benefits of living in Los Angeles was appearing on TV shows. Up at Stanford, I had appeared on one show, which I have described, and been scared stiff. Down in Los Angeles I appeared on so many that I became blase.

Two shows are particularly amusing. The first was, "Beat the Genius". The "Genius" was a masked man who competed against a panel of five contestants. The genius had a buzzer and each of the contestants had a bell. The master of ceremonies would read a question, and whoever had the answer would ring the buzzer or the bell. If the answer was incorrect, the side was penalized and the other was allowed to answer the question at leisure.

The incentive was a trip to Las Vegas, all expenses paid. There was, however, no danger of this. In the first place, the master of ceremonies asked questions to which he knew the genius had the answer and it was very unlikely that anyone on the panel would know the answer. Secondly, one of the members of the panel was a shill. If the score became uncomfortably close, the shill would give wrong answers to make sure that the panel would lose.

The situation was slightly different when I was one of the panel contestants. In the first place, my head is filled with all kinds of miscellaneous information. I have a very good memory and all kinds of facts just stick in it. Secondly, one of the features of the program were questions on arithmetic. The master of ceremonies would read at a very fast rate a sequence of integers interspersed with pluses and minuses and ask for the total. Nobody on the panel would dare to hazard a guess and the genius considered this his province.

A deep dark secret is that I can do rapid arithmetic. I never advertised this since one of my pet gripes is that the public thinks that the ability to do mathematics is associated with the ability to do arithmetic.

I decided, however, to have some fun. When these questions came up, to the surprise of both the genius and the master of ceremonies, I came up with the answers.

Towards the end, we were actually ahead and the master of ceremonies got a little frantic. The shill gave incorrect answer after incorrect answer, and we managed to lose. That made little difference to me since I didn't want to go to Las Vegas anyway.

After the show, the master of ceremonies asked me if I would fill in for the genius during his vacation.

Then, there was the Joe Pines show. Joe Pines delighted in getting someone who believed in flying saucers, spiritualism, ESP, or some such obsession. Then he would hold them up to ridicule. The audience loved it. Also, he liked to get a pompous member of the middle-class and stick pins in him.

When the producer called me up to invite me on this show he warned me that Joe might push me around. I assured him that there was nothing to fear. At the time, I was working on mathematics in medicine and I thought that the Joe Pines show would reach a good audience.

The person before me on the show believed in flying saucers and Joe had his usual fun with him. During the intermission, Joe and I chatted and I found him a highly intelligent person. He had realized that the audience loved this format and he made a good deal of money out of it.

When we were on the air, he started to attack immediately. First he elicited the information that I was a mathematician. Then, he asked why society wanted mathematicians. I replied that mathematicians were a luxury, not a necessity like him.

Then, he asked me a bit about hospitals. I went into my prepared speech which was to the effect that all the results of modern technology should be used for health. After this talk, he said that now that we were in the hospital what job would there be for him? I replied that there was the squack box, the one that said, "Calling Dr. Kildaire", and that would be his job.

I was not invited back after the commercial.

One day, I was called up by a Mr. Anthony. The name was very familiar. In New York, we used to call him Mr. Agony. He invited me to appear on his radio show. I thought it would be amusing.

What made his radio show interesting was that the listeners could call in immediately with comments of what was said. I thought, it would be amusing to go on the show for half an hour. I ended up being on the show for an hour and a half.

As usual, I spoke for several minutes about the application of modern technology to medicine. Then various questions came in.

I thought that it was worthwhile to point out that it was Kennedy who got us into Vietnam. I mentioned that he had 20,000 troops plus an uncounted number in the Navy before Johnson took office. An irate listener called in to point out that it was only 18,000.

I also sounded off about the man in space program, which I called the moondoggle. There must have been an editorial on this in some newspaper because several listeners called in with the identical question, "Weren't the planets put there by the Creator so that man could walk on them?" There were several things I could have said, but I wanted to be diplomatic, so all I said was, "I have no idea what was in the mind of the Creator."

With my return to California, my allergies started acting up.

When I was up at Stanford, I took it for granted that when I went down to Los Angeles I wouldn't sleep well. However, when I returned north, things returned to normal. When I joined RAND things became different. The situation got worse and worse. I found that doing mathematics was very helpful. When I had an asthma attack, I would turn my mind to mathematics and gradually my breathing would become normal.

If it became too bad, we would go to Cantors's delicatessen on Fairfax to get something to eat. The trip plus the eating made things better.

One evening, about three o'clock in the morning, we were counting out our pennies to see what we could order. This was observed by the man in the next booth who invited us to be his guest. When the waitress came over to take our order she was very rude to him. When she had left we asked him why he endured such treatment. He sighed, and said that she was the niece of the grand duchess. If he treated her as he should have she would complain to the grand duchess. At that time there was a big colony of Russian emigrés in Los Angeles, like Dimitri Tiomkin, and Misha Auer.

Finally, I got status asthmaticus, and I realized something had to be done. I went to the Piness-Bookman Clinic but I didn't have much hope that they could do anything. To my surprise their treatment worked. Thus, since 1955, I have taken hypodermic injections every week.

The allergist and the psychiatrist are constantly at each other's throats. That is unfortunate, since the rest of the medical profession is down on both. The trouble is that nobody knows what the state variables are. Many cases can be given where treatment has been very helpful but nobody knows why.

But, the emotional turmoil of my marriage with Betty Jo was taking its toll. First, I got meniere syndrome. This laid me low for a couple weeks and then I couldn't drive. Fortunately, Bob Kalaba and Ricky Karush drove me around. When I finally returned to RAND I had to hold up my head with my right hand while I wrote with my left.

Then, I became a monster. I was returning by train from one of my trips to New York, when I woke up with a strange feeling. I turned on the light and looked in the mirror. My face was grotesque and my eyes were practically swollen shut. I had giant hives. Fortunately, I had some vaseline so I wouldn't scratch my face.

I went to the hospital in Chicago and got a shot of benadril, which did nothing. The intern wanted to give me cortisone, but I knew enough not to take a drug where the dose was not known.

In the terminal, I bought a pair of dark glasses to the consternation of the girl behind the counter. She practically fainted. It was very interesting to see the reactions of passers-by. Some stared; some averted their eyes.

I decided that I would not eat in the dining room on the train so as not to ruin somebody else's dinner. I had my dinner brought to me by a waiter. When I opened the door he took one look at me and dropped the tray.

When I returned to Los Angeles, I went to my dermatologist, Dr. Hosmer, who gave me a shot of cortisone. He asked me how I had endured the trip. I responded, "Vaseline and whiskey." For several weeks I came into RAND only at night and left messages for my secretary. Finally the condition cleared up.

But, I had to live on cortisone. The emotional turmoil caused ugly red blotches all over my body. I knew it wasn't healthy to live on cortisone but I had no choice.

Finally, in 1962, I left the house. I realized that Betty Jo and I were not good for each other. I knew this action would hurt Eric and Kirstie. As a matter of fact, the reason I had delayed in leaving was because of Betty Jo's accident and because of the children. I felt, however, that the best example I could set for them was that each person should live his own life. I didn't think they would be grateful later if I said that I had sacrificed my life for them.

Being a bachelor again after all this time was an interesting experience. It was nice to come and go as I pleased. However, there were disadvantages. I was used to cooking and shopping. As a matter of fact, I enjoyed shopping.

First of all, I found that I had to be more circumspect. It was alright to flirt when I was married, but when I was single, girls took it seriously. Secondly, I had to make dates. When one is married, one has an automatic date each weekend. This is not the case when one is single, and the weekends come very quickly. If one is not careful, one spends a lonely weekend.

I took advantage of all the time I had to do reading and to improve my chess. I kept to my resolution not to do any mathematical work after eleven p.m. After that time, I would play through famous games and learn various openings. My game improved considerably. A high point was getting a draw with Reshevsky in simultaneous play against sixty people.

I actually had a won game, but when he offered a draw I was so overjoyed that I accepted immediately. I had played badly in the opening and he had gotten careless. I then made a combination which destroyed his position and exposed his king.

The problem of dates disappeared when I started going with Nina. Since she was a working girl, when she made dinner for me, we had a casserole which she could put in the oven in the morning. They were quite tasty, and together with such staples as lamb chops and fish, we did quite well. I have never been a fussy eater, although, I should have have been considering how my mother cooked. My only feeding problem was in getting enough food.

Imagine my surprise to find after we were married that Nina was a gifted and imaginative cook. Only vanity has prevented me from getting overweight.

I noticed Nina in June of 1961, but I thought she was Stuart Dreyfus' girlfriend so I did nothing. She was a very pretty girl with a very good figure. In December of 1961, I found out that I could get acquainted with her without stepping on anybody's toes. It seemed like a safe relationship. Nina had joined the Peace Corps and was going to Liberia in a few months. She had no desire to get married. In addition, there was an eighteen-year difference in our ages and her best friend Mary Jane, her godmother, and her mother were strongly opposed to me. On my part I had no desire to get involved since I was still emotionally upset. After all one does not break up a twenty-one year marriage easily. Naturally, we fell in love. When the divorce from Betty Jo became final, we got married.

Nina bears a strong resemblance to Aphrodite in the famous painting by Botticelli. My private name for this painting is "Venus on the half shell". Most people know the myth of the creation of Aphrodite from the sea-foam. They would be rather shocked if they knew the full myth. We are closer to the primitive than we would like to think. The fairytales collected by the brothers Grimm, aptly named, illustrate that.

Nina also bears a close resemblance to Alice in the well-known illustration of "Alice in Wonderland".

Lewis Carroll (Charles Dodgson) was a professional mathematician who was very interested in logic. Many of the passages in "Alice in Wonderland" and "Through the Looking Glass" can only be understood knowing this fact.

Like "Gulliver's Travels", which has also become a children's book, his books can be read on many levels.

Nina's mother is a professional artist and her father is a professional musician, so we had lots to talk about.

In addition, we were both very much interested in archaeology, classics and history which we discussed at my favorite restaurants, and I was delighted to find that she knew Latin. In addition, we shared a common interest in jazz. Furthermore, we both enjoyed foreign movies. She did not have my taste for Dixieland, but in return she knew far more about jazz than I did and introduced me to the modern jazz quartet. I call it courting music.

Nina was a rarity; she was a native Californian. She was also a tenth-generation American. Indeed, one of her ancestors was Pocahontas. She liked to tell people at parties that she was part Indian.

The state of Virginia had magnanimously passed a law allowing the descendents of Pocahontas to intermarry.

I had corresponded with Wladimir Swarc while he was in Poland. When he came to Los Angeles, at the invitation of George Kosmetzky, he wanted to see me and Andy Vaszonyi. George had been a professor of economics at Harvard, a member of the original brain trust of Kennedy. He had gone into private consulting and made a great deal of money. He had built a fine house in Bel Air which had been completely burnt down in the Bel Air fire. He built a bigger one of which he was very proud.

At his house, he told me he had a treat for me, Commander Walker who was Von Braun's right-hand man. I said, "Oh," politely.

I waited until Commander Walker took off his coat. Then I asked, "Commander Walker, how does it feel to work with a Nazi war criminal?" Von Braun was a war criminal as far as the English were concerned. He had worked at Peenemunde on the V2 for the Nazis. The British had repeatedly bombed Peenemunde since they knew this was the center of research and production of the V2. During one of the bombings, the underground killed the first three men engaged in research. In the darkness, they missed Von Braun who was number four.

Von Braun knew that if he set foot in English soil he would be tried and hanged. Consequently, he was careful not to travel and stayed in Huntsville, Alabama, protected by the Pentagon.

When the whitewash picture, "I Reached for the Stars" was shown in England, public protest was so great that it was withdrawn.

Commander Walker had a strong grievance against Hitler. He felt that Hitler was a poor strategist.

I left Commander Walker sitting between Wladimir Swarc and Andy Vaszonyi, both of whom had dozens of relatives and hundreds of friends killed by the Nazis. We were not invited back.

The marriage ceremony was performed by Eustace Haydon, Brownlee's father. He had been a very famous history of religion professor at the University of Chicago. He was also an ordained Baptist minister as well as a humanist. The marriage was held in the house of John Richardson in Malibu.

Eustace Haydon also married Ralph Day and Henry Miller's youngest daughter, Valentine. Through this connection, I became quite friendly with Henry Miller and we had many interesting discussions. I told him how much I had appreciated his writing while growing up and how much I agreed with his philosophy that one should use one's body the way one wants. Unfortunately, that marriage didn't take. Two years ago, Ralph married a girl, Gail Levy that he had known in high school.

Assimilation is proceeding at a fast pace, despite the efforts of priests, ministers and rabbis. Toleration is doing what persecution never could.

At first, we lived in an apartment at 4th and San Vicente. We constantly looked for a house. For four years we could find nothing. The Sunday before the Saturday when we were leaving for Stockholm, Nina wanted to go looking as usual. I didn't want to because I thought that it was just our luck that we would find something just when we were going away. Sure enough, we found a house we both liked. One of the difficulties that we had was that we had an entirely different taste in houses.

I didn't think it would be possible to buy the house in six days but it was. The house is a one story, rectangular house, which can be described as ranch style. It has a magnificent front yard and back yard, and a swimming pool. The house is divided into three parts. The center part is a large living room ideal for parties. On one side is a kitchen, a bathroom, and two rooms which can be used for bedrooms. On the other side is our bedroom, my den, and two bathrooms. At the end of the house is essentially a separate apartment, a large bedroom, a bathroom, and a large closet. It is a very roomy house.

As soon as I saw the large living room I said, "Parties!" We had some good parties there, including New Year parties. These were enlivened by Elaine taking off her clothes and strolling around. Those who knew her were amused by this and doubly amused to see the shock of other people who didn't know her.

One of the amusing sights was to see a woman who liked to take off her own clothes trying to restrain Elaine.

At parties at her own house, Elaine also liked to take off her clothes.

Then there was the famous party at Shirley's. There is no point in describing this because nobody who was not there would believe what occurred. Even those who were there like myself think of it more of fantasy than reality.

When Nina and I got married, it was necessary to reorganize my social life. Fortunately, most of the friends that we had before were my friends. Only a few people were dropped. This was easily made up by the new people that we met.

At the time that I met Nina, John Richardson was going out with Gloria Stockdale. Although both married other people, Gloria became Nina's best friend.

Gloria had been raised in Mexico City and spoke Spanish fluently. She also spoke German fluently because friends of the family were German. In addition, she had a great gift for small talk. Consequently, we often took her along when we had to entertain foreign visitors.

She would often come up to our apartment on San Vicente and we would sit around and gossip. One night, something that was said triggered an idea. I called up United Airlines and got a passenger agent. I pointed out that United Airlines had half fare for a wife. What about two wives?

The girl on the other end of the line said that was illegal. I was very stern. "Young lady," I said, "I am a Moslem. If I wanted it would be legal to have four wives." She digested this a moment and asked why I wanted to take both of them on a trip. I responded that they were very fond of each other and it would be impossible to leave one of them home.

There was a long silence, and then the official voice broke, she giggled, "Why not take me and leave both of them at home?"

CHAPTER 15

GUILT BY ASSOCIATION – 1954

Up at Stanford, after lunch I had the custom to browse in the bookstore. While doing so, I would scan the headlines. One day my attention was caught by a headline which read, "Army Sergeant Arrested for Espionage".

Stories of that type were quite common. Usually, over a few drinks, someone who had been at Los Alamos showed a photograph standing with one of the A-bombs like a fisherman with a catch. He was then reported to the FBI, slapped on the wrist, and the photograph confiscated.

What was unusual was that this story was in the headlines. I read the full story after purchasing the paper. It seemed that Greenglass, the army sergeant, had taken various secret papers from Fuchs, in the theoretical division, at Los Alamos to his wife in Albuquerque who had then taken them to the Rosenbergs in New York. The communist background of Klaus Fuchs was well known to the British. That is why they would not let him work on radar and had exiled him to New Mexico.

I knew exactly where the papers had changed hands and the name Greenglass was quite familiar to me.

The story is the following. When Betty Jo had gone to Fort Oglethorpe for basic training, our apartment in Albuquerque was vacant. We kept it since the rent was only $30.00 a month and I would go to Albuquerque about once every two weeks. This was well known. Berderson approached me and asked me if I would let Greenglass stay in the apartment. I had met Greenglass several months before. He was not the type of person I would associate with in New York and I saw no reason why I should associate with him in Los Alamos. I told Berderson that Greenglass was persona non grata in my office.

Then, pressure was brought on me. Several people said that I was being anti-Semitic. I replied that I was not being anti-Semitic, merely anti-boor. However, Greenglass' wife was pregnant and I knew full well how difficult it was to get housing in wartime. I figured that Greenglass should be regarded as an ally, like the Russians or Chinese.

Reluctantly, I agree to let them use our apartment for two weeks. When the two-week period was up, they showed no indication of leaving. I told Berderson to tell Greenglass that I would be in Albuquerque next weekend and would dispossess them myself. When I came, Ruth Greenglass was waiting for me. She threw the key in the dirt and stalked away.

That was the last I saw of her and I thought the last of the incident. I waited for a visit from the FBI which was not long in coming. Two young men, one a graduate of CCNY and the other of Harvard appeared at my office. Without preliminaries, one said, "Do you know that Greenglass named you as a candidate for Soviet espionage?"

I was not at all fazed by the question. In the first place, I had not been a Soviet espionage agent. In the second place, I was familiar with the Canadian spy trials in which an innocent man, Israel Halperin, had been put in jail for several months for the same reason. Tucker had worked very hard to establish Halperin's innocence and to provide money for his family.

I told the FBI men the full story. Fortunately, up at Los Alamos, we had had a very close knit group, Norman Greenspan, Murray Peshkin, Benjamin Berderson, Peter Lax, and Milt Wing. All of them substantiated my story, and all knew how I felt about Greenglass. I am sure that the FBI men had asked them first before seeing me.

Then I shifted to the attack. How was it, I wanted to know, that a person of Greenglass' known association with communist groups was at Los Alamos. The FBI men were quite apologetic. It seems that during the war the security at Los Alamos was handled by the Army, not by the FBI.

We ended up on quite a friendly note. The FBI man from Harvard said that he only had to mention Harvard to be considered a flaming radical.

This appeared to close the incident. There was no trouble with my security at RAND and when I went to work on the H-bomb, again this was not mentioned.

I made no secret of the Greenglass affair. Whenever I went to parties, and some Cassandra would say the country was going to the dogs as far as personal liberties were concerned, I would tell the Greenglass story. I pointed out that in some countries, like Russia, I would either be in jail or dead.

After the war, we had a reunion in Peter Lax's parents' apartment in New York. After some preliminary discussion the room divided into two groups over the hypothetical question: If Greenglass had the necessary intelligence should he be admitted to Princeton?

In 1952, the situation was different. An evil man, Joe McCarthy, supported by Cardinal Spellman and Joe Kennedy, was on the rampage. One can count the lives he ruined and the laboratories he destroyed, but it is not possible to count the people who refused to work for the government if security was required. Nor is it possible to estimate the college professors who decided to give "safe courses", and the students who were turned off by that. No enemy agent could have caused so much damage. Why he had so much power, and why he was tolerated for so long, will interest social historians for hundreds of years.

Incidentally, J.F.K. was one of the few senators who did not vote for the censure of McCarthy. He dodged the issue by spending a few days in the hospital claiming his back was acting up.

Ironically, McCarthy who hounded so many homosexuals out of government service and some to suicide was probably a homosexual himself.

Hank Greenspun, the editor of the Las Vegas Sun, published the names and dates of assignations of McCarthy in Chicago hotels and challenged McCarthy to sue him if the information was not correct. Nothing was ever done.

When McCarthy went on his rampage, John Williams had the melancholy task of telling McKinsey, a fine mathematician, that he could not stay at RAND because he had lost his clearance. McKinsey, naturally wanted to know on what grounds. John Williams replied that the grounds were the usual ones, fear of blackmail and emotional instability.

McKinsey was very indignant. There certainly was no fear of blackmail since he had never hidden the fact that he was a homosexual. And as far as emotional instability went, he had lived with the same young man for seven years which was far longer than the average marriage.

McKinsey got a position easily at Stanford. The president of Stanford then was Sterling. When Sterling was head of the Huntington Library, his initials were J.E.W. When he became president of Stanford, the trustees asked him to drop one of the initials. He dropped the E and was known as J.W. Sterling.

Edward R. Murrow performed a great public service by attacking McCarthy on TV. His attacks were very effective. Unknown to him, and to McCarthy, Murrow's chief assistant had been mixed up with the YCL when young. At least ten thousand people knew this. It was certainly worth about 100 thousand or a million dollars to McCarthy to know about this. However, it was a well kept secret.

When TV is attacked by critics, and they have plenty of ammunition, it should be remembered that TV destroyed McCarthy and helped destroy Nixon.

In 1954, I got a letter from the AEC which listed several points. The Greenglass affair, the fact that Betty Jo's younger brother, Robert, had been a communist, and the names I had given the FBI at Princeton, at the time when I was barraged by communist propaganda.

Today, the letter seems absurd. After all, the Greenglass affair had been thoroughly discussed and Betty Jo's younger brother was only thirteen when we got married. But, in those days it was quite a serious charge.

It was interesting to see the reaction of various people at RAND. Some avoided me like the plague; some went out of their way to invite me to parties. I remembered who did what.

I had to make a decision. Should I stand and fight or should I retreat. A prudent thing to do would just have been to have left RAND and joined a university.

In the first place, I am not prudent. In the second place, I was innocent. As a matter of fact, I had always been anti-communist. It reminds me of one of my father's favorite stories. A man was crossing Union Square where a riot was in progress. The police were clubbing the rioters. As the man got closer a policeman started to club him. The man protested, "Don't hit me, I'm an anti-communist." The policeman clubbed him, saying, "I don't care what kind of a communist you are."

The question was how to defend.

First, I decided to be a little prudent. I wanted to sell the house on Bundy so that I would not have to worry about a large mortgage. Someone at RAND told a real estate agent that I was having security troubles and had to sell. When the agent called up, I was ready for him. I told him that it was an exclusive neighborhood and we weren't interested in people who worried about money. I intimated strongly that he must be a very seedy agent to represent such people and then I hung up. He called up my real estate agent and complained bitterly. He said that in thirty years as a real estate agent he had never met anybody so arrogant and obnoxious. Obviously I did not have to sell.

The next day the same agent called up with an offer which was $500 under my price. I decided to put the house on the market for the same price I had paid for it. We accepted the offer and were free of the house. That is how we moved to 728 24th Street. The house there was on the market for $20,000 having just been put up for sale a half hour before. We offered $19,500 which was accepted.

Then, I made sure that I had university jobs to go to. I told the whole story to Dean Boelter at UCLA and had a position in the Department of Engineering waiting for me. Courant came to visit me and assured me that there would always be a place for me at NYU.

This visit by Courant helped greatly in alleviating my mental anguish. I knew he had suffered a far greater ordeal at the hands of the Nazis. He probably came at Peter Lax's urging. Peter had told him the facts of my case.

The visit by Courant was all the kinder since I knew he was still irked over the Siegel incident. Siegel was a skiing companion and an old friend. Courant had had a great deal to do with Siegel's career.

Courant was a rare combination of a fine mathematician and a fine administrator. In addition, he knew how to handle young mathematicians and had helped many of them.

Lefschetz was a fine mathematician but a poor administrator. With the blessing of the University authorities, Tucker handled all the details of the mathematics department.

I was quite friendly with von Neumann at that time. However, he had just become an AEC commissioner and I thought that this contact would embarrass him. Consequently, I avoided him on his visits to RAND.

The first step was to see Uncle Alfred. In his position as top legal officer for civil service, he had been asked by F.D.R. to be the first security board. He handled the first 3,000 cases until it started interfering with his other work. In addition, he got tired of being smeared on the floor of Congress by people like Dies, and seeing headlines in the Washington Times-Herald like "Russian born Alfred Klein clears another communist." He went to the Civil Service Commission and asked that a board be set up.

He was not happy at the current situation. There were no legal guidelines, as there had been for security. He had been asked to testify by Jerry Vorhies, the Congressman that Nixon beat, when hearings on the new loyalty bill were held. He said that the military had had the power for many years and had not abused it. He doubted whether a civilian agency would. Unfortunately, he was wrong. The AEC abused the power repeatedly, and he was very sad about that. Nevertheless, he offered to help me in any way he could.

We felt that a good defense would be a sketch of my background, showing that I was consistently anti-communist.

To begin with, we pointed out that my father and uncle Jack had been in the army in World War I. A cousin of my grandmother, Alvin, had been gassed in World War I. My father had been consistently anti-communist and pro-British. We mentioned his involvement with the American Legion and the Jewish War Veterans.

Arthur, at the age of forty-two, had volunteered for the Air Force in World War II. He had gone through basic training, breaking three ribs and a finger in the process. He was supposed to be a bombardier. Fortunately, when it came time to go overseas they decided he was too old. I say, fortunately, because the casualty rate was about ninety-five percent.

I was never reticent about my opinions, and many people knew how I stood politically.

From thirteen to seventeen, I was a Boy Scout. During that time my main interests were mathematics and athletics.

In college, I wrote to the school newspaper urging the support of France and Britain. This was 1939 during the Russo-Nazi pact and was not the party line. The letter was printed because the editors who were strongly pro-communist, wanted to show what a warmonger I was.

I had a certain amount of difficulty getting a copy of that letter. When I wrote to the Dean asking for a copy, I was informed that copies of the school newspaper were not available. I wrote back explaining why I wanted a copy. The Dean was very nice about it and I received a photostatic copy by return mail.

In Belleville and in Madison, I was too busy to spend my time on political matters. In Princeton, in 1943 I had long discussions with Herb Bailey.

In San Diego, I must have discussed these matters with Glen Camp, but I have no memory of doing so.

At Los Alamos, as I have said above, we had a very close knit group. Milt Wing, Peter Lax, Norman Greenspan, Murray Peshkin, Berderson, all knew my political views.

In Princeton, from 1946 to 1948, I had many discussions with Herb Bailey and Pete Stevenson.

At Stanford, I had long discussions with Bob Weinstock and others.

Down in Los Angeles, I had many discussions with Ernst Straus and others.

All of this was substantiated by various letters. My best friend from the age of thirteen on was Norman Greenspan. Herb Bailey wrote a letter for me and Pete Stevenson testified for me. Al Tucker was willing to but he thought that a letter from him would hurt rather than help. For several years, he had been active on behalf of Israel Halperin who had been falsely accused in Canada.

Milt Wing, and the others wrote letters substantiating my statements. Bob Weinstock wrote a letter telling about the discussions I had with him. When Ernst Straus heard about this, he wrote a letter telling about the discussions I had with him before going to work on the H-bomb.

Ted Harris also testified for me at the hearing. We had had many conversations about my political attitudes and he recounted some of them.

Meanwhile, the military sent me essentially the same letter, and I sent back the same defence. In about a month, the military decided there was nothing to the charges and my top secret clearance held. There I was, top secret from the military, and a security risk as far as the AEC was concerned.

I also answered the charges in the letter from the AEC. I gave again the details of the Greenglass affair and pointed out that all the statements could easily be checked. I pointed out that Robert Kates, Betty Jo's younger brother, was thirteen when we got married.

Those were dangerous times. Everyone who wrote a letter was well aware of the danger. They felt, like I did, that it was a time to stand up and be counted.

The hearing was held in downtown Los Angeles. There were three civilian members and an observer from the AEC from San Francisco.

At the very beginning, the board said that I shouldn't waste any time over the Greenglass affair. It had been thoroughly examined.

They wanted to know how close my association was with Robert Kates. I pointed out that I had not seen much of him during the war. After the war, he had spent a week at our house in Stanford. Both Betty Jo and I had long discussions with him about his political attitude. When we saw it was a waste of time, we decided to have nothing further to do with him. It should be pointed out that several years later he changed his attitudes and returned to school. He got his Ph.D. and is now a professor of geography, a member of the National Academy of Sciences.

One of the board members asked me how long I had had the letter from Brooklyn College in my possession. I told him the difficulty I had in getting it.

The observer from San Francisco was very helpful. Time and time again, he asked questions which gave me a chance to show my attitudes. In addition, he had a copy of a letter to PM which I had forgotten about. Again, this was an anti-communist stand.

Eddie Kanner testified about my Boy Scout days. In addition he testified how at parties I would cite the Greenglass affair as an example of how an innocent person was still judged innocent in this country. Pete Stevenson testified about the many discussions with me at Princeton and up at Stanford.

The hearing ended on a friendly note. One of the board members was an engineer who wanted to know about dynamic programming.

The San Francisco agency was going to clear me. About twenty-four hours before the letter was sent out, my case was transferred to Albuquerque, and the AEC there judged that the letter was correct. I was not surprised, since I had expected all along that I would be found guilty. However, I appealed. Dick Best, the security man at RAND, tried to cheer me up, but I asked him to find one case where an appeal had been granted. He was unable to.

The summer meeting of the American Mathematical Society was in Laramie, Wyoming. I had been invited to give an hour talk there on dynamic programming. I thought it would be a pleasant drive. That was the first time I was in Laramie. The second time was ten years later when I got the Norbert Wiener award for applied mathematics. When I returned, I found, much to my surprise, that my appeal had been granted.

The first thing I wanted to do was to visit Los Alamos. There, I found that an open tennis tournament was going to be held. Playing tennis at 8,000 feet is quite interesting. It is not at all the tennis at sea level because the air density is so different. Consider the lob. If you allow the ball to bounce it bounces over the fence. Secondly, all ground strokes must have a lot of top spin, otherwise the ball just travels virtually in a straight line. For that reason, every serve is an ace. It was a pleasure to serve at Los Alamos.

They didn't know how to play doubles. I took a C player as a partner and had a great deal of fun poaching. We won the doubles tournament easily. It gave the C player a great thrill. Never again would he rise to such dizzy heights. I also entered the singles. It was quite an effort to play tennis at that altitude. One had to get used to it. I thought that it would be amusing to wear an oxygen pack on my back like an astronaut. I easily got to the finals.

In the finals, I met a really good player. His wife would not allow him to play tennis except for the tournament. I was ahead four to two in the final set when I thought he wanted to win much more than I did. So, I let down and he won.

At the same time that I had trouble with the AEC, many people at RAND also had trouble. Herman Kahn was as thoroughly anti-communist as I was and so was his wife. She was the daughter of a banker from Yonkers. Unfortunately, her two older sisters were both communists. In those days, this was the basis for a charge of guilt by association.

Herman hired Martin Gang, a well-known lawyer who specialized in civil liberties, and was completely exonerated.

However, the episode scarred Herman irretrievably. Before the accusation he had been working on a Ph.D. in theoretical physics under Feynman, and had two books on Monte Carlo methods and operations research. After the accusation, he dropped all of these and published the unfortunate book on thermonuclear war.

Brownlee Haydon had trouble because of his father. One girl at RAND had trouble because her father, forty years before, had joined a burial society which subsequently was taken over by the communists. She became hysterial and saw McCarthyism as a prelude to Hitlerism. Dick Best asked me to talk to her. I am glad to say that she was cleared. One of my friends got into trouble because during the war when asked his religious affiliation he put down "Pagan".

There were amusing notes too. A friend of mine was approached by the FBI who informed him that he had been seen at several communist meetings. He said he had never been a communist. However, the FBI man persisted and gave the dates. My friend searched his memory and finally found the solution. He had been going with a girl at the time who said she would not go to bed with him unless he attended meetings. Naturally, he went. This explanation was completely satisfactory to the FBI man and there was no further trouble.

A final postscript to this sorry mess. In 1964, I received a telephone call from Air Force security near the airport. They wanted to ask me some questions and I could bring a lawyer if I wanted. Everyone else at RAND who had had clearance difficulty with the AEC received the same phone call. Dick Best urged me to go. However, I felt that this was a clear example of double jeopardy, and I ignored the call. About one week later, I got another call.

"Did I wish to co-operate?"

"I was delighted to co-operate," I replied. I was so willing to co-operate I wanted to make sure that they had the correct answers to their questions. "Would they be kind enough to put their questions down on paper so I could give them the precise answers?"

I heard no more from them. They recognized a trap when they saw one. I was prepared to raise holy hell, if I got a letter from them, and they must have known it.

CHAPTER 16

USC 1965

Why did I leave RAND?

At RAND, I had complete freedom to work on important problems with people like Stuart Dreyfus, Bob Kalaba, Vasudevan, Sueo Ueno, John Jacques, and others. I had a good salary, a private secretary, an unlimited travel budget and an expense account. But, I did not have students.

There had been some talk over the years about making RAND into a university, but nothing came of it. I had helped several people in various ways get their Ph.D's; Stuart Dreyfus, Bob Kalaba, Masanao Aoki, Dick Beckwith, Dave Adorno, Marshall Freimer, and others. I had also given lectures at various universities from time to time. If, however, I wanted to carry out this program systematically, I had to go to a university.

I had complete freedom but it wasn't clear how long it would last. The intellectual climate at RAND had changed. If I wanted to continue my research, it became obvious that I would have to go to a university.

I had been offered various university positions in the past. The most attractive was in Denver from the medical school of the University of Colorado. However, I did not want to leave the Los Angeles area. There were several reasons for this. In the first place, there was Eric and Kirstie; secondly, I had many friends in the Los Angeles area; thirdly, I had a very lucrative consulting arrangement with the Hughes Research Laboratory; fourthly, there was the climate. The climate in Los Angeles is not ideal. However, if one goes East in January or February, one soon appreciates it.

The most logical candidate was UCLA where I had many friends and contacts in mathematics, engineering and medicine. I looked into this first. The salary was not high, but that did not concern me. I knew I could make as much money as I wanted by consulting or card playing.

What did concern me was the many rules and regulations. I had been used to living a very unconstrained life and the idea of putting myself into a cage did not seem attractive.

I didn't think there were any possibilities at USC, but to be thorough, I decided to look into it. I called up Al Whiteman, who was equally pessimistic about the chances. However, he got in touch with Zohrab Kaprielian, who was then chairman of the department of electrical engineering. Kaprielian had remarkable administrative ability and a keen judgment of people. I had met him several years before when I gave a talk at USC. He was then Topping's right-hand man in the administration of the university.

Kaprielian made an appointment with the dean of the medical school, Roger Egeberg.

The day of the appointment, there was a torrential downpour. I was not anxious to go from RAND to USC and then to the medical school in that weather. USC is about fifteen miles from RAND in south central Los Angeles. It is bounded by Jefferson and Exposition Blvds. on one side, and by Figueroa and Vermont on the other. The medical school is about three miles away, associated with the County Hospital.

Kaprielian called me up and told me the trouble he had gone to in arranging the appointment and how difficult it was to catch Egeberg in town. Reluctantly, I agreed to go.

Egeberg was a huge man with a very salty way of speaking. He was forever apologizing to my secretary for certain expressions. He had been in New Guinea during the war. There, he had a constant fight against various jungle infections, particularly malaria. Often, it was impossible to field a full contingent of soldiers.

While he was carrying on this fight, he got some forms from Washington about VD. In his usual fashion, he scrawled some obscene comments and sent the forms back. The bureaucrat in a comfortable office in the Pentagon wanted him court-martialled. MacArthur, who had a keen sense of humor, saved Egeberg by transferring him to Tokyo.

One day in Tokyo, Egeberg was examining a soldier. In walked the mistress of one of MacArthur's generals who wanted instant attention. Egeberg told her she would have to wait her turn. She complained to the general and Egeberg was in the soup again. To save him this time, MacArthur made him his personal physician, and this is the way he ended the war.

Egeberg also had a fight with the AMA. He believed that everybody was entitled to good medical care.

Yet, despite all this, Egeberg was quite diplomatic. He was Topping's right-hand man in running the medical school.

The interview went very well. Egeberg talked to me for a while and then commented I would solve all their problems in one year. I replied that it would take two years. Then he asked me how much I wanted. Considering that it was the medical school, I replied that $25,000 a year seemed a good figure. This was quite agreeable to Egeberg.

Kaprielian asked me to sit in the anteroom while he spoke to Egeberg. He asked Egeberg whether any committees had to be consulted. Egeberg laughed and said the committees would agree to anything he thought was right. And that is how I became a professor of mathematics, engineering and medicine at USC.

I brought a good group with me. My secretary Jeanette Blood, came as my secretary at USC. My research assistant Ricky Karush, continued in that role. I also had Bob Kalaba, Stan Azen, and various consultants like John Jacques and Fred Grodins.

I had a quite definite program. The first task was to use computers in various parts of the hospital. I did not make the mistake that IBM had made five years before of trying to computerize the hospital at one time.

It has been pointed out by many people that the hospital is the last vestige of feudalism, with the heads of the various departments as feudal barons. They are very jealous of their power, and there is little possibility of their cooperating.

But, it is much more than that. Different doctors want different data. A cardiologist wants to know different things from an orthopedic man; someone doing research on diabetes wants different data than a neurosurgeon. The problem of communicating data is not trivial.

I decided to use the Tom Sawyer approach. I would find one department and show how useful computers were. Fortunately, the head of clinical pharmacology, Bob Maronde was very interested in the use of computers. We decided that the initial use would be quite unsophisticated. All we wanted to do was to inform the doctor what drugs had been given over the last month to the patient.

I was very lucky to get Fleur Mitchell to carry out this work. I had known Fleur since she was about twenty from RAND. At the moment, she was doing some computer programming for an aircraft company. Today she is an expert in the application of computers to medical problems.

Bob Maronde also told me of the magnitude of the side effect problem. I had been aware of the problem in the administration of drugs, but I had not realized the full magnitude. Because there is a time-lag, most physicians are not aware of this either. It is true, fortunately, that the problem has come to be recognized. Mathematically, the side effect problem can be viewed as a control problem; we want to get a therapeutic level at one side, with a nontoxic level elsewhere.

I also was very fortunate to make contact with Roger Jelliffe, a cardiologist, godson of Roger Egeberg, who was interested in determining dosage of digoxin and digitoxin. It turns out that very simple compartmental models can determine a very accurate dosage. I had June Buell work with him in the construction of various models.

There are very interesting mathematical problems connected with compartmental models. However, organs are not symmetrical in shape or homogeneous. This motivated a continuing interest in the solution in partial differential equations over irregular regions. Here dynamic programming and invariant imbedding can be used very successfully. This motivated a book.[1]

The application of dynamic programming to multi-dimensional variational problems raises a number of interesting and novel mathematical problems.

[1] R. Bellman and E. Angel, *Dynamic Programming and Partial Differential Equations,* (Academic Press, Inc., 1972).

In general, one can expect that physiology will have the same influence on mathematics as the physical universe had in the eighteenth century. It will stimulate all kinds of new investigations, and will give rise to many new branches of pure mathematics.

Some years ago, in St. Louis, I gave a talk entitled, "On the Application of Medicine to Mathematics". As may be imagined, I had quite a time keeping that title. All sorts of people wanted to be helpful and invert the words.

Computers are also useful for the monitoring of people with heart trouble. The mathematical problems, however, are considerable. I discussed this question with Julian Haywood, a cardiologist who knows a great deal about computers, and further discussions with him were held with Bob Kalaba and John Richardson.

With Rajko Tomovic I studied the muscular system. We enunciated a principle of maximum autonomy. This was a good example of decentralization. This aroused my interest in the control of large systems.

I next turned my attention to the location of a tumor. Here, a search process is involved. Working with Hiroshi Sugiyama and Bayesteh Kashef, we developed the theory of scan-rescan processes. Here, again, dynamic programming can be used to good avail to reduce the time involved and improve the accuracy. The same method can be used to find other medical abnormalities and there are many industrial and scientific applications.

Once the tumor has been located, there is the question of radiation dosimetry. Here, again, the side effect problem is important. Radiation causes damage both to the tumor and to healthy tissue. It turns out that the same techniques that are used in radiative transfer can be used here. Sueo Ueno, Vasudevan, and I made a number of interesting mathematical investigations.

I had met Hiroshi Sugiyama at UCLA. He had a charming wife, Yoshiko. Bayesteh Kashef was a theoretical physicist. She now has a top position in Iran.

In general, there is a great need for the application of modern physics to medicine. One of the most exciting ideas is that of neutron capture therapy. Suppose that we have a tumor which is so deep it is inoperable. By means of an injection, a suitable radioactive chemical which is selectively absorbed can be administered. Then, appropriate radiation is used. The reaction between the radiation and the radioactive chemical is short range, strong enough to destroy the tumor without damaging the healthy tissue surrounding. This is the basic idea. There are many technical details before the method will work.

The method was tried unsuccessfully several years ago. With modern techniques, it is being tried again by Yori Ueno, a nephew of Sueo Ueno, in Japan.

I also wanted to continue the work on psychiatric simulation. Here, I was fortunate to be able to bring to USC Polly Kell who knew a great deal about psychology and psychiatry. Our results are contained in a book.[2]

Much more has to be done in that area.

Polly had worked at Resthaven, a mental hospital near Chinatown, and knew the director of research Joe Krofchek, quite well. Joe wanted to make Resthaven a model for the whole country. Simulation would play an essential role. Polly and I spent a great deal of time with Joe and Tim Brown. When Joe had time, we would have a good lunch at a nearby restaurant in Chinatown. When he didn't have time, we had a mediocre free lunch at Resthaven.

The work on biostatistics was headed by Stan Azen. Stan had worked for me at RAND as a programmer, and then had gotten his Ph.D. in statistics with Afifi. He and Afifi wrote a modern book on statistics showing how the computer could be used. Many calculations which were once difficult could now be done easily.

That gave an idea of the program in the medical school. I want to emphasize, however, that many leads were pursued before good directions were obtained. This is typical of research. As I have said elsewhere, the secret of success is failure. One had to expect that many promising directions will not pan out.

The support for this program was from the NIH, National Institutes of Health. In 1965, I got two years of support, essentially a continuation of my grant at RAND. In 1967, I got a five-year grant, for $200,000 a year. Indefinite support from the NIH seemed assured.

[2] R. Bellman and C.P. Smith, *Simulation in Human Systems — Decision-Making in Psychotherapy* (John Wiley & Sons, Inc., New York, 1973).

With this money, I was able to pursue a systematic program. In the first place, many first-rate people were able to come for a period of several weeks to several months. Let me mention Lotfi Zadeh, John Jacques, Rutherford Aris, Karl Astrom, Magnus Giertz, Tosio Odanaka, Ichiro Nabeshima, Sunji Osaki, and others. I was also able to support a number of graduate students. Some were good, some weren't. Let me only mention the good ones.

My first graduate student was Austin Esogbue, an Ibo from Nigeria. He worked in operations research in hospitals. Since then he has branched out and is now an expert on this and water resource.

Austin had some very garish costumes. When he came to a party dressed in one of these he put all the women to shame.

Then there was Art Lew and Ed Angel. Art became an expert in computers and is now at the University of Hawaii. Ed worked in dynamic programming and invariant imbedding and is now at the University of Rochester.

Chris Shoemaker and Carlos Ford-Livene worked on problems of pest control. This is a very serious problem, either with or without DDT. I was first made aware of the importance of this problem by Ken Watt. If control is exerted incorrectly, the situation can become worse rather than better.

Carlos decided to get his Ph.D. ten years after his master's. At the time he decided to get his Ph.D., the mathematics department at USC decided to make the standards very much higher. They gave him a written test which I couldn't have passed myself. The result was that they wanted to disqualify him. I pointed out that only I could disqualify a student, and, fortunately, that was a University regulation.

At the time that Chris Shoemaker got her Ph.D., jobs for mathematicians were very hard to get. Most Ph.D.'s were unable to find positions. Chris had three offers. The point is that there is always a job for a person who fills a need. The reason that most of the other Ph.D.'s could not find positions was that there was no need for them. Many professors pay no attention to this. They are rather callous about what happens to their students after they got their degrees. I have always felt that a subject should be studied with a position in mind. There are many interesting areas of mathematics which are over populated. For example, I would not direct a student to analytic number theory.

John Casti worked in invariant imbedding and dynamic programming, and is now spending a year at the Courant Institute.

Peter Poon worked in invariant imbedding and is now at JPL, Jet Propulsion Laboratory.

Andy Yakush is at Loma Linda, interested in the administration of drugs. He is working closely with Roger Jelliffe.

Milan Sedlar went back to Belgrade, where he is now director of a computing laboratory.

Milan is a very strong chess player, far stronger than I am. I enjoyed playing with him. His game would go down and mine would go up. Through him, I met many of the leading chess players. In 1962, the Piatagorsky competition was held in Santa Monica. Milan was a personal friend of the Yugoslavian champion Ivkov. Through Ivkov, we met Larsen and Spassky.

I took them to the Luau and fed them fogcutters. I felt a little guilty about this but knew that chess games were not held until five p.m. Chess masters do not sleep well.

The next day, Larsen was to play Petrosian, then the world champion. Larsen made a queen sacrifice and won brilliantly. I took a small amount of credit for this.

Liljana, Milan's wife, was learning English but did not speak well at the time. Fortunately, Nina's girlhood friend, Donica, came from a Serbian background and spoke rudimentary Serbian. She was able to communicate with Liljana, and thus Liljana was able to work for us in the office. We certainly needed her help.

There were several good journals devoted to theoretical biology and the application of mathematics to medicine. However, with the rapid increase of research in these fields, new journals were needed. Consequently, I started a new journal, *Mathematical Biosciences,* supported by American Elsevier. This was operated like JMAA. In the beginning, Jeanette Blood was editorial assistant. As her administrative chores increased this task was taken over by Polly Kell. I remained as editor for the first twenty-two volumes, then John Jacques became editor.

We also had a weekly seminar, inviting people up and down the coast so that the travel expenses were not too great. Also, we had talks from people who were passing through.

Simultaneously, I started a program in applied mathematics. My aim was to make USC a center of applied mathematics, a Courant Institute west. The two main activities were mathematical physics using invariant imbedding and the numerical solution of functional equations. There was no competition with the Courant Institute since different methods were used.

This motivated differential approximation and the work on splines. Splines could also be used to alleviate the curse of dimensionality.

I gave a two-year cycle of courses, dynamic programming, control theory, invariant imbedding, and the mathematical biosciences. The purpose of these lectures was threefold. In the first place through these lectures these methods were made available to many people. Secondly, I got graduate students this way. Thirdly, I enjoy lecturing. When I lectured I always gave the material from a new point of view. It was seldom that I didn't get several ideas this way.

I don't believe in grades for graduate courses, but the Dean does. It is necessary to give a mid-term and a final grade. Theoretically, one is supposed to give examinations. I would have the students make up their own examinations. Some of them protested. I told them it was good practice for the outside world. If the examination was too easy, they could do very well; if the examination was too hard, they would do very poorly. The final was supposed to be an amplification of the mid-term. A requirement was that every student have access to a computer and numerical results were to be given.

I tried to get computers into the medical education at the medical school. I had many talks with the director of medical education, Abrahamson and with Roger Egeberg and Franz Bauer, the Assistant Dean. It is not easy to introduce a new course in an already overcrowded curriculum. Although I pushed very hard and was on various committees for the introduction of new courses, I never succeeded. A new generation of medical students is coming up and they will automatically use computers.

Every university has a lot of politics, and the same is true of medical schools. Having a joint appointment I had a great deal of opportunity to engage in politics. I avoided this as far as possible. However, I could not avoid it completely. Bruce Waxman at NIH was willing to give me five million dollars worth of computer provided it was IBM. Topping, probably under pressure from the board of trustees, wanted the computer to be Honeywell. This went on for several months and finally I had no computer. I did not want a Honeywell computer since I felt that the students would receive training in a computer which was not very common.

I became interested in the plight of minorities as far as education was concerned. The long term solution is easy. We must improve the schools, the curriculum, the teachers, and supply jobs for the graduates. But we want to do something now. It is imperative to provide jobs for the graduates of today. I felt that computers could do that easily. A graduate could get a job using a computer in various ways. If he or she went on to college, this training in the use of computers would be very valuable.

We called the program, "The Summer Soul" program. It was carried out by my graduate students. The first year the program was administered by Fleur Mitchell. The second year, it was administered by Carlos Ford-Livene.

At RAND, I also got some money from the NSF for training. This time the training was for chairmen of engineering departments. The idea was to make them aware of recent developments. Bob Kalaba and I gave some lectures, and we used various girls at RAND for social purposes.

Everything was going well, then I had a series of setbacks. To begin with Polly Kell and I tried to get support from the NIMH, National Institute of Mental Health. A site committee was sent out and they voted not to support us. This was a minor disappointment since I didn't expect any support in the first place. Then Joe Krofchek got into a disagreement with his board of trustees and resigned his position. That ended the Resthaven plans. But, the most serious of all was that the NIH changed its policy. Henceforth, it would not support large programs. This was a body blow.

However, it was not fatal. It was only a matter of time before the

NCI, National Cancer Institute, supported our program. Sure enough Nixon announced that two billion dollars would be available for cancer research. The experts in the field were to gather in Warrentown, Virginia, a suburb of Washington, to divide up the pie. I was chairman of a committee on the use of mathematical methods. The other members of the committee were, John Jacques, Fred Grodins, Bob Rosen, Monas Berman, and John Hearon.

It did not begin auspiciously. We were to meet in the VIP lounge at the National Airport in Washington, D.C. and be taken by car to Warrentown. When I asked a clerk at Eastern Airlines where the VIP lounge was, I was told it didn't exist anymore. Fortunately, a passerby overheard the conversation and directed me to the VIP lounge.

I was naturally irate, and asked to see the manager. He was equally bland and said the clerk had instructions to tell people that there was no VIP lounge. When I wrote to Eastern Airlines I didn't even receive an answer.

At Warrentown, we had a good time deciding how we would spend the money. Alas, it was a typical Nixon trick. He posed for TV cameras and gave away pens, but not a penny ever appeared.

I tried to get support from the NIH and the NCI without success. Reluctantly, I dismantled the research group I had so painstakingly built up. After the initial disappointment wore off, I figured it was all for the best. The direction of these programs had consumed a great deal of time and effort. It was time to write some books and to strike out in new directions.

To begin with, I wanted to collect some results on artificial intelligence that I had done over the years. These constitute a book.[3]

I had done a great deal of work on decision processes in connection with dynamic programming, both of deterministic type and those involving chance events. I had done some work on learning processes in the early days of RAND, but I got seriously interested when I came across a paper by W.R. Thompson. This was devoted to the interesting question of how one introduces a new drug. I came across the paper in

[3] Bellman, R., *An Introduction to Artificial Intelligence — Can Computers Think?* (Boyd and Fraser Publishing Company, San Francisco, 1978).

the usual way, by accident. I was looking through the *American Journal of Mathematics* for a paper on analytic number theory when I spotted this. Since the title was "A Problem of Apportionment", I was curious to see what anybody was writing on that in 1934.

This question leads to a great number of interesting analytic questions and even more, requires a large number of assumptions. I finally decided to treat learning as changing an initial probability distribution on the basis of observation.

My work on consciousness came about in the following way. I was seated at my desk working on something when the phone rang. It was Jerzy Neyman. Would I speak at a forthcoming Berkeley symposium? I agreed and thought no more about it.

When the program came out, I was horrified to see that I was scheduled to speak at a conference on evolution. What did I know about evolution, and how could I say something meaningful?

I had always been interested in consciousness, and always ask myself how far down the phylum consciousness went. It was obvious that dogs were conscious, because one could see them dream. Were lobsters conscious? This was not an idle question in view of the way it was recommended to cook them. I thought long and hard, and finally decided to talk about the evolution of consciousness as a control process for overriding instinct.

The talk was quite successful, and there were many questions. Finally, someone asked how I stood on the Darwin-Wallace theory of evolution. I knew that this theory had several flaws. Probably the most serious is that there has not been sufficient time to explain the great variety of species.

I answered that no one expected one theory to cover all cases. It was remarkable that a theory existed that could explain so much.

In the book I carefully stayed away from creativity. No one understands much about creativity. However, I could not resist putting in a chapter on humor. I had read Aristophanes, Rabelais, Voltaire, Swift, Leacock, and, of course, Mark Twain. In addition, I had read many lesser humorists and much about humor. I did not want to talk about humor in general. What fascinated me was that a new type of humor had emerged, one which could not be found in medieval or classical times. It was based on the Russell theory of types and gave me a chance to say a few words about paradoxes.

If there are paradoxes in mathematics, think of how many paradoxes there must be in ordinary speech. The existence of paradoxes involves logic. This led naturally to the question of local logics. It seems to me that it is no more natural to expect that a universal logic will hold than that a universal geometry holds.

I also had a chapter on communication as a control process. If one balances the cost of transmission with the cost of doing something with the message, one sees that there is no such thing as a perfect message. The "theory of information" where one is only interested in the rate of transmission of messages emerges as a special case.

Then I wanted to collect some results on compartmental models that seemed both interesting and useful. These constitute a book.[4]

With Hiroshi Sugiyama and Bayesteh Kashef, we decided to write up our results on scan-rescan processes. With Vasudevan and Seuo Ueno we are going to write up our results on radiation dosimetry. With Austin Esogbue we are going to present some results on the application of dynamic programming to operations research in hospitals.

I was fortunate enough to join forces with Stanley Lee. He is trained in chemical engineering and has acquired an extensive knowledge of applied mathematics. With him, we are going to investigate the various mathematical problems involved in energy. Different types of energy lead to quite interesting mathematical problems. Thus, for example, coal-gasification leads to highly nonlinear differential equations and many questions of numerical solution. Geothermal energy leads to free boundary problems. Solar energy involves radiative transfer and thus the use of invariant imbedding. Tidal energy involves dynamic programming.

Nuclear energy would appear to be a panacea. However, the question of the disposal of radioactive waste is a serious one.

All uses of energy involve scheduling problems and thus dynamic programming.

[4] Bellman, R., *Mathematical Methods in Medicine* (World Scientific Publishing Company, Singapore, 1983).

Another direction of research is fuzzy systems. This will greatly increase the use of mathematics from the inanimate to the animate. In the past, mathematics has been used for the analysis of physical systems. With fuzzy systems and computer simulation we can study many processes in the social sciences.

There are many fringe benefits to being at USC. To begin with, faculty children go to the University free. Kirstie went to Santa Barbara for one year and then transferred to USC, where she graduated with high honors. At present, she is getting a Ph.D. in San Diego in neurophysiology.

USC is near many fine restaurants. It is very close to Chinatown and to Little Tokyo. Only a few blocks away, there is a Korean neighborhood.

It is not far from USC to Hollywood, which means the Pickwick Bookstore where I love to browse. Also, the University itself has many libraries where one can keep up with literature.

In general, I try to avoid university functions. I am not naturally a hale fellow well met and they impose a strain on me.

In 1967, a conference on control theory was held at USC and a considerable Russian contingent was supposed to come. This included Pontryagin, Gamkrelidze, Mischenko, Mitropolsky, and others. I felt I had to attend. Furthermore, Pontryagin had entertained us in Moscow and we wanted to reciprocate.

One evening, we threw a party for them. The four named above came and a mathematician named Kharaksvili. The reason he came along was that his wife, Victoria, was the daughter of the political boss of Georgia. She wanted to see Disneyland. She made it a condition that Pontryagin and his associates could come if and only if her husband came.

We had invited in addition to other friends Genia D'Arsen. Genia had been born in Leningrad. Her parents were the Mischevskis, a prince and princess. Genia was a countess, but never used the title.

Nina met her through French tutoring, and they soon became good friends. I liked Genia too and we often went out to Scandia because Genia knew the owners. Genia at first had made her living running a dress shop for the movie colony and had many connections there. As a matter of fact, she brought Anne Baxter to this party. This added a touch of glamor and I'm sure the Russian visitors liked that.

Genia spoke fluent Russian of course. When Alex Letov was visiting I introduced him to Genia and they had a very pleasant conversation. At the party, she and Pontryagin hit it off and spent a good deal of time talking.

I decided to have some fun. I introduced Genia to Victoria under Genia's family name. As I had expected, a look of horror crossed Victoria's face. She reacted the way a daughter of a Republican banker would act upon being introduced to a communist. I have told the incident to many Russian visitors and they all enjoyed it.

Ordinarily, Pontryagin travelled with his wife. Unfortunately, at the moment she was ill and had to remain in Moscow. We discussed making a telephone call to Moscow. Pontryagin thought that this would be too difficult, considering the time here and there. We told him that the only time that would be required would be the time in Moscow. To convince him, we placed a call. The connection to Moscow was made almost immediately, and then it took a half hour to locate Pontryagin's wife. He was delighted to talk to her, and it cost us $35, but we felt it was worth it.

I also make it a policy to accept all invitations to speak at USC. Consequently, when Dave Malone, who was the faculty advisor, invited me to speak before the USC chapter of Phi Beta Kappa, I accepted. The title of my talk was the unpronounceable A(B)MCHITKA.

The background is the following. Amchitka is an island in the Aleutians where the AEC decided to do some underground testing. Above surface testing had been banned by a treaty between Russia and the United States when it was found that the fallout did dangerous things. This treaty was ratified despite a tearful plea by Teller before Congress.

The organization of which I am a director, CNR, Committee for Nuclear Responsibility, was opposed to the test. In the first place, we didn't think it necessary. But far more important is the fact that there is a chance of an earthquake.

The energy released by an H-bomb is small compared to an earthquake. However, in an earthquake region everything is very unstable.

The H-bomb might just be the trigger for an earthquake. An earthquake there would produce dangerous tidal waves in California and Japan.

The CNR sued to prevent the test. We didn't expect to win, but we felt that it was necessary to sue. The matter was taken up to the Supreme Court which allowed the test by a vote of five to four. I was surprised by the closeness.

I gave the same talk before an engineering alumni meeting. I thought it was very important that people like this understand our position. A very fine line must be walked. On one hand, it is important to have weapons to deal with Russia. On the other hand, we have many other things to do with money. Consequently, there is no point in having too many weapons.

CHAPTER 17

THE CENTER 1969-75

My first visit to The Center, as the Center for the Study of Democratic Institutions is called, was in November of 1962, the day that Kennedy was shot in Dallas. My talk was scheduled for eleven o'clock and Kennedy was shot at a quarter to eleven. My talk should have been cancelled, but wasn't. I have no memory of what I talked about, nor did Brownlee Haydon who was there that day, and I am sure that the audience has no memory either. We were all busy speculating on the consequence and whether the assassin belonged to the extreme right or the extreme left.

Poor Kennedy! All he wanted to do was to make love to beautiful women but his father wanted him to be president. I like Truman's remark that he wasn't afraid of the Pope but of the pop.

That evening I went to a party. Naturally, the assassination was talked about at great length. I commented that at last we had in Johnson a good president. Several people there were outraged. I pointed out that these were the same people who a few years before had been ardent Stevenson supporters.

I supported Kennedy because I thought it important to beat Nixon. My principal argument was that Stevenson was a loser. In retrospect, I don't think Nixon could have done as much damage as Kennedy did with the Bay of Pigs fiasco, Vietnam, and the man in space. Hindsight is always 20/20.

At the time, I did not want to associate with The Center. I knew what The Center had done in opposing McCarthy. Hutchins had been one of the few who had been willing to attack McCarthy publicly. Naturally, McCarthy retaliated by calling Hutchins and The Center communist. Incidentally, the first senator to attack McCarthy was

Margaret Chase Smith. McCarthy tried to destroy her but without success.

I admired The Center but there were too many people there whose ideas I didn't like, such as Ping Ferry. I liked Ping personally, but our ideas were diametrically opposed.

I did have a warm spot for Ping because he gave me a chance to make a good pun. At one meeting, after I spoke, Ping got up and said, "I listen to the prophets."

I interrupted, saying, "Ping, I listen to the non-profits."

In 1969, I read in the Los Angeles Times that The Center was being reorganized. People like Ping Ferry were out. I wrote to Hutchins, stating that I was interested in questions which he was considering and offered my services. He wrote back, saying that The Center was reconsidering its program and open to new suggestions. He invited me to a three-day conference where such matters were to be discussed.

I accepted the invitation and Nina and I stayed at the Biltmore. Many interesting people were at the conference, Jerry Weisner, the president of MIT, Bertrand de Juvenal, who is a son-in-law of Collette, Kenneth Boulding, Alexander King, Marcia Eliade, and others. First, we listened to the program of The Center and then made suggestions as to what we thought The Center should study. Many suggestions were made. Kenneth Boulding who didn't like Hutchins or The Center suggested that The Center should become a school for five-year olds. Alexander King said why five, why not three?

I suggested that The Center should study the systems of society. It is clear that such a study is needed.

The mathematician has much to offer to the study of our culture. Some typical questions are:

What different kinds of systems are there?

What are the objectives of these systems?

What kinds of interactions between systems are there?

How does one describe these systems analytically?

What decisions are made in each system and who makes them?

What data are available to the decision makers?

What control mechanisms exist, and who exerts them?

What analytic tools are available for treating these questions?

One could continue with a number of other questions. I think it is clear that this is a fruitful field for mathematical investigation.

The historian, sociologist, psychologist and many others, have made great contributions to the analysis of the American society. I feel strongly that the mathematician has much to offer. He can tell what system exists, what methods are used to operate these systems, what control mechanisms are used, what the flow of information is, the interaction between various systems, and the objectives.

As a result of the meeting, various people who attended were invited to be associates of The Center. I was among those.

The Center is located a few miles east of Santa Barbara. Santa Barbara is a charming city about ninety-five miles north of Los Angeles, an easy drive. The Center is situated on a large estate. The principal building is rectangular with the entrance at one end, offices along two sides, and a conference room along the fourth. On one side of the conference room is a dining area and a kitchen. On the other side is a projection booth so that the proceedings can be photographed and taped.

When the weather is nice the eating is done right outside the conference room. There is a large pool which has no water, with a wire screen so that no one will fall in.

The building is done in Roman style with a courtyard inside.

The conference room is taken up by a large rectangular table around which the senior fellows sat. This table is about eight feet by thirty feet. At one end sat Hutchins and the speaker. The Center revolves around Hutchins. He is quite tall, about six feet three inches, and very handsome. His training is law and the humanities. He has a prejudice against science, particularly, computers. I spent a great deal of time trying to tell him how computers could be useful in the humanities, but I don't think it took. Harry Ashmore usually sat in a chair to the left of Hutchins. Ashmore's official title was president. The senior fellows occupied the same seats at every meeting. These meetings were from eleven to one. At one o'clock one drank and ate.

On the left hand side sat Rex Tugwell. He had been governor of Puerto Rico and Secretary of Interior under F.D.R. His project was writing a new constitution. I thought this was a waste of time. We can do anything we want with the constitution we have. Furthermore, I told him occasionally that we want inefficiency in our system. My favorite comment was that efficiency was fascism.

The big struggle today is against big government. We want decentralization. The attempts of Nixon to become a dictator show how important it is to have checks and balances.

Elizabeth Mann-Borgese, was one of the two daughters of Thomas Mann. Her main interest was establishing a rule of law in the oceans, about which I will speak more below.

Ritchie Calder was a labor peer. He was originally a journalist.

Frank Kelley was vice president of The Center.

On the right hand side sat Norton Ginsburg and John Cogley together with various research assistants. Norton Ginsburg was a geographer. John Cogley was in charge of the publication program of The Center which was extensive. The Center published a magazine every month, a Center report, and various pamphlets containing interesting talks and discussions.

At the far end of the table sat Harvey Wheeler and John Wilkinson. I usually sat there, except when I was speaking.

Harvey Wheeler was a political scientist interested in the constitutionalization of science. John Wilkinson was a polymath. He had taught chemistry and philosophy. However, his strongest point was philology. He knew all modern languages and ancient ones like Egyptian and Sumarian. He had spent some years in Turkey which gave him an opportunity to become familiar with Anatolian languages.

The main programs of the Center were connected with law, as one would expect knowing Hutchins' interest and background. One of these was concerned with a law of the sea, called "Pacem in Maribus". This was a take off on the famous encyclical of the Pope called "Pacem in Terris". A second was the constitutionalization of science.

The Pacem in Maribus program was under the leadership of Elizabeth Mann-Borgese. The program was important for several reasons. Probably, the most important was that of food supply. The earth is over populated, and a great deal of the food must come from the oceans.

An analysis of beef shows that it is uneconomic, certainly in a hungry world. I think that it takes about eight pounds of cereal to produce one pound of beef. It is clear that our food habits have to change. Already, we are eating more fish. Unfortunately, there is not enough fish. We can remedy this to some extent by eating more shellfish. But, we face the same problem. There is not enough shellfish.

We will certainly have to become more vegetarian. Furthermore, we will have to start eating insects, as is done in many parts of the world. One advantage of this is that it will automatically act as pest control.

We also heard a great deal about the "green revolution". This was a set of techniques for increasing the yield of current crops and adding some others. This program was faulty for several reasons. In the first place, it was merely postponing the problems of over population. In the second place, the new crops were not stable. They are not resistant to various blights, and there was a good chance that the whole crop would be destroyed leaving the native population open to starvation.

The program on constitutionalization of science was headed by Harvey Wheeler. It is clear that we cannot let science go its own way, but it is no easy matter to figure out how to control it.

In this connection, Harvey studied many things. In particular, he had various people write reviews of Skinner's book, "Beyond Dignity". This was a bad book for several reasons. However, it is not easy to point out the flaws in a work. I liked the title of my review, "Pigeons on the Grass, Alas", but the review itself was not satisfying to me. What was necessary was a discussion of mathematical modelling.

The basic idea is quite simple. A model of the process is made, then this model is analyzed mathematically; finally, the results of this analysis are interpreted in connection with the original process. Many notable examples of the success of this method can be given. However, the method must be used carefully.

The model of psychology which Skinner constructed, essentially, a "black box" model, was a good one about fifty years ago. With the increase in knowledge of the components of the "black box", a more sophisticated model should be used. Secondly, it is always dangerous to interpret the results of a simple model for a complex society, and this is what Skinner did.

The same is true about psychiatry. One hundred years ago, when

Freud developed his ideas they were a significant contribution. To use these same models now creates great difficulties.

The Center also ran several large affairs in New York and Los Angeles. This one was devoted to ecology and held at the Beverly Hilton in Los Angeles. Several Senior Fellows, associates, and people interested in the area gave talks. I spoke and all I remember about my talk was that I said that ecology must be a good thing because the DAR was against it. At the speakers' table, I found myself seated next to Eddie Albert. He had a very effective talk pointing out how the use of DDT was making a certain species of bird extinct by destroying their eggs.

I told him how much I had always admired him as an actor, and that the first picture I remembered him in was "Brother Rat". He told me the other "two rats" were Wayne Morris and Ronald Reagan. As a result of this picture he had gotten quite friendly with Reagan.

We continued the conversation and turned to other topics. He told me how a leading conservative had been quite radical in his youth. As a matter of fact he had stayed up with him all night to convince him not to join the communist party. In view of later behavior he now regretted this action.

I wonder how many members of the Republican right wing, for which Reagan is the spokesman, are aware of Reagan's early days.

The first meeting in which Pacem in Maribus would be discussed was held in Malta. Malta had been opened up to the public only a few months before. Prior to that, it was a military base, the unsinkable aircraft carrier. Since we had never been to Malta and since we were very much interested in the topic, we went eagerly.

The meetings were a waste of time. Speaker after speaker gave talks on how wonderful it was to do research on the oceans. I listened with impatience. Finally, I got up, interrupting the proceedings, and said that I had not come 7,000 miles to hear paeans of praise for ocean research. This caused a temporary interruption, but then the meeting went on as planned.

However, as usual, we enjoyed the sights. We went to many local museums, but the highlight was a neolithic shrine. This had been discovered while putting in some gas lines.

The Douglases also attended the meeting. One evening we observed Kathy Douglas dining alone, and we invited her over to our table. She and Nina hit it off and spent a great deal of time together sightseeing.

Fortunately, I could only spend three days at the meetings because I was chairman of a two-week meeting in Dubrovnik.

A second meeting to study the problem of pollution in the Mediterranean was held in Split. I wrote a paper, "Mathematical Methods in the Mediterranean" pointing out that simulation could be used to study this problem effectively. The speeches were excellent, complete with interpreters, but no numbers.

We had, however, an excellent time sightseeing. Bengt Lundholm was also at the meeting and we wandered around Split looking at the old parts. In addition, when the emperor Diocletian retired, he built a palace at Split, formerly called Spalato. This palace is in a good state of preservation.

Milan came down to see us and we had a joyous reunion. At Zagreb, we had a few hours to spend with Vana. She was on her way to India to study Tibetan philosophy. With Bengt, we went to Stockholm after the meeting.

Flying in and out of Malta was nerve-wracking because of the possibility of strikes by both the Italians and the British. When we arrived in Rome on Thursday, I heaved a sigh of relief, only to find that there was no flight that day to Dubrovnik. As usual, the schedule was not to be trusted. I decided the simplest thing to do was to fly to Split, about fifty miles from Dubrovnik, rent a car and drive up the coast. I made all the plans for renting a car in Rome. It was a good plan, except that there are no cars for rent in Split. There was an office, but no cars.

Stymied again! There were, however, taxis. I asked how much they wanted for a ride to Dubrovnik. The price was $60. I used an infallible technique. I took out four $10 bills and showed them. Finally, one taxi cab driver said he would accept the $40. We loaded the luggage in the car. They made one last attempt. They wanted to drive me in one taxi and Nina in another. This attempt was easily repulsed.

We arrived in Dubrovnik without incident after giving the taxicab driver instructions as to how to get into the town and to our hotel.

When we got there, they gave us the worst room in the hotel. Not only was the air conditioning broken, but the room was directly over the entrance. We spent a sleepless night. The next morning, bright and early, I saw the manager. He said nothing could be done since the hotel was filled up.

I went to Rajko Tomavic and told him that if the room were not changed we would take the afternoon plane to Rome. He had a brief conversation with the manager and obviously someone must have moved out in the meanwhile. We were moved to a fine room overlooking the Adriatic.

I greatly enjoyed The Center. The discussions were often stimulating and I met a number of interesting people. If a meeting was two or three days, I would drive up with Nina. At first, we stayed at the Biltmore. Then The Center had a fight with the Biltmore over dress. After that we stayed at various motels.

Two young lawyers, who were attending a conference at the Center had long hair which went over their collars. For this reason, the Biltmore wouldn't let them eat in the dining room.

For the same reason, because of long hair the head of the Greek Orthodox Church, who was attending a conference on religion at the Center, was denied a room at the Biltmore by the manager. As I left, the prelate, a giant of a man, remarked mildly that his predecessor had dressed the same way for over 1,500 years.

I imagine that the manager would have denied a room to Jesus Christ for the same reasons.

One of our friends decided to take his wife for a Sunday drive up the coast and have dinner at a posh restaurant in Santa Barbara. She was wearing a very expensive pants suit. The maitre de at the restaurant was firm but apologetic. She could not dine at the restaurant in pants.

"Very well," she said, and to the amusement of her husband and the consternation of the maitre de, she took off her pants. There was no rule against very short skirts and she was now attired properly for dinner. The offending pants were neatly draped over the front seat of their car.

If it was a one-day meeting, I occasionally drove up with Polly Kell or Anne Friedland. I attended meetings which were of interest to me.

That averaged out to about once every two weeks. My closest connections at The Center were with Harvey Wheeler and John Wilkinson. Occasionally, I would play tennis with Harvey. John had developed the concept of retrospective futurology. Put in simple terms, this means that if one can predict the past one can believe predictions about the future. This involved mathematical models of past societies. Because of John's knowledge of science and philosophy, he understood what computers could do in the social sciences. We spent a great deal of time together discussing these matters.

Finally, I decided to pursue an old dream, the decipherment of Etruscan. With my familiarity with computers and John's knowledge of philology, we made a good team.

In 1975, The Center was reorganized again. Hutchins fired all the senior fellows. Alex Comfort, Harvey Wheeler, and John Wilkinson started a new institute, Institute for Higher Studies, with which I decided to affiliate.

Alex Comfort had become a senior fellow in 1972. The proceeds from his book, "Joys of Sex", helped support The Center.

CHAPTER 18

TRAVELS: STOCKHOLM, PARIS, MOSCOW-LENINGRAD, DUBROVNIK, ROME, WEST BERLIN, LONDON, JAPAN, TAIWAN, NEW ZEALAND, BRAZIL, MEXICO, CANADA

Nina and I travelled extensively, both in United States and abroad. I travelled for three reasons. First, I had new theories and new problems to present. I gave lectures on dynamic programming, invariant imbedding, and the mathematical biosciences. A good idea of what I talked about can be gained from my University of Kentucky lectures.[1]

Secondly, I wanted to find out what was being done elsewhere. Frequently one group in an area didn't know what another group was doing. Often, this cross pollenization was very useful.

Thirdly, I wanted to see how people lived, to observe other cultures, and other artifacts, both in United States and abroad.

I was particularly interested in places where centers of applied mathematics was being formed. For example, Goran Borg in Stockholm, Arthur Beaumont in Waterloo, George Adomian in Atlanta, Milt Wing in Dallas, Marion Moore in Arlington, Bob Stoll in Cleveland, Tosio Kitagawa in Japan and many others. Frequently, Nina and I flew up to San Francisco. I would spend the day at Berkeley with Lotfi and others. Nina would spend the day in San Francisco shopping. At the end of the day, we met in Chinatown and Lotfi usually brought some other people along.

We visited many of the major cities and many of the small cities, such as Manchester, Tennessee, Arlington, Texas, Rochester, Minnesota, Potsdam, New York, Blacksburg, West Virginia and many other cities of that size. Here, we shall only describe our visits to New York City and to Columbia, South Carolina.

[1] R. Bellman, *Some Vistas of Modern Mathematics* (University of Kentucky Press, Lexington, Kentucky, 1968).

We often went to New York, either going or coming from Europe. During the day, I would usually see publishers and Peter Lax at the Courant Institute. Nina would go shopping.

Usually the shopping expeditions were quite successful. She would order several things and have them delivered. Once, she got a dress at Bonwit Teller which was quite defective. She sent it back, with a returned receipt to make sure that the store received it. Nevertheless, in a few weeks she got a bill. She sent them a xerox copy of the receipt to show that she had sent the dress back and it had been received. But, the store was stubborn. The bills kept coming and Nina kept writing. The matter dragged on for months.

Finally, I said I would take care of it. The president of the store was Mildred Tustin, a well-known business woman. I wrote directly to her. I began, "Dear Millie" and recounted some imaginary incidents which had taken place at a party in Beverly Hills. I am sure that this titilated her secretary.

At the end of that letter I mentioned that Nina was having some difficulties and asked that her secretary look into it. Within a week I received a letter from the secretary informing us that Miss Tustin was in Europe and that the matter would be looked into. We received no more bills.

We had our favorite restaurants to go to and would occasionally go down to Greenwich Village to a nightclub. On Saturdays we went to the Metropolitan Museum and other museums such as the Museum of Modern Art and the Guggenheim Museum. Occasionally, we would have lunch at the Metropolitan. This was a very attractive area. The dining area was around a pool which had a fountain and several statues by Milles. Milles had a very interesting style. His statues are suspended by an iron wire through one foot and seem to be standing in air. This gives a wonderful impression of movement and freedom.

The dining area was rectangular with the self-service bar at one end and tables on the other three sides.

Much of what we saw at the Museum of Modern Art I didn't like. However, there was always at least one thing worth seeing. In particular, in the theatre downstairs they showed classic movies. I saw "The Cabinet of Dr. Caligerri" that way.

Also, we saw the exhibition of new musical instruments by Pierre Baschet.

At the Guggenheim Museum, we picked up a reproduction of a picture by Kandinsky for Kirstie. He was one of her favorite painters.

I was not enthusiastic that the Metropolitan Museum had spent five million dollars for a Rembrandt, "I was still contemplating the bust of Homer." I thought that the money could have been better used to subsidize young American artists. I was also quite irked when they hung a large canvas by Jackson Pollock, "the drip and dry man" as I called him. However, I realize how many theses would be written in the future explaining why so many of the American public accepted this nonsense.

Jackson Pollock is a representative of what I call the "slash and burn" school. Many of the members of the school have to paint the way they do because they can't draw. However, this is not uniformly true. For example, Picasso was a master of classical art at twenty-one.

In the evenings, we occasionally went to stage shows. I had a very simple method of getting tickets which usually worked. I would go to the box-office a half hour before show time and ask for cancellations.

If the weather was clement, we walked back to Essex House. If the weather was inclement, we took a taxi. Getting a taxi in New York is not easy. To begin with, there are not enough cabs. Secondly, the natives have an unpleasant habit of shortstopping.

At the airport, the simplest thing to do was to walk from a domestic to a foreign flight.

One evening, this happened several times. I made up my mind it would not happen again. When it was tried, I hit the forearm sharply of the person who was reaching for the door. He got pugnacious and wanted to fight. What was amusing was that he was only about five feet and two inches. I easily held him off with one hand while his wife restrained him. As he went away, I opened the door of the cab only to find another pugnacious five feet and two inches individual. I thought the world had gone mad. However, it was a joke. It was Walter Winchell who had observed the proceedings and decided to tease me.

On one visit to New York, I decided to visit the IBM Research Center at Yorktown Heights. The trip was easy since they sent a car for me and took me back. I gave a talk on the application of dynamic programming to chess and checkers and explained why the ideas of Newell, Simon and Shaw would have great difficulty. I was shown various advances in the use of computers. I was particularly impressed with the light pen. By using this device one could construct circuits from circuit components. It immediately occurred to me that the same method could be useful in philology constructing words from prefixes, stems, and suffixes. Subsequently, I discussed this with John Wilkinson.

On one visit to New York, we ran across Mina Rees at the airport. She was the head of the mathematics branch of ONR, Office of Naval Research, during the war and for several years afterwards. Hitler provided the tremendous spurt in the level of American mathematics and science by driving so many refugees to these shores. Mina Rees provided the money for the support of many of these and for the support for many students that they trained. Many people, like myself, got their Ph. D.s through an ONR grant. Mina Rees is too modest to speak of the great role that she played in raising American mathematics to the level that it is now.

We shared a cab into Manhattan. The taxicab driver, illegally, wanted to charge us each the full fare. We pointed out the regulations to him. We have had trouble with taxicab drivers in New York, Paris, and Kyoto. In general, it is necessary to watch them very carefully.

We spent several days in Columbia, South Carolina, because Western Union wanted to modernize and Tom Jones the president of the University of South Carolina was part of the team.

I was not anxious to be a consultant to Western Union. However, I was interested always in communication and was curious as to how Western Union operated.

This operation was under the leadership of Bernie Weitzer. He had been a pupil of Hal Shapiro who had recommended me. Over a dinner at the Cock and Bull, Bernie described what he wanted to do. I agreed to lend my services.

We met first in New York, to find out how Western Union operated. I was pleasantly surprised to find that John Kemeny and Lotfi were also on the team. John had developed a very simple, useful computer language called BASIC.

In Columbia, we listened to a representative from an operations research company who explained how scanning would allow the customer to write his message in any form. This scanning would automatically determine the state and the city.

In the first place, I didn't believe, the method would work. In the second place, it was against my general principles. I believe strongly that a problem should be prepared for the computer. It is very inefficient to expect the computer to do all the work. I pointed out that companies would be glad to use a standard format in return for quicker service.

After the meeting, we were introduced to the state legislature by Tom Jones. The University is right across the street from the legislature. The House of Representatives stopped their work and the speaker welcomed us. He introduced each person, and then gave a little talk. In the course of the talk, he welcomed us and then looking directly at me and said, "If you get into trouble, we will get you out."

We would not do as much travelling now. It is too expensive and with all the hijacking, too dangerous.

STOCKHOLM

In 1964, I was invited to give lectures at KTH, Konigliches Technische Hochschule, by Goran Borg, three lectures a week for six weeks. I had met Goran while at RAND. We had spent a considerable time in discussion of applied mathematics and the interaction between mathematics and society.

We stayed at the hotel Diplomatt, so called because there are so many embassies there. It also had the name Strandbagen Hotel. At first, I used to take a taxi to KTH, then I discovered it was a pleasant walk, and I walked both ways.

I also gave some lectures on dynamic programming at the Swedish School of Business Economics. Since it was the end of the term, I was invited to the graduation lunch. They have a charming custom. Every member of the class gets up and tells a story, with each one topping the previous. After all the stories, the professor turned to me and asked me to contribute. I had not expected this, but, fortunately, did have a story to tell. Some years before, when I was concerned with the business game I had corresponded with a Professor Frenckner at the same school. We corresponded back and forth and became quite friendly. In one of my letters I mentioned that I had seen the Bergman movie, "Smiles of a Summer Night". Frenckner said that the Bergman movies did not give a true picture of Swedish life, and said that I must not stay away from Stockholm because I thought it was filled with high bosomed bare breasted women. I wrote back that that would not deter me. This story was greeted with a great deal of laughter.

After the laughter died down, the professor got up and said, "I am Frenckner."

We got quite friendly with Frenckner and had dinner at his house several times. He had been on the general staff during the war, and knew a great deal about the relations between Sweden and Germany. Three times it was thought that Sweden would be invaded by the Nazis. But each time, Hitler realized it would cost too many men who were needed on the Russian front. The Swedes were very defensive about the neutrality of Sweden during World War II, and it was hardly possible to have a five-minute conversation with a Swede before he gave some apologies about this neutrality.

Stockholm is a very compact city, and is easy to walk over the entire downtown area. In this way, we got to know the city quite well.

Goran was an excellent host. He took us to many delightful inns around Stockholm, and showed us many features of interest. In particular, we visited the Mittag Leffler Library, a sinecure which was held by Otto Frostman. Thereby hangs a tale.

There is no Nobel prize in mathematics. Niels Bohr had a very simple explanation for this. He said that Mittag Leffler had seduced Nobel's wife. When it was pointed out that Nobel never had married Bohr said, "Never let facts interfere with a good story."

The true story is the following. When Nobel got the idea of giving prizes, he went to Mittag Leffler, the leading man of Swedish science and a very well-known mathematician, to discuss it. Mittag Leffler thought the idea was bad and said so. Nobel went ahead anyway. But he was so incensed at Mittag Leffler's attitude that he wanted to make sure that no prize be given for work in theoretical physics because he was afraid that Mittag Leffler would get a prize that way.

For example, Einstein never got the Nobel prize for relativity theory. This injunction has been gradually ignored over time and several theoretical physicists have gotten a Nobel prize.

Goran also took us to Uppsala, the university from which he had graduated. He took us at class reunion time and it was very pleasant. But the most exciting thing was to see the midnight celebration of the arrival of spring. One had the feeling of slipping back several thousand years and seeing a very primitive ritual. Considering the winter in Stockholm, every spring is indeed a miracle.

Goran had two pupils, Magnus Giertz and Karl Astrom. Magnus was interested in classical analysis, and became the chairman of the department after Goran became Rector. Karl became professor of control theory at Lund and is very much interested in the mathematical biosciences. Whenever we visited Stockholm, we would visit Lund to see the Astroms, and then take the hydrofoil to Copenhagen. Either we would spend several days in Copenhagen or take the SAS plane there.

Copenhagen is a charming town and we greatly enjoyed visiting it. It has many fine restaurants, museums, and parks. A principal attraction is Tivoli, an amusement park. This did not impress me greatly since I had grown up next to Coney Island. However, whenever we would visit Copenhagen, we would visit Tivoli.

While in Stockholm I wanted to find out what research was being done at Karolinska. I had a good entry in the form of Aage Moller, who worked on the physiology of the ear. I had him give several lectures on this at USC.

I found that they were doing a great deal as far as computerizing the hospital. These were the days of thalidomide. It is estimated that there are 50,000 thalidomide cases in Europe. The only reason we don't have this curse in this country is the bravery of one woman. She held out against the drug companies and insisted that thalidomide had not been tested sufficiently to be released for general use.

Eighteen that had originally worked on missiles decided to do something for thalidomide victims. They designed a vest and a carbon dioxide container that could be used to activate artificial arms. With the aid of this container, a great many things could be done. I saw a demonstration of this on a five-year old girl who had no arms.

When I went to the demonstration I asked that the address be written down. The taxicab driver looked at the address and then looked at me sadly. The man in the information booth looked at the address and then looked at me sadly. It turned out that the only place that work could be done was at the Alcoholic Institute.

In 1969, Goran invited me to put down the things we had been discussing on the relation between mathematics and society.[2]

We rented some rooms in the country and a car. I drank and drove under the happy impression that the strict Swedish laws did not pertain to foreigners. By the time I found out, I was safely home.

This was the only time we went to Europe in a sensible fashion, by boat. There was no jet lag since the clocks were advanced a little bit everyday. By the time we landed at Le Havre, we were on European time. We took France with Steve and Anne Friedland. Every evening we had dinner together, along with two other couples. One couple, a German engineer and his wife was quite boring. The other couple were from Mississippi and quite interesting. He was a former state senator who had been voted out of office because he was not segregationist enough. His wife was a former state Congresswoman who he had retired by marrying her.

They came from Fayette, Mississippi, the town that Medgar Evers' brother was mayor of. Anne asked Mrs. Cato how she felt having a black mayor. Mrs. Cato replied that if the northern press would leave him alone she was sure he would do a good job.

We stayed a night in Paris and then went on to Oslo to see Sem Jacobson. He was doing some interesting things in neurophysiology, and I had him give a talk on that at USC.

Sem had been in the underground during the war. He owed his survival to a close study of German psychology. For example, when he wanted to travel he always used the VIP car of a German troop train. When the Gestapo wanted to check papers, the Gestapo officer was usually thrown out bodily by an irate general or admiral. After spend-

[2] That was the origin of R. Bellman and G. Borg, *Mathematics, Systems and Society*, FEK — Report No. 2, From the Committee on Research Economics, Swedish Natural Science Research Council (NFR), Berlingska Boktrycheriet, Lund (March 1972).

ing three days in Oslo we went on to Stockholm and the Friedlands went on to Israel.

The Swedes have a serious problem with alcoholism. Consequently, they have very strict laws about drinking and driving. This makes parties very amusing. Really, there are two parties, one for those who drink and one for those who drive.

What is amusing is that the Swedes think that the Finns drink too much.

Except for 1969, we stayed in the center of the city and dined out every night. As a result, we systematically sampled all the restaurants of downtown Stockholm. We probably knew them better than most people who lived in Stockholm. One thing we noticed was that many menus contained eggs Bellman, chicken Bellman, or some other dish with the name Bellman attached. The name Bellman is a very famous name in Sweden like Shakespeare in England or United States. Carl Michael Bellman lived in the eighteenth century and wrote a great deal of music and poetry.

We know from history that Swedish soldiers penetrated very far into Russia, certainly as far as Kiev. Most likely the name Bellman stems from this.

It became very expensive to stay in hotels in Stockholm. Fortunately, one of the professors at KTH, left an apartment house to KTH. One of the apartments in this apartment house is reserved for visitors. We call this place, "The Museum" because of the many objects of art which the professor collected. He travelled widely, and had excellent taste.

Our chief form of amusement was going to movies. Most of the movies were from Hollywood with Swedish subtitles. As usual, those subtitles were not very accurate. Frequently, we were the center of many eyes because we laughed at various statements which were not in the subtitles.

We also did a lot of sightseeing and there is much to see in Stockholm.

To begin with there are many palaces. I saw most of them, and Nina saw all of them. Secondly, there is Old Town. This is one corner of Stockholm which is carefully preserved to be the way it was in the seventeenth century. The outsides of the houses are in the original form, but the insides have been modernized. Old Town has many shops and restaurants. We ate in many of the restaurants and browsed through many of the shops. In one of the shops, we bought a door knocker which adorns our front door. In another shop, we always picked up some ornaments for our Christmas tree.

Then there is Skansen. This is a park which had many features. Most interesting to us were the original dwellings which had been moved from various parts of Sweden. These dwellings covered all periods, and one could get a good idea of Swedish life from them. Some of them were used for movie sets by Bergman.

There are many interesting museums and exhibits in Stockholm. One of the most interesting exhibits is connected with the Vasa. The Vasa was a warship, the pride of the Swedish Navy. In the seventeenth century, it was launched, sailed a few miles and then capsized. The king had wanted the Vasa to be the mightiest warship afloat and had put too many canons on the deck. Disasters like this make archaelogists happy. They preserve many objects which would otherwise have been used and discarded. As a result of the capsizing of the Vasa, we have a good idea of what life was like in the seventeenth century.

Magnus used to say plaintively, "We made a mistake in the seventeenth century, and they won't let us forget it."

Another interesting exhibit was the home of Milles, with a number of his statues in the courtyard. We had first seen his work in the Metropolitan, and wanted very much to see more of it.

We also went to two operas, Aida and La Belle Helene. Goran took us to La Belle Helene, which the members of the opera greatly enjoyed.

We like Stockholm immensely, and whenever we are in Europe, we try to spend a couple of days in Stockholm. I give some lectures at KTH on my latest work and Nina goes shopping. The Swedes manufacture very interesting glassware and import other interesting work from Finland.

On one visit, Magnus challenged me to give a talk on dynamic programming, predestination and free will. This fit in with my recent ideas on artificial intelligence, and I was able to show how the idea of levels enables us to discuss the old philosophical question of predestination versus free will. The idea of level is a transliteration of the theory of types of Russell.

We financed our first trip to Stockholm by buying a Volvo for Nina. This was a gear shift car because Nina knows I don't like to drive those. The engine blew up after 900 miles because a connecting rod was put in backwards. Fortunately, this was covered by the warranty. After we got a new engine, properly installed, the car behaved beautifully.

I have always admired the Scandinavians, witness the names Eric and Kirstie, and association with many Swedes only increase this admiration. They are very civilized people, particularly as far as sex and religion are concerned. However, they are very formal in other ways. I shocked them with the sport coats I wore, and I was forever scandalizing them by taking off my jacket when lecturing. Another thing which shocked them was my attitude towards Kennedy. I pointed out that he had a great European reputation but was a very poor American president.

PARIS

In 1964, I was invited by Electricite de France to give four weeks of lectures on dynamic programming in Paris. I accepted, since that would give us a chance to see Paris.

The students were very competent. However, they would not ask questions. Finally, I interrupted my lecture to ask them why they did not ask questions. They replied that they had been trained not to ask questions.

Sometimes I took a taxi, sometimes the Metro, and sometimes I walked. Occasionally, I was given a lift by Marie-Claude, a student in the class. She had a small car into which I could barely fit. Marie-Claude was a very sweet girl except when she got behind the wheel. Then she became a tigress. She drove in a very reckless fashion, and I fully expected that we would get into an accident. The other drivers would occasionally make unflattering remarks. Then, Marie-Claude would lean her head out of the window and yell, "A Toi."

We stayed at a small hotel, Hotel Aiglon, at 242 Blvd. Raspail. This is quite centrally located.

There were several interesting shops on the Blvd. Raspail and on the side streets, in which we browsed. One of the shops had wood products from Spain. One of these was a reproduction of an eighteenth century canon. I bought it and carried it home on the plane so that it would not be damaged.

The Blvd. Raspail intersects the Blvd. St. Germain, along which there are also many interesting shops. It is a short walk to the Seine. Along both banks of the Seine were bookstalls where one could buy books and maps. Much of this stuff was junk but if one looked long enough, one found something worthwhile. We found a very fine map which we had framed and which now hangs in our living room. I am sorry that we didn't buy more of them. Across the Seine is the Louvre. Further on is the English Tea Room. We had lunch there frequently. This had a good bookstore underneath. The bookstore had a complete selection of Penguin books which are not available in the United States. The Penguin series had many good books on archaeology. We read everything that Leonard Cottrell wrote. A few hundred yards further on, across a dangerous intersection, was the Champs Élysées.

It is quite a job to get fed in Paris. If one goes to a neighborhood restaurant one has to go at the right time or else there is no service. For that reason we appreciated La Coupole, the famous restaurant on the Blvd. St. Germain. La Coupole served continuously, and we often ate there.

One of the advantages of dining in Europe is that one gets used to having wine. Good wine is very expensive.

We saw the standard sights of Paris. The Eiffel Tower, Notre Dame, and various other places.

I resisted going to Napoleon's tomb. I have always had a low opinion of Napoleon. I regard him as a barbarian in a class with Attila of the Hun, Genghis Khan, and Hitler. Finally, I gave in. His tomb, in a military museum, is a fine example of primitive art. However, we should not point any fingers. There are more examples of the primitive in the United States.

For example, practically every daily newspaper has a column on astrology. One of my friends, a fine mathematician, is very much concerned with this nonsense. When he was director of research at a local aircraft company, the space shots he was responsible for were carefully made in accordance with astrological charts.

In 1799, Laplace was invited to give some lectures on probability theory and applications, in Paris. The only restriction was that he was to use no mathematical symbols. These are fine lectures, and in all probability they will never be surpassed. They are available in translation.[3]

They should be read by everyone interested in probability theory, and certainly by everyone working in operations research.

In the foreword, he says that at last we have seen the end of the superstition of astrology. I do not think we will ever see the end of it. People like to believe in magic.

Nina and I are museum buffs. Whenever we travel, we go to the local museums. We have been to all the famous museums, the Metropolitan, the Louvre, the British Museum, the Hermitage, and the Prado. It is a pleasure to go to a museum with Nina because she knows much more about art and sculpture than I do. When we went to the Louvre she gave me some interesting lectures on Greek sculptures.

The Louvre has among its art treasures the famous painting, the Mona Lisa. Naturally, we went to see it. I have never understood why this portrait is famous.

We knew it took weeks to see a museum of any size. Consequently, we made no attempt to see the Louvre on one visit. We frequently went there, and every time we went to Paris we paid a visit to the Louvre.

The Egyptian collection at the Louvre is more extensive than the one at the Metropolitan.

Paris has several smaller museums which we visited. Our favorite was the Musee de Cluny, which had tapestries showing the Virgin and the unicorn. This was a favorite medieval theme.

We wanted to see Versailles, about thirty miles outside of Paris. I rented a car, which unfortunately, was a European car with five gear positions. Nina offered to drive and I should have let her. However, my male chauvinism interfered and I insisted on driving. I was always starting the car in second, and we spent a very unpleasant time put-

[3] Laplace, P. S., *A Philosophical Essay on Probabilities* (Dover Publications, Inc., 1951).

putting along. On the way back, in the Bois de Bologne, I was so busy trying to get the car into the proper gear that I didn't notice a traffic policeman stopping traffic. I drove illegally, practically under his nose. He was delighted at this clear infraction. He came up to the car and said some few unflattering things in French. However, I pretended that I didn't understand French at all, and merely said, "Que?" He tried again. Again, I said, "Que?" Finally, he got exasperated and said, "Allez." Again I said, "Que?" Finally, he started shouting, "Allez, allez," and we drove off. I felt sorry for the next motorist he stopped.

We enjoyed seeing Versailles very much, especially the gardens which have been much copied.

While I gave my lectures Nina went shopping in Paris department stores. She got a very interesting set of plates with astrological designs which we use for dinner parties.

One day, while she was shopping I decided to visit Pigalle, to see if they still sold filthy postcards to tourists. I wandered around, and sure enough there was a "psst". One had to be very careful because de Gaulle had cracked down on pornography. One person asked me if I was interested and then we repaired to a cafe where a confederate showed me some photographs. I commented that these photographs were quite prosaic and that in Los Angeles one could get much more interesting ones.

At the mention of Los Angeles, the man who had first attracted my attention picked up his ears. Did I know Disneyland, he wanted to know. I knew Disneyland very well because every Russian wanted to go there particularly because Khrushchev couldn't.

He had spent his vacation in Los Angeles and had gone to Disneyland many times. We ended up talking about Disneyland for an hour.

In May of 1968, I was invited to spend a month giving some lectures at IRIA and the Sorbonne. IRIA is located in Versailles, in a former NATO camp. Nearby, is Fountainbleau where Rudy Kalman had his establishment. Rudy spent six months at Stanford and six months in Fontainbleau. Pierre Faurre was his assistant. Pierre came to IRIA to listen to my lectures and would give me a lift back to Paris.

This time we stayed at the Hotel Cayre, located at Number 4 Boulevard Raspail. Arrangements had been made for us at a hotel near the Sorbonne, Hotel Select. However, I was very suspicious of any academic arrangement, and preferred to pick my own hotel. This turned out to be quite fortunate. In May of 1968, France was near civil war and there were many demonstrations in Paris. These demonstrations were called "manifestations", and made going to restaurants quite a feat. It was necessary to pick a route which avoided manifestations.

I was afraid with all the troubles in France that there would be no foreign flights so we cut our stay short. However, it was too late. Air France decided to bus the passengers to Leige. It was quite an interesting bus trip and we had a good chance to see the French countryside. When we got to Leige, the bus driver got lost. Several times he had to call Paris to get directions, but got lost each time. Finally, at about three o'clock in the morning, he found the airport. We took a half empty plane to New York.

There were many reasons for the manifestations. One of them was that the French had made a classic mistake. They had educated many people but had no jobs for them.

The second time I saw Versailles it was at the invitation of Marois who headed Institut de la Vie. This was an organizing meeting for a meeting later that year in Bordeau. The theme of the meeting was the impact of computers upon society.

Because of other commitments, I arrived a day late. There were several "ugly" Americans present who wanted to show some movies of space shots. Who had invited them, and why, I don't know. The host, Marois was too polite to put his foot down. When I got there, I said that these movies were completely inappropriate and they were shelved. I had to step on several toes hard and I am sure that I aroused some dislike.

Bordeau is a charming town. The meeting was the usual hot air. But, we enjoyed greatly the farewell dinner which was held in a wine cellar. Indeed, one of the attractions of going to Bordeau was the fine wine we had available very cheaply.

I was chairman of one of the sessions. One of the hard things about being chairman is keeping the speakers within their allotted time. Tukey used to stand up in front of the speaker if he spoke too long.

Another chairman would use an alarm clock. A buzzer would sound about one minute before time, giving the speaker a chance to conclude his talk. If he continued, the alarm would go off making further speech impossible.

I also had a very useful trick when I had to edit proceedings. If the speaker was too dilatory, I would write to him that if I did not get the polished manuscript, I would use the transcript. This threat never failed. Everybody sounds like Eisenhower when he speaks.

There were many people to see in Paris. To begin with there was Claude Berge, who knew Nina because he had spent several months at RAND. Not only was he a fine mathematician, but a well-known modern sculptor. Through him we met Jeanne Le Becque who owned a small antique shop on Rue Jacob. This was between our hotel and the Seine and was within easy walking distance. We would frequently visit her at the end of the day and then go out to a restaurant. She was unmarried and had five older brothers who were unmarried. However, she broke this tradition. She married an American and now lives in Boston.

At IRIA we met Nikita Moiseev, his nickname is Nicky, a mathematician based in Moscow. We became quite friendly with him. He spoke no English, but fluent French. He had learned his French from a French governess.

One evening, we called him up inviting him to dinner, in my halting French. He replied, "Les etudiants." It seems that his hotel was surrounded by students who were in turn surrounded by police. He was effectively quarantined. When we saw him the next day, we asked him why he didn't join in the demonstration. He replied, "Cela ne me regarde pas," which means, "It is none of my business."

Because of the demonstrations, I did not get to give my lectures at Sorbonne. I did, however, have an interesting conversation with Fortet. He had written an interesting paper on connections between dynamic programming and the principle of Fermat. Conversely, one can use dynamic programming for the minimum principles of mathematical physics. For example, with dynamic programming one has a very simple derivation of the eikonal equation. In addition, the Hamilton-Jacobi equation of mechanics can easily be derived.

Jacques Lions was the head of the mathematics section of IRIA. Through him we met Bob Lattes. Lattes had started out playing bridge until he became bridge champion of the world. Then he turned to mathematics working with Lions. They wrote a book which I translated into English for my Elsevier series. It was on improperly posed problems, a topic which has always interested me.

After working in mathematics for a few years Lattes became a businessman. We got to be quite friendly and Lattes invited us to spend a weekend in his summer chateau in a small village, about thirty miles outside Paris. The second floor, where the bedrooms were had the usual low ceilings and one had to be careful to avoid bumping one's head. The bedroom where we slept was quite dusty and I spent a sleepless night, which I did not tell Lattes about.

Lattes had been in the underground during the war, living on forged papers. He often used to say that if computers were available then he would not be alive.

Arnold Kaufman came to see me. He is a very good writer of mathematical books and several in translation appear in the Academic Press series.

We saw Rudy Kalman quite frequently. Fortunately, my visit coincided with his six months in France.

We also looked up Pierre Baschet whose exhibit of new musical instruments we had seen in New York in the Museum of Modern Art. Pierre had a shop not far from our hotel.

It was enjoyable to eat in La Coupole and to stroll down the Champs Élysées. But, it was far more than that. When we saw Roman ruins, the cathedral of Notre Dame plus Vendome, or the Quai d'Orsay, we had a sense of history. One gets an indescribable thrill from a city which is two thousand years old.

MOSCOW-LENINGRAD

In 1966, the International Congress of Mathematicians was held in Moscow. I was invited to give an hour talk on dynamic programming. Naturally, I accepted.

We had read a great deal about Russia and were very anxious to go there and see for ourselves.

We took Andrea, Nina's mother, and Jeanette Blood, my secretary. We thought it would be a good reward for her years of service.

We decided to make a grand tour of it. One week in Rome, two weeks in Dubrovnik, overnight in Belgrade, ten days in Moscow, four days in Leningrad, and five days in Stockholm.

It is no easy matter to go to Russia. In addition to getting a visa, everything has to be arranged through Intourist. Four rates are available and I chose the lowest. Intourist tries to extract as much money as possible from Americans. There are different rates for Americans than for Europeans. I was warned by several friends that choosing the lowest rates means that we would stay in a pigpen. However, I knew that the Russians had translated many of my books and many roubles were available in Moscow. I felt that once we got to Russia, it would be easy to arrange for better accommodations, and I was right.

After the heat in Rome and Dubrovnik, the temperature of Moscow, about 75°, was very pleasant. We stayed at the Hotel Ukraine, a fine example of what is called Stalin baroque. This was a massive building which could easily house many hundreds of the visiting mathematicians. As I had expected my friends, Aisermann and Letov, had arranged for a large suite in the hotel. We had one, and two floors underneath us, Andrea and Jeanette had another.

I had met Letov in Atlantic City some years before. He was very patrician in appearance and in manners. Aisermann, we met for the first time in Moscow. Aisermann was very kind to us, and spent a great deal of time showing us around. In particular, he took me to the publishers, Mir, and got me several thousand roubles.

I gave several hundred each to Nina, Andrea and Jeanette. Many things could be bought, amber, fur hats, shirts, and several other things. But, many things like silver objects and rugs, could only be bought for dollars. For roubles they were state treasures.

I had read once that Sesue Hayakawa, the screen villian, made five thousand dollars a week back in the days when there was no income tax. With this money, he gave a three-day party, with a different band every eight hours. I had always wanted to do the same thing. Here was my opportunity. The Russians have no hard currency, and roubles are not worth anything outside of Russia. As a matter of fact, it is illegal to take roubles out of Russia.

Unfortunately, when I mentioned this idea to Aisermann and Letov, they were scandalized. Since I didn't want to hurt their feelings, I shelved the idea. I ended up depositing the excess roubles in a bank which was located in the Hotel Ukraine. The interest was 5/7 of a percent per year. Letov, with a twinkle in his eyes thanked me for my confidence in the Soviet economy.

It is no easy thing to get fed in Russia. The reason is that meals take a very long time. For that reason, we decided that if we were to do anything else, we had better limit ourselves to two meals a day. However, we had a snack in the morning. There was a snack bar where one could get coffee and caviar. The idea of having caviar for breakfast was very appealing. We ate from chest-high tables, standing up, something I had not done since my days at CCNY.

When we first came to Moscow, we had dinner at the Hotel Ukraine with Aisermann and Letov. They assured me that one could drink as much vodka as desired, provided one ate at the same time. This is not true. After six drinks, I was roaring drunk. I thought, "What a scandal. If I try to get up, I will fall flat on my face." By that time, the meal was over. The only thing left was dessert. I had all the desserts possible and got a reputation which plagued me in Russia for liking desserts. However, as a result of my forced feeding, I was sober enough to walk to my room without scandal. It was, of course, a practical joke which Aisermann and Letov were playing on me.

The meetings were held at the University of Moscow, a great skyscraper building, at the other end of town. We were taken there by car, so I never did have a chance to ride on the famous Moscow subway. I was nervous about my talk and it wasn't one of my best efforts. However, I consoled myself with the thought that most of the audience didn't understand English well anyway. I also was the chairman of one session.

We saw the usual sights, the Kremlin and Lenin's tomb. There was a line about two blocks long of people waiting to see Lenin's tomb but Aisermann had no compunction in putting us near the beginning of the line. This excited no comment. The same thing happened at the main post office. One of Richard Jones' daughters collected stamps and I had promised him a fine selection of Russian stamps. I asked Mark to take me to the post office so I could get current issues. When we got there, all the lines were quite long. But Mark went to the head of one line and told the people behind us that this line would be closed for some time. Again, no comment.

What interested us most was the Agricultural Exhibition. This was a large park, which had several exhibits and restaurants from every part of Russia. Going into these restaurants one could sample exotic food. In addition, there was a very garish fountain filled with semi-precious stones.

Fortunately, we didn't have to eat many meals at the hotel, because we were invited out often. First of all, we went to Pontryagin's apartment. He was an academician and therefore resided in an apartment house which was reserved for academicians. The apartment was quite spacious, but the kitchen was small and primitive.

I had a short conversation with Pontryagin. He asked me what I thought of differential games. I replied, "Not much," and gave him several reasons.

Later on, there was dancing. I have never danced well and just sat on the sidelines. Diliberto danced with Nina. While dancing he complained about American students, saying they didn't work hard enough and were not willing to put in the extra twenty percent which was necessary for success. Then he noticed me on the sidelines. He remarked to Nina it was amazing that one so athletic didn't dance. Nina replied that while he and she had been learning how to dance I had been putting in the extra twenty percent.

One of the minor drawbacks to travel is that one has to associate occasionally with people that one would never associate with in this country.

Pontryagin had been blind since the age of thirteen. His mother had learned French and German so she could read mathematical papers to him. It was quite an inspiration to see Pontryagin and Lefschetz together, a blind mathematician and a mathematician without hands.

Pontryagin was quite a brave man. One day, a representative of

Pravda came to him and asked for examples of how dialectical materialism had been helpful to him. Pontryagin said he would think about it and asked the man from Pravda to come back in a few weeks.

As a result of this there was a great debate, should Pontryagin be shot or merely sent to jail. Finally, it was decided to do nothing because of his scientific eminence.

We were also invited to dinner at the apartment of Lerner. This apartment was beautifully furnished as a result of the travels of Lerner. Lerner was also an academician and lived in the same apartment house.

Several years ago Lerner wanted to emigrate to Israel. His request was refused but all his positions were taken away. His children were allowed to emigrate to Israel.

His daughter, much to Lerner's disgust, is very much interested in abstract mathematics. There is always conflict between the generations, regardless of culture.

We were also invited to have dinner at the apartment of Letov. Letov lived in a very small apartment, with his wife and son. The son had to sleep in the kitchen. However, Letov was very proud of his car. He and several other people who own cars, had built a garage. In the Moscow winter, this was needed.

I always thought that Letov had a high position in the KGB because he travelled alone. Not only that, in Moscow, he was the only Russian that was willing to visit us in our hotel rooms.

Several years later, Letov came to Los Angeles with his wife. However, this was not the woman we had met in Moscow. Nina and I debated what to do. There were three possibilities. In the first place, Letov may have divorced and remarried. Secondly, he may just have been taking a girlfriend on a tour of United States. In either case, it was none of our business. Or, he may have been using the classic device for getting another Russian agent into United States. In this case, the professionals were certainly aware of this. We knew of too many cases where well-meaning amateurs had upset carefully laid plans. Consequently, we decided not to play amateur spy catcher.

On this trip, Letov gave a talk at USC on his work. He was studying a basic problem; how do you control a system when you don't have access to all the state variables. This problem arose in the operation of Sputnik.

Letov spoke in Russian, with Milan translating into English. Every once in a while, Letov did not like the translation and gave an English translation which he preferred.

Some years later, John Casti went to Moscow to spend several months working with Letov on this problem.

We also were invited to dinner and a party at the apartment of Gamkrelidze. There, we met several Americans whom we knew, and a Russian, Michael Bruch. Bruch spoke faultless English, and had a newspaper job in Moscow. We met him later in Los Angeles, and learned that he was now doing some work for Arnold Hammer. We also thought that Bruch was connected with the KGB because he travelled alone too.

Some years later, Gamkrelidze and Mischenko spent several months at UCLA. Since they were spending a long period of time, they decided to drive a car. Nina took them down to the DMV.

They excited a great deal of attention when they gave their home address as Moscow.

Rivas commented that this was the only place in United States that he had to wait on line. Nina replied that whenever anything was run by the state one had to stand in line.

Since it was the summer time all the theatres and other attractions were closed. Moscow has a great circus, which we saw in Sao Paolo. The Bolshoi ballet we saw several times in Los Angeles, and other Russian dancers as well. We saw a film showing how hard people trained for the Bolshoi ballet in Paris.

One evening, at about nine-thirty, we called up Rivas and asked what we should do. He replied, "Go to sleep."

There were many people we knew at the Congress. We spent several hours with Stan Ulam and took some pictures to commemorate the event. We met Norman Levinson and his wife. I had not seen Norman since Princeton. Elaine and Frank Haight were also there. They had a room in the same hotel. Elaine, with her customary verve threw a party. She got some caviar and vodka and soon the hotel room was filled with mathematicians from many countries.

The Lerners took us on a picnic to Zgorsk, the center of the Greek orthodox church. It was very interesting to see the various churches, the handsome tall priests and the devout. They were country women dressed in black for the most part. About one in a hundred was a man. The priest asked me to write something in the visitor's book. I thought that the establishment was owned by the state and committed a faux pas. I wrote, "I look forward to the day when all these churches are museums."

Lerner was more diplomatic. When the priest asked him to translate, he said that I had written that the churches were as beautiful as museums.

One day, in my hotel room I received a telephone call from a Rumanian mathematician who wanted to see me. I invited him to come up to my room but he preferred to talk to me in the lobby. He asked me if I were sympathetic to socialism, which is what communism is called in communist countries. I asked him why he asked. I replied that I was just interested in making money.

He started telling me how difficult life was for a Jew in Rumania. Then he took out pictures of his wife and child. Then he told me that he wanted to come to the United States and that it took a lot of money to bribe a border guard. Did I know of any agencies which would supply this money. In retrospect, I am sure that he had the CIA in mind. I told him that it might be a good idea to go to Israel if life in Rumania was so difficult.

He persisted. Would USC supply the money to bribe border guards? That was a very funny thought.

In the middle of Moscow, the whole thing was not funny. I was in a quandary. If I ignored it, I was compounding a felony. If I reported it, the authorities would naturally ask, "Why me?" I decided to do nothing.

The next day I got another telephone call from a Rumanian mathematician who wanted to meet me in the lobby. This time the conversation was in French. I wanted to say that I knew what he would say, but my French wasn't up to it. All I said was, "Continuez." He went through the same routine complete with a picture of his wife and baby.

I would have enjoyed my Moscow visit were it not for the entrapment attempts. I didn't tell Nina about these until we were in Stockholm. I did not want to mar her trip.

After Moscow, we flew to Leningrad. The Russians are very inefficient. I started getting our Leningrad tickets several days in advance. With liberal gifts of lipstick, which Nina had brought in great supply, I persuaded the woman in charge of travel to go down and get the tickets herself. Finally, we got them.

When it came time for the flight, we were put in a special room so that we could not talk to Russians. On the plane, we were shepherded to seats with blacked out windows, presumably so we couldn't see fortifications on the ground below. We pointed out that someone had vomited in these seats and we would take others. The woman official in charge wasn't happy about this but there was little she could do.

In Leningrad, we stayed at the Hotel Europa. This was once a luxury hotel, but quite rundown. However, the food there was very much better than in Moscow and they even had a band which made a valiant attempt to play American jazz. In addition they served Russian champagne which is quite good. It is called champagnska. We also had caviar with every meal.

Leningrad is much more of a European city than Moscow. We greatly enjoyed looking at the shop windows. I suddenly realized in Leningrad what was missing in Moscow. Nobody laughed in Moscow.

In Leningrad, I went to the Institute of Mathematics. I had lunch there and we talked about this and that. Among other things, they showed us the bullet holes which German bullets had made. Several people told me that their chief memory of World War II was hunger.

After some discussion, the senior professor asked me what I thought of Russia. I replied that ten days in Moscow and four days in Leningrad did not make me an expert. In addition, I had VIP treatment so I had little opportunity to see normal life.

The professor said that he realized that, but he wanted my impressions anyway.

I said that it was obvious that the Russian state treated scientists very well. It gave them everything it had but it didn't have much. I pointed out that a factory worker in United States lived much better than a senior professor in Russia. My chief impression was that of visiting poor relations.

The main street of Leningrad is Nevsky Prospekt. We enjoyed walking along this. They still had the plaque which informed citizens to walk on one side of the street where German shells did not land. Along Nevsky Prospekt we came across a salesman who was selling picture books of Leningrad for one rouble. These were of an uncomfortable size, about twelve by twenty-four. I bought one and carried it on the plane so that I could give it to Genia. She had been born in Leningrad, back in days when it was called Petrograd, and enjoyed the pictures greatly.

The first sight we wanted to see was the Hermitage. We were struck by the number of old masters which the Russians possessed. For example, there were so many Rembrandts that they were mounted one above the other.

As usual, we wished we had several weeks to view this collection.

We were also taken to the Palace of Peter and saw several of his personal things.

Finally, we were taken to the summer palace, which the Russians have remodeled in great style. I wish they had kept up the Europa the same way. Nina endeared herself to the guards at the palace by taking pictures of them with her polaroid camera. As a result, we were allowed to look at the furniture close up and even sit in the chairs.

When travelling, one learns to keep an eye on one's luggage. It was just as well. When we were ready to leave Leningrad, a bus tour was leaving at the same time. If I had not guarded our luggage it would have ended up on the steppes of central Asia.

When we boarded the plane for Helsinki, I noticed with amusement how our fellow passengers crowded to get in. I have never felt as happy as when our plane landed in Helsinki and we disembarked. We had several hours to wait for a plane to Stockholm. In the Helsinki airport we enjoyed the selection and quality of food.

In Moscow, I wanted to make sure that we had hotel accommodations in Stockholm. The Moscow operator refused to believe that one could get a telephone number in Stockholm just by asking. This was unheard of in Moscow. I solved the problem by making it a multi-stage process. I saw Frostman and asked him for his home number. When I spoke to his wife, I asked her to call Goran.

DUBROVNIK

We met Rajko Tomovic on the plane coming back from Paris in 1964. Rajko, and his wife Lubitza, were on the way to UCLA where he had been invited by Walter Karplus. Rajko was an electronics engineer who was interested in artificial arms. At the moment he was supported by the AEC who wanted to use these devices for handling radioactive material. Rajko had also designed some excellent prosthetic arms. However, the VA did not use them. The VA has been consistently reactionary, and refuses to use any modern technology for veterans.

Rajko was also a member of parliament in Yugoslavia and knew Tito well.

He had led a very fascinating life. When the Germans occupied Yugoslavia, he joined an underground group. This group was betrayed by one of the members and everyone else but Rajko was shot. Rajko had been a personal friend of the person who betrayed the group, so he was sent to a concentration camp.

In the camp, he became a communist. His activities came to the attention of the authorities, and it was decided to execute him. It was necessary to smuggle him out of the camp. This was done by dressing him as a moslem woman with a veil. The German guards were told that if they lifted the veil it would mean instant death. Rajko, however, had a pistol in each hand prepared to shoot some German guards before he was shot. However, he managed to leave the camp safely and became a partisan. Lubitza, his wife, was also a partisan.

Rajko's independence of spirit got him into trouble many times with the Russians.

He and Lubitza took an apartment in Santa Monica. At this apartment, we met Max Palevsky. It gave me great amusement. Max Palevsky was worth about 100 million dollars being friendly with a communist.

We also became friendly with an army colonel who probably worked for the CIA. We saw him quite frequently since he had designs on Gloria which never materialized. One night we went out to dinner with him, Rajko and Gloria. In the course of the conversation I mentioned that Rajko was a member of the parliament of Yugoslavia.

This disturbed the colonel greatly. He took me aside and said, "Don't you realize who I am?" I said I did, but I thought the contact would be quite useful.

We also became quite friendly with Rajko. He invited us in 1966 to spend two weeks in Dubrovnik giving some lectures on dynamic programming and control theory. Since we wanted to see Yugoslavia first-hand, I accepted.

It turned out to be quite convenient, two weeks before the International Congress in Moscow.

According to Rajko, we were to live in a villa in Dubrovnik. This villa turned out to be a private house. Every summer, the family that owned the house would live in the basement and rent out the house. They made money from this rental and by furnishing meals too.

Lubitza also spent some time at the villa. She was a very attractive woman. One day, intending to compliment her, I said she was as glamorous as an international spy. She heard only the word "spy" and never forgave me.

The heart of the modern city of Dubrovnik is the ancient walled city state of Ragusa. This was ideally situated for independence. The Adriatic is on one side and steep cliffs on the other.

The modern city has spread out in all possible directions. Our "villa" was to the south, the luxury hotels were to the north, and there were private homes on the steep cliffs. The lectures were given at the Art Museum. This was once a private home. The pictures in the Art Museum were terrible.

One of the bedrooms on the second floor had been converted into a classroom. There the lectures were held. Because of the heat in the summer, the best time to lecture was in the early morning.

To get to the Art Museum, one took a Toonerville trolley to the borders of the old city, walked through the old city and then walked a couple of blocks to the Art Museum. The old city had essentially one main street, along which there were many interesting shops.

In the central square, there was an outdoor market during the day. Seeing the pushcarts reminded me of shopping along Second Avenue with my grandmother.

In one of those, we got a rug. The person who sold the rug said that the workmanship was not good anymore. The rug was only guaranteed for 500 years, whereas before it had been guaranteed for several thousand years.

We enjoyed greatly exploring the old city. For a very modest fee, we could walk on the battlements. In addition, tours were organized to nearby places of interest. On an island, a few miles offshore was the home of Boscovich, a very famous Yugoslavian scientist of the eighteenth century.

In travelling, it was essential to locate where the Paris Herald Tribune was sold. The New York Herald Tribune was defunct, but the New York Times still published the European version. In addition, there were reprints of articles of interest from the New York Times. By reading this, we could keep up with what was going on in the United States. In Stockholm and Copenhagen, we knew where to buy it. In Paris, it was sold in Le Drug Store, both the one on the Champs Elysee and the one on Boulevard St. Germain. We were delighted to find that there were two places in Dubrovnik where one could buy a Herald Tribune.

There was also a group of six Russians who had a "villa" of their own. This was the way we first met Gamkrelidze. One night, there was a poor vaudeville show at the Excelsior. We commented on how poor it was. Gamkrelidze said, "Enjoy this, there is nothing like it in Moscow."

We enjoyed Dubrovnik very much. Consequently, in 1968 we came back.

This time, we stayed at one of the luxury hotels, the Argentina, thanks to Rajko. This was much more convenient for going to the Art Museum, and of course very much more pleasant. Our room looked out over the Adriatic.

A lot of people we knew were there at the same time. John Richardson, Bob Lattes, Georgio Segre, and Tosio Kitagawa all gave lectures. In addition, there were two Russians, Mark Aisermann and Yuri Tsypkin.

Tsypkin had survived the war. The Russians had a very simple method for clearing mine fields. They used the first wave of the infantry. When infantrymen were too valuable, they used a special contingent for this purpose. Tsypkin had been in this contingent.

Mark Aisermann had been in the tank corp during the war working up from an enlisted man to an officer. He had sixty relatives. The Nazis had killed fifty-nine, leaving one aunt.

There was a very pretty Yugoslavian girl working in the office at the Art Museum named Vana. She spoke fluent English since she had worked in London for several years for the Yugoslavian government. She was very much interested in philosophy and would spend hours with Tosio discussing this.

Jeanette and Fleur also came for two weeks to spend their vacation there.

Driving in Dubrovnik is rather difficult. Naturally, no cars are allowed in the old city. In 1966, there was terrible traffic congestion. By 1968, Yugoslavia had discovered one-way streets. This reduced the congestion, but made it quite a feat to get places.

In 1968, Russian tanks went into Czechoslovakia. Czechoslovakia had to be independent and the Russians didn't like that. The situation in Yugoslavia was very tense, because it seemed as if the Russians would invade Yugoslavia too. It was clear, however, that the Yugoslavians would fight. The Russians thought it over and decided not to pay the price.

Many Yugoslavians were very rude to Aisermann and Tsypkin. This was very foolish, because they had far less control over what the Russian military did than we do over what the Pentagon does.

We went home by way of Copenhagen. Joined by John Richardson. I felt quite at home wandering through the Tivoli, the large amusement park of Copenhagen because I had grown up next to Coney Island. Copenhagen is a charming city and whenever we went to Europe we tried to spend a few days there. We got to know the downtown section quite well.

In 1970, I organized a two-week course on the mathematical biosciences. I had John Jacques talk on pharmacokinetics and chemotherapy, Homer Warner talk on medical data and computers, and George Moore talk on neurophysiology. In addition, I gave some lectures on my work.

Steve Friedland who was on his way to Greece with Anne gave an excellent talk on nuclear medicine.

After leaving Dubrovnik, we went to Madrid so we could see the Prado. They have a magnificent collection of Spanish masters. But what intrigued us most was the bust of a woman from about the Eighth century B.C. with a hair-do which we have not seen before or since. The origin of this bust is unknown. In general, very little has been done in Spain in connection with archaeology.

The visit to Madrid was almost our undoing. We took a 747 from Madrid to Kennedy airport. As the pilot was preparing to land, he observed that a TWA 747 had not moved away as it should have. At the last moment he made like a dive bomber. We barely avoided a collision. It was quite a feat to do that in a 747. It was the only time that we have a close shave while travelling.

We had several whiskeys after we landed to settle down.

We enjoyed Dubrovnik very much. The place is charming, the people are nice, and the food is good. In addition, everything was quite cheap.

Eric inherited my appetite. For a main course he would have a Chateaubriand for two. At Dubrovnik prices we could afford it.

ROME

Our first visit to Rome was in 1963 when we went around the world. Paris, Zurich, Rome, Tokyo, Kyoto.

There were several amusing features about travelling abroad while at RAND. In the first place, the travel office wanted to give me a card which stated that I had the rank of colonel if captured by the enemy. This, naturally, provoked my curiosity. I asked, "What enemy?" I had the impression we were at peace and had no enemies. In any case, if captured by the unknown enemy I preferred the rank of noncombatant. I refused the card.

Secondly, we were given a paper to read which said we were to leave our vices at home. Again, this provoked my curiosity. I said there were two cases. Either, what I did ordinarily was a vice, or there were vices I wasn't familiar with. The last case was really painful. I asked the girl in the travel office to be more specific. She couldn't be.

In Paris, we stayed overnight, so we didn't care particularly about the accommodations. In Zurich, I was chairman of a session of IFAC, which is International Federation for Automatic Control.

Our accommodations were really bad. I lost faith in what the travel office had booked for us. I called up the Hilton at Rome and arranged a room for us, and cancelled the other arrangements.

In 1963, the Hilton had just opened and the service was excellent.

I wanted to see Aldo Ghizzetti who was a director of a center for applied mathematics, and Nina wanted to see a childhood friend, "Punky" Francesca Coombs. Punky was an architect. She had taken a degree in architecture at Berkeley, a five-year course.

The first day she was in Rome, she met a Sicilian policeman and fell madly in love with him. Neither we nor her family were enthusiastic about this union, but she married him and came back with him to San Bernadino where they are now living. She is a city planner and he is a construction worker.

We wanted very much to see the Roman ruins, the Colosseum, and the Vatican.

We were quite fortunate, because at that time the Colosseum was still open to tourists. Now, it has been closed because it is felt that it is unsafe. We visited the Colosseum several times, and got a thrill each time. We could see where the wild animals were kept below the main floor.

One of the best things that Christianity did was to put an end to the gladiatorial games. There is still a great deal of barbarity in the world, witness the Nazis, and United States in Vietnam. However, there is no question that the world has gotten more civilized.

It was possible to buy postcards which showed what the Colosseum looked like originally. It was when built a magnificent structure. We had a wonderful time exploring the ruins and identifying various structures.

I have a heretical view. Either the ruins should be reconstructed or bulldozed.

The next stop was the Vatican. We had seen pictures of St. Peter's innumerable times in the movies and had read a great deal about it. Now, we had the opportunity to see it close up and see the inside. We were not disappointed. It is a magnificent structure, and has many interesting things inside.

I was not impressed by the famous Sistine Chapel. It looks far better on postcards.

We pursued our favorite hobby when travelling, eating in Japanese restaurants. We have eaten in Japanese restaurants in San Francisco, New York, Washington, Montreal, Honolulu and Tuscon, Arizona. In Europe, we have eaten in Japanese restaurants in Copenhagen, Paris, and West Berlin. Rome had exactly one, which wasn't very good.

The most interesting restaurant in Rome was Mea Petacchi. This was started by an American who thought Rome should have a typical Italian restaurant. By coincidence, we met him on the plane and he told us all about it. That is how we happened to go to this restaurant. It had many delightful features, and we enjoyed it greatly.

Rome is an antiquarian's delight. It would take years to see all the points of interest. We saw some in 1963, and we greatly enjoyed just wandering around. We had seen many Italian pictures which had different views of Rome.

In the evening, we enjoyed strolling down Via Veneta. We would pick some sidewalk café and have some wine there. We had the usual troubles with Roman waiters. Although the tip is automatically added to the bill, when they saw an American, they wanted an extra tip and were quite insulting when they didn't get it.

The airport of Rome, the Leonardo da Vinci Airport, is about ten miles out of the city.

I used to be a great admirer of da Vinci. The more I read about him, the more I agreed with Michelangelo, a contemporary who didn't have a high opinion of him.

It is worthwhile to arrive during the day because on the trip from the airport, one can see many excavations. In addition, one traverses the famous Appian Way and it is a thrill to see this road still in use.

In 1966, on our way to Dubrovnik and Moscow, we stayed in Rome again at the Hilton. The service had deteriorated greatly, and after a few days we moved to the Hotel Eden. This is a charming hotel, one block off the Via Veneta. When we visited Rome again, we stayed there.

Once again, with Andrea and Jeanette, we went to see the Roman ruins and the Colosseum. In addition, we went to the Vatican. We also saw many other things which we had not seen on our first visit.

We intersected with Eric and Skip in Rome. Eric had graduated from high school that spring and didn't want to go to college immediately. I agreed with him. I have always felt that there should be at least a year between high school and college. Preferably, that time should be spent in travel.

We were going to Europe three times that year. Consequently, we thought it would be fairly safe to send Eric and Skip to travel in Europe. They had many adventures due to the fact that they constantly underestimated the difficulty and time required to send money abroad. The worst was in Dijon. They were marooned in a hotel room without food or money, and an irate hotel manager threatened to send them to jail. Fortunately, we were in Aberdeen at the time. However, it was the Easter weekend and there was no American Express Office in Dijon. However, there was a Thomas Cook and Son Office. A very nice bank manager kept his bank open fifteen minutes after closing time when he heard of the predicament of Eric and Skip.

We were staying at the Station Hotel. Two ragamuffins came to see us, Eric and Skip. Fortunately, it was a university town and people were accustomed to the children of university professors being ragamuffins. Eric and Skip had no difficulty in getting in to see us. We fed and bathed them, and they stayed long enough for Eric to pick up the girl who worked behind the counter in the Station Hotel, Jackie.

She joined Eric and Skip and off they took. When we stayed at the Hilton in Rome, I went to the desk several times saying I was expecting Eric and Skip. When they came, they were informed we were not registered there. However, they persisted and we were reunited. We left them in our room while we changed hotels.

Eric bought a motorcycle with a sidecar to make the trip to Dubrovnik. The motorcycle broke down in about ten miles but they joined us in Dubrovnik anyway. One night when they arrived in Dubrovnik we tried to go to a nightclub. The bouncer there would not let us in, because Skip was wearing jeans. When we saw Rajko, we commented that Yugoslavia was a fine socialist country if a man in jeans could not go to a nightclub. Rajko promised to take it up in parliament.

When Eric and Skip went to the beach, Eric was promptly dubbed Prince Valiant because of his resemblance to the comic strip character.

After we went to Moscow, Eric and Skip joined us in Stockholm. They stayed in Stockholm for several months.

We also wanted to send Kirstie to Europe. We found a tour under the auspices of a professor at UCLA. The charter flight and the hotel came to $1,000. However, the company went bankrupt and we lost the $1,000. Kirstie still has not gone to Europe.

WEST BERLIN

In 1969, I was invited by Schering in West Berlin for a conference on chemotherapy, all expenses paid.

Although I greatly wanted to go, I thought John Jacques could gain more from the conference and make a greater contribution. I wrote to the bureaucrat at the NIH for permission to do this. He wrote back and said that only the principal investigator could travel abroad. I tried several times, but in vain.

I got a first-class ticket, so that I could divide it into two tourist class tickets and take Nina. We stayed at the Hilton. I thought it would be a good idea to come a few days early and get over the jet lag. The bureaucrat in Washington refused to cover my expenses for this on the grounds I had not given previous notification. I am sure that Schering would have covered these expenses too, but I didn't think it was right. The meeting was very successful. Schering was very much interested in drug research. One of the people it supported used an analog computer, which was quite useful. However, I pointed out the greater flexibility of the digital computer. The trouble with an analog computer is that one begins to construct mathematical models which can be treated using an analog computer. In many cases this is not realistic.

I met Torstan Teorell, who had started the mathematical investigation of chemotherapy. He told me that he almost didn't get his degree because of this. His professor thought that this was much too radical.

There was, however, another reason for my going to West Berlin. Because of the Nazi excesses, I had been down on the Germans. I found it very difficult to talk or associate with Germans. I did a little calculation. Obviously, one could not hold people who were born in 1934 responsible for the Nazis. To do so would be as bad as the Nazis. That took care of about one-half of the German people. Continuing this calculation, it hardly seemed fair to blame anybody who was fourteen or less in 1934. This eliminated anybody who was under fifty.

One of the sights of West Berlin which has been carefully preserved is the bombed out Kaiser Wilhelm Church. Around the walls of this church are scenes of famous Prussian military victories. Looking at these, one can see the disease that infected the Junkers. Next to this is a simple wooden church, which has the names of about 5,000 ministers and priests who were killed by the Nazis resisting their ideas. I don't think that many people outside of Germany have a realization of the magnitude of the anti-Nazi sentiment.

After visiting West Berlin, I was cured of my prejudice forever.

In addition, once the meeting was over, we did some sightseeing. We saw the infamous Wall, the Art Museum, the Palace Frederick the Great, and the famous Berlin Zoo. The zoo was only a few hundred yards from the Hilton.

We wanted very much to visit East Berlin. However, the memory of the entrapment attempts in Moscow was still vivid. I knew I didn't work for the CIA, but did the Russians know? I decided I didn't want to put my head in the lion's mouth again. Consequently, we were prudent and stayed in West Berlin.

The food in West Berlin was uniformly good. As a matter of fact, the best Yugoslavian food we tasted was in West Berlin at a restaurant aptly named "Dubrovnik".

LONDON

We never had enough of London. Unfortunately, we were always on the way to some place else, Aberdeen, Dundee, Dubrovnik. I never got an invitation to lecture for four weeks so that we could tramp around to our heart's content.

We had one friend in London, Rex Malik. Rex had an interesting background. His father had been born an untouchable. He joined the British Army, rose to the rank of Sergeant Major and converted to Mohammedanism. He then married a French Catholic woman and Rex and his brother were the products of this marriage. His father than got divorced, converted to Anglicanism, and became a minister.

Rex was a scientific writer whose specialty was computers. He wrote for several monthlies and would occasionally contribute an article to another journal. He frequently travelled to United States and that is how I met him.

When we visited London, either we would see him and his wife Lillian for dinner, or else they would have a party for us at their house.

When Richard Jones was associated with Academic Press he lived in Monterey Park. When Academic Press moved to San Francisco, he decided to go back to England. He and Nora had become American citizens so that they could come back when they wanted.

We saw Richard and Nora Jones in London on one visit and had dinner together at a very famous restaurant, Capability Brown. This restaurant specializes in food which was served several hundred years ago. We had a very amusing dinner.

After several years in England, Richard Jones returned to San Francisco, where he is now medical editor for Addison Wesley.

In London, there are many things to see. As usual, we made no attempt to see them all. Our first stop was the British Museum where we wanted to see the famous Elgin marbles and the Rosetta Stone. It would take months to see all the exhibits at the British museums.

We went to Westminister Abbey and had a great time looking at the graves of famous people.

Then, we went to the Tate Gallery, where there were pictures of all the people who had played a role in English history for the last 300 years. It was quite interesting to see portraits of people who had been just names in books.

Next, we took a tour of the Tower. We had read a great deal about this and were very eager to see it. It is well worth seeing.

One of the things that excited us was the foundations of a temple of Mithra which had been found in the heart of the financial district.

Mithraism was the official religion of the Roman army. As the brief article in the Encyclopedia Britannica indicates, Mithraism and Christianity had many features in common. It is very difficult to find any modern book on Mithraism. There is one Dover reprint of a book which was published in about 1880.

Constantine made Christianity the official state religion in 323 A.D. He was probably involved in a power struggle with the Roman army and this move was designed to weaken the army.

I have always had a passion for Wedgewood china. Every time we went to London, we got a few pieces. Over here, they would be prohibitively expensive.

One of the interesting things about going to London is the ability to go to the theatre. We saw five plays in London. The best, by far, was Canterbury Tales. We also saw Oh, Calcutta. The first half was fun, the second half was terrible. Rex took us to two plays, and we went to see one other, where we couldn't even understand the language.

They speak something resembling English in England, but it is not easy to understand it. When a movie is made for export, it is understandable. When a movie is made for domestic consumption, one wishes there were subtitles.

JAPAN

We first visited Tokyo in 1963.

We made the mistake of taking the "milk train" from Rome to Tokyo. This stops at Tel Aviv, Teheran, New Delhi, Bangkok, Hong Kong and Tokyo. Between stops and meals, we got no sleep for about twenty-four hours.

The ride to the hotel was harrowing. Japanese taxicab drivers are called kamikaze for a good reasons. Yet, I never saw an accident. The best thing to do when taking a taxicab ride is to ignore what is going on outside, if possible.

When we got to Tokyo, we had been booked in the Imperial Hotel, the Frank Lloyd Wright hotel. I took one look at the dusty room and went immediately to the Hilton. It turns out that we had been put in the old section.

On the way to the hotel, I thought I was seeing things. An Eiffel Tower bigger than the original appeared. This is typically Japanese.

The Ginza is brighter than Broadway. The discotheques are deafening. The air-conditioning is enough to make one paranoid about stepping outside.

Every hotel has a shopping arcade, which we enjoyed hugely. We browsed through the shops, and bought several things.

We were in Tokyo for an IRE meeting, where I was on a committee on wave propagation.

Many friends were there. Lotfi Zadeh was there and others. There, also, we met Gluskov for the first time. Nina taught him how to use chopsticks.

There was a reception at the American Embassy. The ambassador Reichauer, was actually there, and I had an interesting conversation with him. I asked him how one reconciled the tremendous interest which the Japanese had in esthetics with their cruelty and barbarity. He said he had speculated on this at great length himself and had the following theory. Japanese men are brought up with clearly defined duties to their emperor, to their family, and so on. If one does not fit into this structure, then there are no rules. The western ideas of charity and good works are completely alien.

Reichauer was an ideal ambassador. He spoke Japanese fluently and had married a Japanese woman. He knew Japan quite well. Some years later, he was wounded in the leg by a Japanese extremist. Fortunately, the wound was not serious.

In 1967, I was invited again to give some lectures in Tokyo. I was supposed to give at least one lecture at the University of Tokyo but the anti-American feeling was so great that it was cancelled.

We stayed again at the Hilton. Before one of the talks, I got the flu. Normally, I would have cancelled the talk, but I decided I had to go through with it. Nina got the idea of using a masseuse. She made me feel much better, and although I still felt a little rocky, I was able to give the talk and go to the ceremonial dinner.

In between the various talks we were able to do a great deal of sightseeing. We were taken to a tea ceremony, which I always felt was rather ridiculous. However, we went through with it, and Nina amazed everybody by her ability to sit cross-legged for a long time. I couldn't.

I had corresponded with Tsutomo Arimizu who was interested in applying dynamic programming to forestry. His professor was the royal gardener. Through this contact, we were able to see the bonsai collection at the Palace. Bonsai are miniature trees, perfect in every detail. When one sees the wizardry of the Japanese in gardening, one understands why they are so popular in Los Angeles.

We were also taken to see the semi-finals of Sumo wrestling. We got quite interested in this, and when we went to Kyoto we followed the results in the local English paper. One of the ways one can tell that the Japanese are getting bigger is that the minimum weight for a Sumo wrestler is now 135, whereas it used to be 110.

Our favorite was a Sumo wrestler who was over six feet tall. He was much taller than the usual wrestler. This tallness was due to the fact that he was half Russian.

The ritual was very interesting to watch. A great deal of this ritual has been eliminated for TV, which is a great shame.

After Tokyo, we went to Kyoto. One of the people in Tokyo had a brother who took care of the Golden Pavilion in Kyoto. Thus, we had the tea ceremony again in the VIP room of the Golden Pavilion. As visitors, we were able to visit certain palaces which are closed to the Japanese public. Sueo was very happy about this. He had wanted to see these palaces.

I gave a lecture on invariant imbedding, arranged by Sueo, at the University of Kyoto.

Sueo took us all around. He said that there were over 1,000 temples in Kyoto but that he would only take us to three. One of the most memorable is the Temple of the Thousand Buddhas. Whenever we visited Kyoto we made sure that we saw this.

At one temple, there were giant wooden warriors at the gate. They were supposed to guard the temple. Sueo, who has spent some time in Paris, turned to us with a grin and said, "Concierges."

He also took us to Nara, which used to be the ancient capital of Japan. One of the features of Nara is the presence of tame deer. Biscuits are sold so that one can feed these deer. Again, there are many interesting temples at Nara.

Sueo also took us to see many sights around Kyoto. One of the most memorable was cormorant fishing. A cord is tied around the throat of the cormorant which is then allowed to dive for fish. Because of the cord it cannot swallow the fish. I am sure that the SPCA would not allow this demonstration in this country. Also, Sueo took us to many different restaurants. One of the most memorable was one that served food in the manner of Manchuria. This is very much like a fondue and the trick is to get enough to eat without scalding oneself.

We saw a bit of Kabuki. I was familiar with Kabuki, because I always saw about an hour of it when a Japanese troupe toured Los Angeles. However, Japanese theatre seats are not made for western frames.

We stayed again at the Miyako, which we enjoyed very much.

In 1970, I was invited by JUSE, Japanese Union of Scientists and Engineers, to give some lectures. The way one gives a lecture generally is with the aid of an interpreter. One talks for a couple of minutes, then the interpreter talks. At first, this is rather disconcerting, but after awhile one realized that one has a lot of time during the translation to prepare for the next bit of speech.

We travelled to Japan this time in a civilized fashion. We stayed two nights in Hawaii and got to know downtown Honolulu quite well. On the trip from Hawaii to Tokyo, we encountered a storm. This forced us to land on Wake Island to get more fuel. While the refueling was taking place, we had a chance to stroll around and see the World War II bunkers. It was quite dramatic. The storm followed us all the way to Tokyo. As we approached Tokyo, the lightning was uncomfortably close. Fortunately, we were not struck.

We finally got to see the King Tut exhibit. The tomb of Tutankhamen had miraculously escaped grave robbers. Hence, we were able to see the splendor with which a pharaoh of ancient Egypt was buried. The exhibit had been in Los Angeles, but the lines were so long that we decided not to go. It was a pleasure to see it in Tokyo.

I had promised Tosio Kitagawa, whom I had met first on one of his trips to the United States, that I would visit Kyushu the next time we came to Japan. I gave a lecture at the University on dynamic programming and then we had a round-table discussion. The subject of the discussion was whether or not Japan should have its man-in-space program. When my opinion was asked, I said that just because United States was squandering its resources was no reason why Japan should squander its.

Kennedy had started the man-in-space activity and the Vietnam adventure to distract attention from the Bay of Pigs fiasco.

In 1964, I had been keynote speaker at a conference on control theory at Stanford and expressed similar opinions. I pointed out that we had many other uses for this money, such as urban systems, health systems, educational systems, pest control, flood control, sources of energy, and many others.

It was more than money. There are just so many trained people in the United States. If they are working on man-in-space problems they cannot work on other problems.

Before the talk, I was going to be on all-purpose consultant at North American at $10,000 a year. After the talk, a vice-president of North American remarked that with a friend like me who needed an enemy. That was the end of my $10,000 a year. I always felt that it was a small price to pay for the privilege of saying what one thought, and referred to this as my $10,000 talk.

We had never stayed in a Japanese inn and thought that we would try it for one night. In a Japanese inn, one sleeps essentially on the floor on a piece of bedding which is rolled up during the day. This was an interesting, if not entirely comfortable, experience. The bathrooms are also interesting. The bathtubs are made to be sat in rather than, western style, to be reclined in. However, they are made to be sat in by Japanese. Hence, they are rather small.

Having tried it for one night, I never want to try it again.

In 1972, on our way to Taiwan we visited Japan again. With us were Virginia Zoitl and Nina's mother, Andrea. They had been given tickets by President Lin. Virginia had arranged the trip and President Lin had very kindly sent her a ticket. Why Andrea got a ticket will be explained below.

This time we reversed the order, just as Kyoto is the reverse of Tokyo. We visited Kyoto first, as a consultant to Tataishi. This was arranged by Hiroshi Sugiyama, who was a consultant to Tataishi.

Tataishi was supporting a large group which was doing research on traffic. This is definitely needed, since there is tremendous congestion in the cities of Japan. It is a wonder that anything moves at all. Japanese streets were never made for automobiles.

The problem is very difficult, and the group had not gotten very far.

We stayed a few days at the Miyako and then moved to a downtown hotel. Once again, we went to Nara and saw the temples and the deer there.

We went out to dinner with Hiroshi and his wife Yoshiko, Sunji Osaki, and two officials from Tataishi. The restaurant we went to was completely western, to our disappointment. Sunji Osaki described what he wanted in a wife. He went on and on about the virtues he required. Finally, this was too much for Yoshiko. She said, "Sunji, why do you think you deserve all this?"

In Tokyo, we were the guests of Fujitsu, the largest Japanese computer manufacturer. Tosio Kitagawa had retired from Kyushu and was starting an institute of applied mathematics for Fujitsu. I was to be a consultant for this institute.

We stayed at the Palace Hotel. I had lunch with the senior people of Fujitsu, and was impressed by their intelligence and ability.

Ikeda, a vice-president of Fujitsu, gave a banquet for us at a Japanese inn. He scoured all the islands of Japan for delicacies. Ikeda was a gourmet and put a great deal of thought into the selection of various foods. Some we recognized, some we didn't. We bravely ate everything.

I remembered as a boy that I had read of the exploration of Roy Chapman Andrews in the Gobi desert. It was necessary to keep the local chiefs happy. Before each dig, there was a ceremonial dinner at which a whole sheep was served. As guest of honor, Andrews was given an eye. He ate it thinking of dinosaurs.

We also made a visit to the manufacturing plant of Fujitsu. There, we were shown propaganda movies. When I commented on this, one of the top officials was very amused. Almost all of the top officials spoke fluent English.

After our stay at the Palace Hotel, we went to Hakkony. Hakkony is a well-known Japanese resort. Tosio Kitagawa had spent his honeymoon there. His institute was to have a building nearby.

After our stay of two days at Hakkony, we returned to Tokyo. This time we stayed at the new Otani. On that site, the original Otani was a well-known Japanese inn. The new Otani was a magnificent hotel, and we enjoyed our stay there greatly.

After Hakkony, Virginia went to stay with some friends in Tokyo. Nina, Andrea and I did some sightseeing. We saw the Meiji Museum. This is a collection of paintings by Japanese artists showing how Japan became a modern nation. It is a painless way of learning a good deal of Japanese history.

TAIWAN

In 1972, I was invited to give some lectures at the Tatung Institute in Taipei. I accepted for several reasons.

In the first place, I felt that a country like Taiwan was very important in that part of the world in showing that capitalism was a viable system. I felt that technical education was very essential for the existence of Taiwan and that I could make a contribution. Secondly, I had never seen Chinese culture before and I was anxious to visit Taiwan. Thirdly, I wanted to stop off in Tokyo and see Tosio. Finally, Andrea was brought up in China. Chinese was her first language.

Andrea was born in Kentucky but at the age of two her parents went to China. Her father founded schools throughout China. He was not a missionary but they knew many missionaries. As a result, Andrea had an abiding hatred of missionaries.

But, there was more than that. Her father had had a very fine voice, and her mother played the piano well. Through a combination of circumstances, her father sang at Chiang Kai-shek's wedding and her mother played the piano. When President Lin heard about this he was very anxious to have Andrea come with us and meet Madam Chiang.

I gave several lectures at the Tatung Institute. Tatung also runs a number of industries. The usual ceremonial tour was arranged for me, seeing a refrigerator plant and so on. I pointed out that I could see refrigerator plants in Los Angeles and I would much rather talk about technical education with President Lin and Dean Lin, no relation.

Dean Lin was very nice to us. He personally took us to two famous temples and to the Art Museum. At the Art Museum we saw a number of cooking urns which had been excavated from tombs. These had quite beautiful carving on the sides. In the stores, one could buy replicas which were made into ice buckets.

President Lin had several dinners for us. One was at our hotel where we heard some Chinese music played on Chinese instruments. It was very melodious. The next night he took us to his favorite restaurant where again we had Manchurian food, which we had first tasted in Kyoto with Sueo.

President Lin wanted us to meet Madam Chiang. On Taiwan she is just referred to as Madam. The best way to meet her is to go to her Thursday prayer meeting which she attended regularly. This prayer meeting was conducted by an old missionary woman, mostly in Chinese, occasionally she would break into English.

I amused myself looking around at the faces. On the subway in New York, I had learned the trick of closing my ears to sound.

After the meeting was over, it lasted only one hour, we were introduced to Madam Chiang. She acknowledged the introduction in a gracious, but perfunctory way. Around the room were several examples of her paintings. Andrea commented that they were quite good. Madam Chiang accepted this in an offhand fashion.

I saw that Andrea's comments had not registered. I said, "Madam Chiang, Mrs. Day is a professional artist. When she said that the paintings are good she means it."

At this, Madam Chiang showed great interest. She then engaged Andrea in a conversation.

Madam Chiang spoke excellent and fluent English. She had gone to school at Bryn Mawr. Indeed, gossip had it that she spoke better English than Chinese. Andrea had forgotten most of her Chinese. When she went into stores, various phrases came back to the astonishment of the merchant. I am sure that if Andrea had stayed in Taiwan for a month she would have been speaking fluent Chinese again.

We returned to our hotel for dinner. Midway through our dinner there was a telephone call from Pearl Chen, Madam Chiang's personal secretary. Would we come to the Palace at four the next afternoon? Naturally, we accepted.

At about three-thirty, a huge black limousine pulled up in front of our hotel. The Palace is about ten miles out of town. As we approached the Palace, the driver started using the two-way radio, giving various passwords. It was like a James Bond movie. As we drove down the driveway to the Palace, every fifty feet, two men with sub-machine guns stopped the car and the driver gave a password. Finally, we got to the Palace, an elegant one-story building.

We did not get to see the whole building, but were ushered into a large dining room where Madam Chiang was. She was a very gracious hostess; serving us some delicious food. She chatted with each one of us in turn, asking me what I did. When I said I was a mathematician, she gave the traditional rejoinder, "That was my worst subject at school." But it was Andrea that she really wanted to talk to.

She took Andrea by the arm and showed her various paintings of hers around the room. They were quite good. Her secretary, Pearl Chen, interrupted every ten minutes to remind Madam Chiang of a five o'clock appointment. Each time, Madam Chiang shook her off.

Finally she had to let Andrea go.

As we were leaving, Andrea admired some roses. The toughest looking character I have ever seen, a colonel, explained what the roses signitied. Madam Chiang insisted that we have the roses. The colonel personally wrapped them. When we returned to the hotel, we gave one to each chambermaid, thrilling them.

However, although we were leaving at noon the next day she had us go to the museum in the morning to see a number of her paintings which had not even been uncrated. Also, she had us visit a hospital for polio victims which she supported. This visit affected me greatly since it brought back the ordeal that Eric had with bulbar polio. A great job had been done on Taiwan in eradicating various diseases, but they had not yet gotten around to polio.

We enjoyed our visit to Taiwan greatly and hope to return. I keep in regular correspondence with President Lin about matters of education.

NEW ZEALAND

In 1971, I was invited to visit New Zealand and give lectures at the principal universities in Wellington, Christchurch, Dunedin, Palmerston North, and Auckland. The visit was arranged by Alex McNabb. Alex had spent two years at USC, and when he returned to New Zealand he was anxious to have me come. Fleur Mitchell had become very friendly with Alex and his wife Max while they were here. Some years later she spent a month in New Zealand.

Alex's specialty was defusion equations. At the moment, he was working on geothermal energy. At that time, geothermal energy was not economic. With the increase in oil prices it is now. Very interesting free boundary problems arise in the consideration of geothermal energy. These problems can be well treated by invariant imbedding.

The time difference between Los Angeles and New Zealand is nineteen hours. However, since one crosses the international date-line, the change is only five hours. We went to New Zealand by easy stages. We stayed two nights in Hawaii, and then flew to Fiji, and then to Auckland.

In Auckland, we stayed at the Intercontinental Hotel for two days, resting up before the tour. Then we flew to Wellington.

In Wellington, I was quite busy. My visit had been timed for the annual meeting of the Mathematics Society and the Operations Research Society. I gave talks at both meetings, as well as lectures at the University.

I also spent some time with the people who were generating hydroelectric power from the system of dams which they had in New Zealand. They were faced with many scheduling problems which could be handled by dynamic programming. However, at the time the dimensionality problem was overwhelming. As a result of the work which I have done since with Vasudevan and Bayesteh Kashef on spline approximations, I can now make a significant contribution to their problems.

I visited the laboratory where Alex works, DSIR, Department of Scientific and Industrial Research. I spent several hours there in discussions with him and other people.

Initially, we stayed in an apartment close to the University. However, the heating in this apartment was very poor. In order to keep warm, we found it necessary to put hot water in the bathtub. That kept the bathroom warm but had little effect on the rest of the apartment. Furthermore, sleeping on the mattress activated the fleas in the mattress. The warmth of our bodies brought them to life.

I wanted to cause no trouble, but gave up after four days. We moved to a Travel Lodge. We had a beautiful view of the bus depot but at least we were warm.

Elaine Haight's brother and sister-in-law lived in Wellington, and had us over for dinner one night. It was a pleasure to be in a warm house.

We also had dinner several times with Alex McNabb. New Zealand dinners are generally good but fattening. Not only one kind of potato is served, but two. Furthermore, after dessert, there is something called a "savory", another kind of dessert. This is generally brought by one of the guests. Both Nina and I gained several pounds from our trip.

We did not have much time to wander about Wellington. However, we did manage to send back a few sheepskins as souvenirs.

We flew next to Christchurch. We stayed at a hotel where the rooms were spacious, the food was good and we were warm.

I gave some lectures at the University, visited some laboratories and had discussions with several faculty members. One of the best things about the trip was the opportunity I had to have discussions with various faculty members.

When I did this, Nina visited the botanical gardens. New Zealand has been isolated for about fifteen million years. As a result, it has very interesting vegetation. It has no animal life to speak of. The wild pigs that abound are descendants of the tame pigs brought by Captain Cook. The bird life is also very interesting and various types of birds may be found in New Zealand and no place else.

In the evening, we had an opportunity to go to movies. We saw, "Tora, Tora", which we promptly dubbed, "Terrible, Terrible". Actually, the movie is quite good as a James Bond movie. It bears as much resemblance to the facts as the usual epic that Hollywood produces about the crusades bears to medieval life. Since it was a joint

Japanese-American production, both sides wanted to gloss over certain episodes. It was quite amusing to see how certain incidents were handled.

The next stop was Dunedin. On the way we saw various hydroelectric installations. It was convenient on the way to stop and see Mt. Cook. We stayed one night at a lodge on the slopes of Mt. Cook. It was very pretty to see Mt. Cook in the moonlight.

I was not, however, as impressed as I could be. After all, I had seen the Rockies, the Grand Canyon and other natural wonders of the southwest. One of the people I was talking to was exasperated by this attitude. He wanted to know why we had come to New Zealand if we were not interested in the natural wonders. I replied that we had come to New Zealand to see the people and the cities.

To get to our next stop, we took a DC 3. I was not happy about the way the pilot flew between mountains, but I knew that the DC 3, the air taxi as it is called, is a very safe place. After a flight of about a half hour we landed at an airfield, where the grass was kept low by sheep. Then, out came the smallest plane I have ever seen. There was room for eleven passengers with one sitting next to the pilot.

The woman in front of us and directly behind the pilot turned around and said, "I'm scared." Nina assured her that there was nothing to be scared about because this airline had the best safety record. This reassured the woman and she made no further comment. After we had disembarked I asked Nina where she had gotten this statistic. "Oh," she said blithely, "I made it up. I was afraid she would start hitting the pilot over the head with her handbag and we would all crash."

We were picked up by car and driven to our motel, which was on the edge of a beautiful lake. While the driver waited, I inspected our quarters. As I had expected, they were frigid. I decided that we would not spend the night in that icebox and asked the driver to take us directly to Dunedin.

It was only a short drive to Dunedin. At Dunedin, we were staying in a good hotel. Spacious quarters, good food, and warm.

Dunedin is the center of medical research in New Zealand. After giving my lecture at the University, I visited the hospital. At the hospital, I met a young doctor who was doing research in hypertension. I knew a little bit about hypertension because Bob Maronde had told me about this research in this area. To my surprise, I learned that Maoris were very subject to hypertension.

Nobody knows what causes hypertension. One can control it somewhat, but one cannot eliminate it.

One cannot draw any parallel between the New Zealand treatment of the Maoris and the treatment of the blacks in the United States.

One evening, we had a very pleasant dinner with the vice-chancellor. We discussed the problems of scientific education at great length.

I scandalized many of my listeners in my lectures. I constantly emphasized that one of the purposes of a university education is to prepare a person for life. In particular, this means that his education should equip him for a job. I pointed out that every educated person should know how a digital computer works. This was not the traditional English view. Education was something a gentleman had, and gentlemen did not engage in trade.

Secondly, I constantly made political remarks. At the time, we had Nixon for president, Reagan for governor and Yorty for Mayor of Los Angeles. I pointed out how embarrassing it was to be represented by these men. In my lectures in Kentucky and Tennessee, they made fun of the governor of California. This was particularly humiliating since in my youth a southern senator had been a stock comedy figure.

Most of my listeners agreed with my feelings, but they felt it wasn't polite to say so in public. In New Zealand, one should not talk about money or politics in public. Sex, of course is taboo.

In all the universities I visited, I did not see a single computing installation. Even the laboratory where Alex worked did not have a computer. I suspect that at the time there was not a single modern digital computer in all of New Zealand. I hope that situation is better now.

Another evening, I was asked to give a description of the new mathematics in the United States. Some of the faculty members were trying to modernize the curriculum. That put me in a quandry. I was all for modernization of the curriculum but was opposed to the excesses of the new math. The motivation was excellent, but the subject matter was atrocious. I decided not to speak about the excesses, but to concentrate on the motivation.

In Dunedin we had a chance to stroll around. Naturally, we went to visit the local museum. It was excellent. For the first time, we learned how the Polynesians did their island hopping. In addition, there was an excellent exhibit of Polynesian life. We had gone to a similar museum in Honolulu and it was very bad.

We went next to Palmerston North, a typical provincial New Zealand town. The university there had originally been an agricultural school.

I gave my lecture at the university and in the evening went to the inevitable faculty party. It was boring as expected, and confirmed my attitude to avoid them in Los Angeles. Positions were already difficult to obtain in United States. There were several Americans there taking advantage of the fact that positions were still available in New Zealand.

Remarkably, there was a very good restaurant in Palmerston North, one that Los Angeles would be proud of. We ate very well in New Zealand, in restaurants and hotels. The only poor meal that we had was in a private home with the evening afterwards even worse. We escaped by my looking at my watch at nine-thirty, and saying it was my bedtime. At the hotel, we had several drinks to recover from the awful experience.

We had been warned before going to New Zealand that we would be served only mutton. That is not the case at all. Actually, the restaurants and hotels have a wide selection. In any case, we both like mutton.

Alex McNabb was driving us because he wanted to show us the geothermal installations personally. All of New Zealand is volcanic, but the region around Rotorua is particularly active. There was a good exhibit there, and Alex did not have to give explanations. Then we went to visit Rotorua itself. Boards had been laid, so we could walk quite close to the various hot springs. It was eerily beautiful.

Right close by was a luxury hotel. Several people said that the volcano underneath would explode any minute. However, several others said it wouldn't.

We stayed the night at the hotel. That was the only place in New Zealand where my allergies acted up. Rotorua is in the middle of a forest, and most likely I was affected by various pollen.

This is also Maori country. After we had spent the night at Rotorua, we proceeded in the direction of Auckland. A few miles further on, there was a very interesting exhibit of Maori buildings.

We arrived in Auckland without incident. We stayed again at the Intercontinental Hotel. Then, I went to the University, and gave my lecture. After that, we met several of the faculty members.

Then, we had several days to ourselves to wander about Auckland. I was not used to the pace of the trip and welcomed this opportunity. One evening, we spent with Frank Haight and his new wife Mary. The last time we had seen Frank was in Moscow in 1966. In 1975, we saw him in Chicago. Mathematicians do get around these days.

On the way home, we planned to spend several days in Tahiti. It was a great disappointment. The main town Papeete, has little to recommend it. The only thing I recall about Tahiti is that I got an atrocious haircut there. This was the year that I had three haircuts, one in Stockholm, one in Wellington, and one in Tahiti. It took six months for my hair to return to normal after the haircut in Tahiti.

Tahiti is the creation of press agents.

BRAZIL

I met Leo Roberto Borges-Vieira at my lectures in Paris in 1964. He was obviously non-French and lonely. I invited him to have dinner with Nina and me. His French was as bad as his English, but we managed to communicate, and became very friendly.

In 1966, he invited me to spend a month in Sao Paulo giving lectures at the university. Since we had never been to South America, I accepted with alacrity.

We went to Brazil by way of New York. We spent three days in Rio de Janeiro, courtesy of IBM, and then flew to Sao Paulo, about 220 miles away.

About all I knew about South America was that Portuguese was spoken in Brazil. This was no handicap to me since I didn't speak Spanish. As a matter of fact, I thought that Sao Paulo was a small university town of about 300,000. I was delightfully surprised to find that Sao Paulo had a population of over ten million and a skyline bigger than New York's.

We stayed at the Excelsior Hotel, right in downtown Sao Paulo. The dining room was on the top floor, and I was quite amused to see that all the neon signs were in English. The food was excellent, so there was little incentive to sample the many restaurants that abounded.

The university is about five miles outside of town. I was driven there everyday and that was the most dangerous part of the trip. The car in which I was driven was quite small, and I saw traffic accidents each way. The driving in Sao Paulo is worse than that in Tokyo, if that can be imagined. The architectural style of the university is quite interesting. The architects have made considerable use of the climate. In Mexico City, I saw similar architecture at the university. Nothing like that exists in the United States.

I lectured on dynamic programming, control theory, and invariant imbedding. Leo was trying to modernize the curriculum. The trouble is that the tradition in Brazil is law, not engineering. Brazil is a very rich country, but it doesn't have the manpower to exploit its natural resources.

Leo had a friend who was a statistician attached to the hospital, Maria-Alice Valdez. She took me around the hospital and explained the many problems they had in public health because of the proximity of the jungle. When we returned to the United States the public health officer read us an impressive list of diseases to which we had been exposed. I smiled inwardly, because I could have added several others to the list. However, Maria-Alice said that living in the heart of the city there was little danger.

Some years later, Fleur spent some time in Sao Paulo helping Maria-Alice install a medical information system.

She knew the curator of the famous snake farm where they sent poison venom all around the world to combat snake bite. She insisted that we visit the snake farm, and the curator showed me how he handled poisonous snakes. Having a poisonous snake a foot away from one is not pleasant, although the curator assured me there was no danger. I prefer to see it in the movie.

In Sao Paulo, I first met Nestor Distefano. There was a meeting in Sao Paulo and he took this opportunity to get in touch with me. At the time, he was at the University of Buenos Aires. When the military took over, they ruined the University, and drove the intellectuals out or put them in jail.

By diligent search, we had found a restaurant that served real Brazilian food, Casa d'Oro. This was not easy to do. Sao Paulo had many restaurants, serving everything but Brazilian food. Nestor insisted that Portuguese was so smiliar to Spanish that he could order easily. We wanted chicken. He kept asking the waiter for "pollo". The waiter didn't understand. Finally, I said, in English, "We want chicken." "Oh," said the waiter, "why didn't you say so?"

After the military took over in Argentina, Nestor spent some years with me at USC. Then he went on to Berkeley where he had a joint appointment in mechanical engineering and architecture. Sadly, he had a heart attack and died in 1975.

Rio de Janeiro and Sao Paulo are at the southeast corner of Brazil. To counteract the concentration, the capitol, Brasilia, is located 550 miles away. We were supposed to visit it. However, my allergies acted up because we were so close to the equator. I found that I could not sleep at night. I knew exactly what to do because I had had the trouble before. From twelve to about four, I wrote two books. This meant that I could not lecture in the morning at the University.

We enjoyed Sao Paulo very much. On weekends, we explored the city. Sao Paulo has a very good art museum which we visited several times. In addition Leo was a good host, and there were several other people that we met.

MEXICO

I first visited Mexico when I was in San Diego in 1944. It is quite convenient to go to Mexico since San Diego is only thirteen miles above the border. The nearby Mexican town is Tijuana, a typical border town.

However, in addition to the usual tawdry joints which a border town has, Tijuana has a jai alai palace. We often went to the jai alai games and admired greatly the skill of the players. Most of them are Basque.

One of my colleagues at the laboratory had a car, and he invited us to visit Ensenada, about 100 miles below the border. In those days, before the freeway, it was quite a tortuous trip over the mountains to Ensenada. At various points, one was stuck behind water trucks. Ensenada had no source of fresh water and all the water for the hotels and restaurants had to be taken in by truck.

It was quite a thrill to go to a foreign country. In addition, I could not resist the impulse to buy something without using points. I dashed into a grocery and found a can of pineapple, sixty points. I eagerly bought this.

After the war, when I had come to Los Angeles, my tennis group occasionally would arrange a match with the Coronado Hotel. This hotel has all the elegance of fin de siécle. In the evening, we often went to Tijuana to see the jai alai games.

My next trip to Ensenada was in 1954, when Alfred came. I took advantage of being in Ensenada to buy about $100 worth of French wine. Wine is much cheaper in Mexico because there are no comparable duties. The girl in the liquor store assured me I would have no difficulty in bringing in the liquor if I declared it.

When we reached the border, I declared a few other things which we had bought and the wine. The customs man looked at me as if I was crazy. He said to take the wine to another building where it would be examined. It was quite difficult to lug the wine around, but I finally got it on the counter. The man behind the counter took one look at the wine said, "You can't bring that in." I asked what I was supposed to do with it. "Drink it," he said.

I felt rather desperate. I noted however, that I was on the American side of the border and that no one was watching me. I shrugged my shoulders, put the wine back in the car and took off. Thus, I smuggled $100 worth of wine into United States.

Alfred was rather disturbed at the incident. When he returned to Washington, he asked his friend, the head of the customs service about it. The head of the customs service explained the injunction against wine was a state law. The border officials were federal. They were supposed to tell you that you were breaking a state law but they had no authority to enforce it.

I wanted very much to see Mexico City. I finally had the opportunity in 1960. The American Physical Society had its annual meeting in Mexico City. For the only time in my life, I gave a ticket paper. This is my name for a twenty-minute talk designed to supply transportation to a desired place. The talk was on some aspect of invariant imbedding.

The meetings were held at the university, giving me a fine opportunity to see the famous murals. I had seen pictures of these murals, and many movies of them. They are even more magnificent close up than in pictures. They express all the fire and passion of the Spanish and Indian soul which is rarely present in Anglo-Saxon tradition.

The meetings were not peaceful. There was a great deal of anti-American sentiment and the students went around on the outside chanting. This was rather disturbing.

We went to Mexico City with the Friedlands. After the meetings, we wanted to see the pyramids, about ten miles outside the city. Anne and I very intrepidly climbed to the top of one of the pyramids. The ascent is quite easy until about fifty feet from the top, then it gets very steep. However, we made it. As we were enjoying the view, we were buzzed by a plane and had to fall on our stomachs to avoid being hit.

Anne and I both have a fear of heights. Consequently the descent was neither easy nor pleasant.

In addition to the pyramids there are many temples well worth seeing.

One night, we went to a nightclub. There were many people there including Gene Guth. He was based at Oak Ridge, but often came to RAND. During the day, we would discuss various problems in chemical physics, and at night we would go to various restaurants and nightclubs. Gene considered himself a ladies' man.

One evening we went to the Greek Village, where they had a belly dancer. After the show, I went backstage and gave her five dollars and asked her to make a fuss over Gene. This was quite successful, particularly because she got one of her veils entangled with his glasses.

In Mexico City, I saw a chance to continue the joke. I went backstage and gave the performer a mass of pesos and asked her again to make a fuss over Gene. The others were not aware of my giving the performer any money. Gene was quite gratified at this.

We stayed at one of the luxury hotels on the main street of Mexico City, Avenue de la Revolucion. We were very careful about the water, fresh fruits, salads, etc. We were even careful about the way we brushed our teeth. However, I think that the ice cubes in our drinks at the night club did us in. In any case, the next day I had a very high fever, 105° and felt very sick. Anne also had the same thing.

We called the doctor, who patted us on the head and said time would take care of it. I felt sure that we were going to spend at least a week in bed. Miraculously, we were better the next day, in time for the plane.

When we arrived in Los Angeles the Friedlands had no difficulty. The customs officer regarded me very suspiciously. He engaged me in conversation, asking where I had gone to school, where I had been in the army, etc. Finally, he asked for some documents. I took out my RAND ID card, which had my picture on it, and hoped that would satisfy him. He looked at the ID card and wanted to know what organization that was. I then took out my Hughes consulting card and showed it to him. Obviously, he thought I had a host of forged documents.

He looked me straight in the eye and said, "A lot of people from Central Europe who speak fluent English are coming in by way of Mexico." If I had the time, I would have thrown up my hands in horror and said I was caught. However, I had other things to do. I never satisfied him, but reluctantly, he had to let me in.

Mexico City is a very beautiful city and I was anxious to return.

I had my opportunity in 1967. I was invited to give some lectures at the University of Mexico. Reservations had been made for us at the President Hotel. This was quite convenient to the downtown section, and in addition it was only a half block away from the finest restaurant in Mexico City, La Fonda del Refugio. We had dinner there often.

While I lectured at the University, Nina went to see the pyramids. Since I had been there last, they had built a beautiful anthropology museum. It is probably the finest museum of its kind in the world. We went there quite often.

In addition,we took several rides on the subway. While building the subway a small pyramid had been found. Therefore, in one of the downtown stations in Mexico City, there is a perfect little pyramid.

We never had enough of Mexico City. About a year later, I was invited to give a lecture about fifty miles out of Mexico City. I agreed to give the lecture provided that my expenses in Mexico City were covered for three days. After that lecture we returned to Mexico City, and stayed at the President Hotel again, and had a chance to wander around for three days.

There are two advantages to travel. In the first place, it is good to see what others think. Secondly, it is so good to come home. I think one only appreciates the United States when one goes someplace else for awhile.

CANADA

We visited several universities in Canada; Calgary, Toronto, Waterloo, and Western Ontario.

We enjoyed these visits enormously. Canada is a charming country and Canadians are very nice. Really, there is no such thing as an average Canadian since there has been so much immigration.

We visited the University of Waterloo several times. Here, Arthur Beaumont has built up an applied mathematics program which has had a tremendous effect on Canada. It was a pleasure to help in this.

One of the advantages of flying to Montreal was in visiting any university in upstate New York. I used to have some fun with the customs officials. They always ask two questions:

"How long do you expect to stay in Canada?"

"What is the purpose of your visit?"

To the first, I would say, "About ten minutes." This was the length of time it took to pick up a rented car. To the second, I would say, "To visit upstate New York."

One time, we visited Potsdam, New York, where Clarkson Institute of Technology is, that way. I gave some technical talks during the day and a popular talk during the evening. I made my usual remarks about how foolish and dangerous the ideas of Kahn and Teller were. One member of the audience became quite agitated and made several sharp remarks. I commented on this later to my host and he laughed, "Teller spoke here last week and he was the chairman of the invitational committee."

I made a promise to myself that we would never go or come from Europe non-stop again. The time change is too much. Next time we go, we shall either go by way of Waterloo and come back by way of Atlanta, or the reverse.

NAME INDEX

RICHARD BELLMAN

Date of birth: 26 August 1920
Place of birth: New York City, New York

Education: B.A., Brooklyn College, 1941
M.A., University of Wisconsin, 1943
Ph.D., Princeton University, 1946

Academic Positions

Assistant Professor of Mathematics, Princeton University	(1946-1948)
Associate Professor of Mathematics, Stanford University	(1948-1952)
Visiting Professor of Engineering, UCLA	(1956)
RAND Corporation, Santa Monica, California	(1953-1965)

Present Position

Professor of Mathematics, Electrical Engineering and Medicine, University of Southern California (1965-)

Honors and Awards

First Norbert Weiner Prize, Applied Mathematics (American Mathematical Society and the Society for Industrial and Applied Mathematics)	(1970)
First Dickson Prize (Carnegie-Mellong University)	(1970)
ALZA Distinguished Lectureship (Biomedical Engineering Society)	(1972)

Doctor of Science (University of Aberdeen, Scotland) (1973)
Doctor of Laws (University of Southern California, Los Angeles) (1974)
Doctor of Mathematics (University of Waterloo, Canada) (1975)
Fellowship (American Academy of Arts and Sciences) (1975)
John Von Neumann Theory Award (Institute of Management Sciences and the Operations Research Society of America) (1976)
Member (National Academy of Engineering) (1977)
Gold Medal for Dynamic Programming (IEEE) (1978)
Fellow of the Society for Mathematical Biology (1980)
Human Relations Commission's "Bicentennial Salute" (Los Angeles, California) (1981)
Member (National Academy of Sciences) (1983)
Heritage Medal (American Council for Control) (1983)

Publications

620 published research papers
40 books
7 monographs
Editor, Journal of Mathematical Analysis and Applications (Academic Press)
Editor, book series, Mathematics in Science and Engineering (Academic Press)

CPSIA information can be obtained
at www.ICGtesting.com
Printed in the USA
LVHW021358120620
657940LV00017B/2820

9 789971 966010